Variable Phase Approach to Potential Scattering

MATHEMATICS
IN SCIENCE
AND ENGINEERING

A SERIES OF MONOGRAPHS AND TEXTBOOKS

Edited by Richard Bellman
University of Southern California

1. TRACY Y. THOMAS. Concepts from Tensor Analysis and Differential Geometry. Second Edition. 1965
2. TRACY Y. THOMAS. Plastic Flow and Fracture in Solids. 1961
3. RUTHERFORD ARIS. The Optimal Design of Chemical Reactors: A Study in Dynamic Programming. 1961
4. JOSEPH LaSALLE and SOLOMON LEFSCHETZ. Stability by Liapunov's Direct Method with Applications. 1961
5. GEORGE LEITMANN (ed.). Optimization Techniques: With Applications to Aerospace Systems. 1962
6. RICHARD BELLMAN and KENNETH L. COOKE. Differential-Difference Equations. 1963
7. FRANK A. HAIGHT. Mathematical Theories of Traffic Flow. 1963
8. F. V. ATKINSON. Discrete and Continuous Boundary Problems. 1964
9. A. JEFFREY and T. TANIUTI. Non-Linear Wave Propagation: With Applications to Physics and Magnetohydrodynamics. 1964
10. JULIUS T. TOU. Optimum Design of Digital Control Systems. 1963
11. HARLEY FLANDERS. Differential Forms: With Applications to the Physical Sciences. 1963
12. SANFORD M. ROBERTS. Dynamic Programming in Chemical Engineering and Process Control. 1964
13. SOLOMON LEFSCHETZ. Stability of Nonlinear Control Systems. 1965
14. DIMITRIS N. CHORAFAS. Systems and Simulation. 1965
15. A. A. PERVOZVANSKII. Random Processes in Nonlinear Control Systems. 1965
16. MARSHALL C. PEASE, III. Methods of Matrix Algebra. 1965
17. V. E. BENES. Mathematical Theory of Connecting Networks and Telephone Traffic. 1965
18. WILLIAM F. AMES. Nonlinear Partial Differential Equations in Engineering. 1965
19. J. ACZÉL. Lectures on Functional Equations and Their Applications. 1966
20. R. E. MURPHY. Adaptive Processes in Economic Systems. 1965
21. S. E. DREYFUS. Dynamic Programming and the Calculus of Variations. 1965
22. A. A. FEL'DBAUM. Optimal Control Systems. 1965

MATHEMATICS IN SCIENCE AND ENGINEERING

In preparation

VARIABLE PHASE APPROACH TO POTENTIAL SCATTERING

F. CALOGERO

ISTITUTO DI FISICA DELL' UNIVERSITÀ DI ROMA
ISTITUTO NAZIONALE DI FISICA NUCLEARE, SEZIONE DI ROMA
ROME, ITALY

1967

ACADEMIC PRESS   New York and London

ACADEMIC PRESS INC.
111 Fifth Avenue, New York, New York 10003

United Kingdom Edition published by
ACADEMIC PRESS INC. (LONDON) LTD.
Berkeley Square House, London W.1

LIBRARY OF CONGRESS CATALOG CARD NUMBER: 66-29675

PRINTED IN THE UNITED STATES OF AMERICA

Foreword

The subject of this monograph is nonrelativistic scattering on a spherically symmetrical potential. More specifically, the discussion is focused on the scattering phase shift δ_l which, for each value of the angular momentum l, represents all the effect of the potential that is relevant for the quantum mechanical description of elastic scattering. The treatment makes no attempt to go beyond the standards of mathematical rigor that are usually considered satisfactory in physics. In fact, whenever possible the emphasis is on the physical understanding rather than the mathematical formalism. It is nevertheless hoped that the number of imprecise or incorrect statements will be minimal.

The fact that a monograph has been written on a subject that is treated in several quantum mechanics textbooks requires some justification. This can be based on the fact that the method employed systematically in this monograph for the investigation of scattering phase shifts (the so-called *variable phase method* or simply the *phase method*), although quite old, is almost unknown, while it deserves a much larger audience. In fact, it is elegant, physical, and powerful, because its basic equations are quite simple, have a very direct physical interpretation, and provide a versatile tool for deriving qualitative and quantitative properties of the scattering phase shifts. We believe that this method of discussing scattering phase shifts should be introduced in all elementary quantum mechanics courses that include a treatment of scattering theory.

It might be objected that nowadays the exact computation of the scattering phase shifts produced by any potential is a trivial computer job. It is nevertheless important (in fact, probably more so) to acquire a physical feeling for the relation between the potential and the phase shift; this feeling, we believe, is provided by the approach described herein. The importance of such physical intuition can hardly be overestimated; it is certainly very helpful in most problems of current physical interest, including those in high-energy physics where a simple potential model is certainly inadequate to describe the dynamics completely.

vii

Incidentally we should mention that the approach described here could also be advantageously employed to compute phase shifts on a computer, a task which may be far from trivial if the number of phase shifts to be evaluated is very large and the accuracy required is very high (as is the case, for instance, in high-energy electron scattering on nuclei). But here we do not discuss this point in any detail, i.e., the questions of the accuracies attainable and the computer time needed to get them. On the other hand, it is worth emphasizing that with the phase approach a scattering phase shift can be computed on a desk computer with reasonable accuracy and in a short time, a fact of great pedagogical importance.

This monograph may be read by anyone who has some knowledge of basic quantum mechanics. Some understanding of elementary scattering theory is also necessary; in Chapter 2 we summarize the basic notions required, but this review is probably too cursory to be of use, unless the reader has some previous understanding of the subject. This monograph has been written with the possibility in mind that some readers may be interested only in certain specific results. For this reason we have tried to make the chapter and appendixes as indepenent from one another as possible. A schematic representation of the logical relations is given in the accompanying chart.

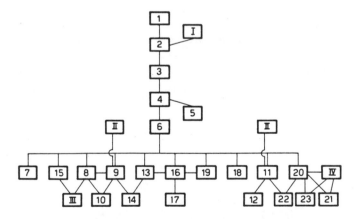

Not all the material in this monograph has previously appeared in print. The major new items are the discussion of bound states and the proof of Levinson's theorem (Chapters 20 and 22 and Appendix IV). Other results that are either new or presented in a new fashion may be found in various places, e.g., in Chapters 18 and 23 and in Appendix III. All the numerical examples presented in Chapters 5, 10, 12, and 21 have been computed for this monograph.

Finally I wish to thank Professor R. Bellman for inviting me to write this monograph; Professor A. Ramakrishnan and Professor R. Vasudevan for their hospitality during the summer of 1964 in Madras and at the summer school in Bangalore, where I gave a series of lectures on the phase approach to scattering theory, which provided the first draft of this monograph; Dr. A. Rambaldi and Dr. A. Morgana for assistance in performing the numerical calculations; Professor M. Ageno for making available the IBM 7040 computer of the Istituto di Sanità in Rome, where some of the numerical computations were performed; Miss A. Di Silvestro, who typed the manuscript, and Mr. F. Bronzini, who drew the graphs; and all those who, at various times, helped me by pointing out relevant references, including Professors J. M. Charap, E. Clementel, S. Geltman, M. Goldberger, T. Kato, J. B. Keller, K. W. McVoy, M. Ross, and D. Zwanziger.

August, 1967   F. CALOGERO

Notation

The notation employed is defined whenever it is introduced, unless it is considered self-explanatory. For the convenience of the reader, a few items are collected here.

(1) Lower case boldface letters indicate three-vectors, except in Chapter 19.

(2) The prime appended to a function indicates differentiation with respect to its argument $[f'(x) \equiv df/dx]$; in the case of a function of several variables, it stands for partial differentiation with respect to the last argument $[f'(x, y) \equiv \partial f(x, y)/\partial y]$.

(3) An equation of the form $x_{a,b} = y_{a,b}$ generally stands for $x_a = y_a$, $x_b = y_b$; similarly $f(\pm, x) = \pm g(\pm, x)$ stands for $f(+, x) = g(+, x)$, $f(-, x) = -g(-, x)$; etc.

(4) The function (or rather distribution) $\theta(x)$ is the so-called step-function: $\theta(x) = 1$ if $x > 0$, $\theta(x) = 0$ if $x < 0$.

Contents

xi

1

Introduction

In this monograph we discuss an approach to the problem of evaluating the scattering phase shifts produced by a spherically symmetrical potential which has several advantages over the traditional approach. In the traditional approach, one first integrates the radial Schrödinger equation—a *second-order linear* differential equation—from the origin to the asymptotic region where the potential is negligible, and then compares the phase of the radial wave function thus obtained with that of a comparison circular function. In the approach discussed in this monograph, one integrates a *first-order nonlinear* differential equation from the origin to the asymptotic region, thereby obtaining directly the value of the scattering phase shift. This approach is termed the "variable phase method" or simply the "phase method," because the dependent variable on which we focus may always be interpreted as a scattering phase shift.

As will be shown in the following chapters, the present method is a very convenient one for deriving general properties of the scattering phase shifts, for obtaining approximate and variational expressions, and for performing numerical computations. A further merit of this approach is its formal simplicity and elegance, and the straightforward physical interpretation that may be given of its basic quantities and equations. In short, it appears that the variable phase approach is in all respects superior to the traditional method for studying scattering phase shifts.

Historically this method is a rather old one; it was used as early as 1924, for instance, in the book by Courant and Hilbert [1] to discuss the asymptotic behavior of Bessel functions. The first application of this approach to scattering theory was given in 1933 by Morse and Allis [2], who derived the equation for S-wave scattering. The generalization to all partial waves was given independently and

1

almost simultaneously by various authors [3–6]. However, the convenience of this approach was never fully recognized, although some of its equations were occasionally rediscovered [7] and used for numerical computations [8, 9] or to discuss certain specific problems [10–12]. This monograph is based mainly on a series of recent contributions that illustrate the convenience of this approach to scattering theory [13–23]. Moreover, it introduces the same type of approach in the bound state problem.

It should be emphasized that this approach also turned out to be a convenient one for treating problems connected with the analytic continuation to complex values of the angular momentum l of the partial wave scattering amplitude [24–26]. However, in this monograph we shall not discuss this kind of topic. In fact we shall always confine ourselves to the physical world of real energies and quantized angular momenta.

Throughout this monograph, unless otherwise explicitly indicated, we adopt units such that $\hbar = 2m = 1$, m being the mass of the scattering particle. In these units k and k^2 will indicate, respectively, the (modulus of) momentum and the energy of the scattering particles.

2

Review of scattering theory

In this chapter we review briefly the elementary theory of scattering on a spherically symmetrical potential $V(r)$.

The scattering situation is described by a stationary wave function $\psi(\mathbf{r})$, which is that solution of the time-independent Schrödinger equation,

$$[\nabla^2 + k^2 - V(r)]\psi(\mathbf{r}) = 0, \tag{1}$$

characterized by the asymptotic boundary conditions

$$\psi(\mathbf{r}) \underset{r\to\infty}{\to} e^{ikz} + f(\theta)\frac{e^{ikr}}{r}. \tag{2}$$

We have assumed here that the incident beam travels parallel to the z axis; the scattering angle θ is the angle between the direction of observation (i.e., the direction of the vector $\mathbf{r}$) and the incident direction. The boundary condition, Eq. (2), corresponds to the experimental setup, the first term representing the incident beam, the second term representing the scattering particles. Note that in order for this asymptotic behavior to be consistent with the Schrödinger equation (1), it is required that the potential vanish asymptotically faster than the first inverse power of r. This we assume throughout. As is well known, the case of an unscreened Coulomb potential requires separate discussion.

The function $f(\theta)$ is the "scattering amplitude," and it yields the differential cross section through

$$\frac{d\sigma(\theta)}{d\Omega} = |f(\theta)|^2. \tag{3}$$

Thus the scattering problem consists in the evaluation of $f(\theta)$.

3

The cylindrical symmetry of the problem is exploited setting

$$\psi(\mathbf{r}) = \frac{1}{r} \sum_{l=0}^{\infty} u_l(r) P_l(\cos \theta), \tag{4}$$

where the P_l's are Legendre polynomials. The factor $1/r$ is taken out for convenience. Note that because $\psi(0)$ must be finite, Eq. (4) implies the boundary condition

$$u_l(0) = 0 \tag{5}$$

for the "radial wave function" $u_l(r)$.

Inserting the *Ansatz* equation (4) into Eq. (1) we obtain the radial Schrödinger equation

$$u_l''(r) + [k^2 - l(l+1)/r^2 - V(r)]u_l(r) = 0. \tag{6}$$

The term $l(l+1)/r^2$ is the centrifugal potential. Note that a positive potential corresponds to a repulsive force, a negative potential to an attractive force; this happens because, although in adherence to the universal convention we talk of *potential*, what it is actually meant is *potential energy*.

We now assume the potential to be less singular in the origin than the centrifugal term, i. e., we assume that

$$\lim_{r \to 0}[r^2 V(r)] = 0. \tag{7a}$$

Such potentials are called "regular," even if they diverge in the origin. The term "singular" is accordingly reserved for the potentials that violate the condition of Eq. (7a). We exclude from consideration potentials that are unbounded at any point other than the origin, except as limiting cases. In the following we consider only regular potentials, unless an explicit statement to the contrary is given; the case of singular potentials is treated in detail in Chapter 15. To be more specific, we generally assume that

$$V(r) \underset{r \to 0}{\to} V_0 \, r^{-m}, \qquad m < 2. \tag{7b}$$

It follows, from the assumption that the potential is regular (Eq. (7a)), that two independent solutions of the radial Schrödinger equation (6) exist, which behave in the origin as r^{l+1} and r^{-l}, respectively. Thus the boundary condition equation (5) is sufficient to identify one solution of the radial Schrödinger equation up to a multiplicative constant, and, in fact, Eq. (5) may now be replaced by the more specific condition

$$u_l(r) \xrightarrow[r \to 0]{} \text{const} \cdot r^{l+1}. \tag{8}$$

The radial wave function thus obtained is real (except possibly for the multiplicative constant), and it defines the "scattering phase shift" δ_l through the comparison of its asymptotic behavior with that of a sine function:

$$u_l(r) \xrightarrow[r \to \infty]{} \text{const} \cdot \sin(kr - l\pi/2 + \delta_l). \tag{9}$$

The term $l\pi/2$ is conventional. The reason for inserting it is that with this definition, all scattering phase shifts vanish when the potential itself vanishes.

The importance of the scattering phase shifts resides in the fact that knowledge of them is equivalent to knowledge of the scattering amplitude. In fact from Eqs. (4), (2), and (9), together with the asymptotic equation

$$e^{ikz} \xrightarrow[r \to \infty]{} \frac{1}{kr} \sum_{l=0}^{\infty} (2l + 1)i^l \sin\left(kr - l\frac{\pi}{2}\right) P_l(\cos \theta), \tag{10}$$

we obtain for the scattering amplitude the expression

$$f(\theta) = \frac{1}{k} \sum_{l=0}^{\infty} (2l + 1)e^{i\delta_l} \sin \delta_l P_l(\cos \theta). \tag{11}$$

We thus see that the scattering amplitude is expressed as a sum over the "partial wave amplitudes"

$$A_l = e^{i\delta_l} \sin \delta_l . \tag{12}$$

It may be shown (see Chapter 11) that, provided the potential vanishes asymptotically exponentially or faster, the partial wave amplitudes vanish when the energy vanishes as follows:

$$A_l = a_l k^{2l+1}[1 + O(k^2)]. \tag{13}$$

Here the coefficients a_l are constant, i. e., energy independent. Thus the higher the angular momentum l is, the faster the corresponding partial wave amplitude vanishes at low energy—a fact that has an obvious semiclassical interpretation. This implies that at low energy, only a few terms contribute appreciably in the partial wave sum equation (11). Therefore, at these energies, the determination of the scattering phase shifts is particularly useful because the knowledge of just a few of them is sufficient to determine the scattering amplitude and thus the differential cross section. On the other hand, at high energy the evaluation of the scattering amplitude through the partial wave sum equation (11) may be difficult because one must first compute many phase shifts and then perform a sum over many terms, which may give rise to large cancellations. At any rate, in this monograph we are not going to be concerned with these problems; instead we shall consider only the problem of evaluating each individual phase shift.

Summarizing, to obtain each scattering phase shift it is necessary to solve a second-order differential equation from the origin to the asymptotic region—i. e., the region where the potential has become negligible—and then to compare the asymptotic behavior of the solution thus constructed with that of an appropriate sine function. A different method for obtaining the scattering phase shifts will be introduced and discussed in the following chapters.

It should be emphasized that the definition of the phase shift now given through Eq. (9) suffers from a $\mathrm{mod}\,(\pi)$ ambiguity. It is customary to remove this ambiguity by normalizing the phase shift so that it vanishes at high energy,

$$\lim_{k \to \infty} \delta_l = 0, \tag{14}$$

and by assuming that it is a continuous function of k. This condition, Eq. (14), cannot be enforced, however, in the case of singular potentials (see Chapter 15) or in the case of Dirac particles (see Chapter 17). Another convention requires the phase shift to be a continuous function of the potential strength, and to vanish as the potential vanishes. This convention is applicable also to singular potentials and in the relativistic case; it is equivalent to the previous one for the case of regular potentials, as will be shown later.

Before closing this chapter we write the integral equation satisfied by the radial wave function, namely,

$$u_l(r) = \hat{\jmath}_l(kr) - k^{-1} \int_0^r ds [\hat{\jmath}_l(kr)\hat{n}_l(ks) - \hat{\jmath}_l(ks)\hat{n}_l(kr)] V(s) u_l(s). \tag{15}$$

The Riccati–Bessel functions $\hat{j}_l$, $\hat{n}_l$ are defined in Appendix I. This integral equation is equivalent to the radial Schrödinger equation (6) (as may be verified by straightforward differentiation, also using the Wronskian identity (I.6)), and to the boundary condition (8). In fact, in place of Eq. (8) we now have the more specific relation

$$u_l(r) \xrightarrow[r\to0]{} \hat{j}_l(kr) \xrightarrow[r\to0]{} (kr)^{l+1}/(2l+1)!!. \tag{16}$$

3

Derivation of the phase equation

In this chapter we present a derivation of the "phase equation," and we introduce the "phase function." A different, albeit equivalent, derivation will be presented in Chapter 6; other derivations will also be given in Chapters 13 and 16, in the framework of more general formulations.

We begin by introducing two auxiliary functions, defined in terms of the radial wave function. These are

$$s_l(r) = -k^{-1} \int_0^r dr'\, V(r') \hat{j}_l(kr') u_l(r'), \tag{1a}$$

$$c_l(r) = 1 - k^{-1} \int_0^r dr'\, V(r') \hat{n}_l(kr') u_l(r'). \tag{1b}$$

From these definitions, and the known behaviors of the functions $V(r)$, $\hat{j}_l(kr)$, $\hat{n}_l(kr)$, and $u_l(r)$ in the neighborhood of the origin, as given by Eqs. (2.7), (2.16), and (I.7), we infer

$$s_l(r) \xrightarrow[r\to0]{} -\frac{V_0 r^{-m}}{k^2}\, \frac{(kr)^{2l+3}}{(2l+3-m)[(2l+1)!!]^2} \xrightarrow[r\to0]{} 0, \tag{2a}$$

$$c_l(r) \xrightarrow[r\to0]{} 1 + \frac{V_0 r^{2-m}}{(2-m)(2l+1)} \xrightarrow[r\to0]{} 1. \tag{2b}$$

We then compare the definitions of the two functions $s_l(r)$, $c_l(r)$, Eqs. (1), with the integral equation satisfied by the radial wave function $u_l(r)$, Eq. (2.15); we obtain

$$u_l(r) = c_l(r) \hat{j}_l(kr) - s_l(r) \hat{n}_l(kr). \tag{3}$$

8

Now we investigate the asymptotic behavior of $u_l(r)$. From the equation above we obtain

$$u_l(r) \xrightarrow[r \to \infty]{} c_l(\infty) \sin\left(kr - l\frac{\pi}{2}\right) + s_l(\infty) \cos\left(kr - l\frac{\pi}{2}\right). \qquad (4)$$

To obtain this asymptotic equation we have used the asymptotic expressions of the Riccati–Bessel functions, Eqs. (I.8), and the fact that the functions $c_l(r)$ and $s_l(r)$ have well-defined asymptotic limits $c_l(\infty)$ and $s_l(\infty)$, as implied by their definitions (Eqs. (1)) and by the assumed asymptotic vanishing of the potential. But now a comparison of Eq. (4) with the definition of the scattering phase shift, Eq. (2.9), yields the equation

$$\tan \delta_l = s_l(\infty)/c_l(\infty). \qquad (5)$$

We see therefore that the knowledge of the asymptotic limits $s_l(\infty)$ and $c_l(\infty)$ implies the knowledge of the tangent of the scattering phase shift.

This relation suggests the introduction of a new function, $t_l(r)$, defined by

$$t_l(r) = s_l(r)/c_l(r). \qquad (6)$$

We obtain, from Eqs. (2), that this function vanishes in the origin exactly in the same manner as the function $s_l(r)$:

$$t_l(r) \xrightarrow[r \to 0]{} -\frac{V_0 \, r^{-m}}{k^2} \frac{(kr)^{2l+3}}{(2l + 3 - m)[(2l + 1)!!]^2} \xrightarrow[r \to 0]{} 0. \qquad (7)$$

On the other hand, from Eq. (5) we infer that the asymptotic behavior of the function $t_l(r)$ yields directly the value of the tangent of the scattering phase shift:

$$\lim_{r \to \infty} t_l(r) \equiv t_l(\infty) = \tan \delta_l . \qquad (8)$$

At this point, therefore, we have learned that we may introduce a function $t_l(r)$ whose value in the origin is known (it vanishes), and whose asymptotic value yields directly the tangent of the scattering phase shift. Now the question is, Is it possible to go from the origin to the asymptotic region? We show that the function $t_l(r)$ satisfies a *first-order differential equation*, so that once its value at the origin is assigned, we can obtain it everywhere; and, in particular, we can evaluate its asymptotic value by integrating this differential equation from the origin to infinity. At this point, of course, the potential will enter into the picture, for after all it is the presence of the potential that produces the scattering phase shift, and it is its detailed shape and magnitude that determine its value.

To arrive at the differential equation whose existence we have already anticipated, we differentiate the equations that define the auxiliary functions $s_l(r)$ and $c_l(r)$, Eqs. (1); we also use Eq. (3) to substitute for $u_l(r)$ in the r.h.s. We thus secure the following system of two coupled first-order linear equations:

$$s_l'(r) = -k^{-1}V(r)\hat{j}_l(kr)[c_l(r)\hat{j}_l(kr) - s_l(r)\hat{n}_l(kr)], \tag{9a}$$

$$c_l'(r) = -k^{-1}V(r)\hat{n}_l(kr)[c_l(r)\hat{j}_l(kr) - s_l(r)\hat{n}_l(kr)]. \tag{9b}$$

Now we multiply the first equation by $c_l(r)$ and the second by $s_l(r)$, subtract the second equation from the first, and divide by $c_l^2(r)$. In this manner we obtain

$$t_l'(r) = -k^{-1}V(r)[\hat{j}_l(kr) - t_l(r)\hat{n}_l(kr)]^2, \tag{10}$$

which is the required equation.

This equation is a generalized Riccati equation, i. e., the simpler nonlinear differential equation. The following should be emphasized, however. Because of the well-known connection between second-order linear differential equations and first-order equations of the Riccati type, the fact that we have succeeded in transforming our problem, which involved the solution of a second-order linear differential equation (the radial Schrödinger equation), into one requiring the integration of a Riccati equation is not startling and does not represent an improvement per se. The advantage, as will be made clear below, resides in the formal simplicity and physical significance of the equation obtained.

As is well known, the solution of a Riccati equation need not be bounded; it may have poles. This may happen in our case too, as implied by Eq. (6) and the fact that $c_l(r)$ might vanish. Therefore we now make a further step, introducing another function $\delta_l(r)$ through the position

$$t_l(r) = \tan \delta_l(r). \tag{11}$$

Then from Eq. (7) we also obtain for $\delta_l(r)$,

$$\delta_l(r) \xrightarrow[r \to 0]{} -\frac{V_0 r^{-m}}{k^2} \frac{(kr)^{2l+3}}{(2l+3-m)[(2l+1)!!]^2} \xrightarrow[r \to 0]{} 0, \tag{12}$$

and from Eq. (8) we find that

$$\lim_{r \to \infty} \delta_l(r) \equiv \delta_l(\infty) = \delta_l . \tag{13}$$

On the other hand, inserting Eq. (11) into Eq. (10), we find for $\delta_l(r)$ the differential equation

$$\delta_l'(r) = -k^{-1}V(r)[\cos \delta_l(r)\hat{j}_l(kr) - \sin \delta_l(r)\hat{n}_l(kr)]^2. \tag{14a}$$

As is obvious from the structure of this equation, the function $\delta_l(r)$ is now bounded. The equation that it satisfies, however, is nonlinear in a more general way.

The function $\delta_l(r)$ is named the "phase function," for reasons that are already apparent, but that will be more evident from the discussion in the following chapter. There we shall discuss this function in more detail; here we simply summarize its main properties, i. e., that it vanishes in the origin (Eq. (12)), it satisfies a first-order nonlinear differential equation (Eq. (14)), and it yields asymptotically directly the value of the scattering phase shift (Eq. (13)). The equation satisfied by the phase function (Eq. (14)) is termed the "phase equation." It will be our main tool for investigating the properties of scattering phase shifts.

The function $t_l(r)$, for obvious reasons, is termed the "tangent function." It has a pole whenever the phase function $\delta_l(r)$ goes through an odd multiple of $\pi/2$, an event that may or may not occur, depending on the potential.

The phase equation (14) becomes particularly simple in the case of S waves, for in that case, using Eqs. (I.5), it becomes

$$\delta_0'(r) = -k^{-1}V(r) \sin^2[kr + \delta_0(r)]. \tag{15}$$

It may be written in a similar form for all l exploiting the amplitudes and phases of the Riccati–Bessel functions introduced in Appendix I. We find that

$$\delta_l'(r) = -k^{-1}V(r)\hat{D}_l^2(kr) \sin^2[\hat{\delta}_l(kr) + \delta_l(r)]. \tag{14b}$$

We end this chapter by introducing two complex functions, which also have definite values in the origin and satisfy Riccati equations, and whose asymptotic values yield, respectively, the partial wave scattering amplitude A_l (Eq. (2.12)) and the "S matrix"

$$S_l = e^{2i\delta_l} = \frac{1 + i \tan \delta_l}{1 - i \tan \delta_l} = 1 + 2iA_l . \tag{16}$$

These functions are characterized by the boundary conditions in the origin,

$$A_l(0) = 0, \tag{17a}$$

$$S_l(0) = 1, \tag{17b}$$

and asymptotically

$$\lim_{r\to\infty} A_l(r) \equiv A_l(\infty) = A_l\,, \tag{18a}$$

$$\lim_{r\to\infty} S_l(r) \equiv S_l(\infty) = S_l\,, \tag{18b}$$

and satisfy the complex differential equations

$$A_l{}'(r) = -k^{-1}V(r)[\hat{j}_l(kr) + A_l(r)\hat{h}_l^{(1)}(kr)]^2, \tag{19a}$$

$$S_l{}'(r) = -(2ik)^{-1}V(r)[\hat{h}_l^{(2)}(kr) - S_l(r)\hat{h}_l^{(1)}(kr)]^2. \tag{19b}$$

The Riccati–Hankel functions $\hat{h}_l^{(1)}$ and $\hat{h}_l^{(2)}$ are defined in Appendix I.

The relations of these functions among themselves and with the phase function and the tangent function are identical to the relations valid asymptotically (Eq. (16)). We refer to the functions $S_l(r)$ and $A_l(r)$, respectively, as the "S-matrix function" and the "scattering amplitude function" (not to be confused with the "amplitude function" of Chapter 6). Whenever this terminology might give rise to confusion, one may add the adjective "interpolating" that has been used sometimes in the literature; it emphasizes the fact that these functions "interpolate" between the value at the origin, which corresponds to no scattering, and the asymptotic value, which yields the correct magnitude for the scattering parameters.

4

Discussion of the phase equation and of the behavior of the phase function. Procedures for the numerical computation of scattering phase shifts

In this chapter we discuss the phase equation, emphasizing its physical significance, the qualitative features of the behavior of the phase function, and the procedures for numerical computations.

The phase equation may be written in either one of the two forms (3.14a) and (3.14b). We emphasize that the condition on the potential in the origin, Eq. (2.7), is sufficient to ensure that the boundary condition in the origin, Eq. (3.12), specifies uniquely one solution of the phase equation, i. e., the phase function. On the other hand, the asymptotic condition on the potential (that it vanish faster than r^{-1} at large r) is sufficient to guarantee that the phase function converges asymptotically to a finite value, which, as we know, is simply the scattering phase shift. Actually the phase function may be identified with a scattering phase shift not only asymptotically, but for all values of r. In fact, it follows from the structure of the phase equation that the value of the phase function $\delta_l(\bar{r})$ at the distance $\bar{r}$ is the scattering phase shift produced by the potential $V(r)\theta(\bar{r} - r)$, i. e., the actual potential amputated of its part extending beyond $\bar{r}$. This remark clarifies the physical significance of the phase function: we now understand that it vanishes in the origin because its value there corresponds to the scattering phase shift produced by a potential that has been completely amputated away! More generally, we now understand the "embedding" philosophy of the present approach: Instead of solving directly the problem P of evaluating the scattering

13

phase shift δ_l produced by the potential $V(r)$, we have set up a family of problems $P(\bar{r})$, consisting in the evaluation of the phase shift $\delta_l(\bar{r})$ produced by the potential $V(r)\theta(\bar{r} - r)$. The family of problems $P(\bar{r})$ interpolates in a continuous fashion from the trivial problem $P(0)$ to our actual problem $P \equiv P(\infty)$. The success of the phase approach depends on the fact that the change with $\bar{r}$ in the solutions of the problems $P(\bar{r})$ is represented by a simple first-order differential equation, the phase equation. We may therefore arrive at the solution of our original problem P, starting from the trivial problem $P(0)$ and varying $\bar{r}$ continuously from 0 to ∞. This is exactly what we are doing when we integrate our phase equation from the origin to infinity.

Returning to the discussion of the phase equation, we emphasize the simple way in which the potential enters into the equation. Note that the term multiplying it has a definite (negative) sign and is bounded. In fact, when r is large with respect to lk^{-1}, its variation is restricted between $-k^{-1}$ and 0, as implied by the asymptotic expressions of the Riccati–Bessel functions (see Appendix I). When r is small with respect to k^{-1}, it vanishes proportionally to r^{2l+2}, as implied by the behavior of the Riccati–Bessel functions in the neighborhood of the origin (see Eq. (I.7)) and the behavior of the phase function itself near the origin (see Eq. (3.12)). In fact, this term is nothing but the square of the radial wave function (normalized as in Eq. (2.16)), times a function that never vanishes and is normalized to the value $-k^{-1}$ in the origin (see Chapter 6). The fact that this term vanishes in the neighborhood of the origin faster as the angular momentum is larger corresponds to the fact that when the angular momentum is large, the particles are prevented by the centrifugal barrier from feeling the innermost part of the potential.

The simple way the potential appears in the phase equation displays clearly that it is the potential itself that gives rise to the phase shift. We immediately see that a positive (repulsive) potential produces a negative phase shift, and a negative (attractive) potential, a positive phase shift. Moreover, it follows from the lemma of Appendix II that if we consider two potentials $V(r)$, $\bar{V}(r)$ such that

$$V(s) \geqslant \bar{V}(s) \qquad \text{for} \quad s \leqslant r, \tag{1}$$

the opposite inequality holds for the corresponding phase functions

$$\delta_l(r) \leqslant \bar{\delta}_l(r), \tag{2}$$

and therefore, as r diverges, also for the corresponding phase shifts.

From the structure of the phase equation, Eq. (3.14b), we may also obtain a lower bound for the phase function, namely,

$$\delta_l(r) \geqslant -\mathring{\delta}_l(kr). \qquad (3)$$

To prove this relationship we remark that it holds in the neighborhood of the origin, as implied by Eqs. (3.12) and (I.20b), and that it must be maintained thereafter; in fact, $\delta_l(r)$ cannot overtake $-\mathring{\delta}_l(kr)$ because, should $\delta_l(r)$ ever reach $-\mathring{\delta}_l(kr)$, then the phase equation would imply that its derivative vanishes, whereas the derivative of $\mathring{\delta}_l(kr)$ is always positive. Actually the condition (3) has a simple physical interpretation in the light of what has been said above, once we recall that $-\mathring{\delta}_l(kr)$ is the scattering phase shift produced by a hard sphere of radius r, i. e., by an infinitely repulsive potential of range r. Then Eq. (3) expresses the simple fact that no potential exists that is more repulsive than an infinitely repulsive potential. Note that we have no similar upper bound for the phase function. In this connection we note incidentally that there is no simple relation between the solutions of two phase equations that differ only by the sign of the potential. This corresponds to the fact that potentials of opposite sign yield quite different phase shifts.

In conclusion, let us summarize our discussion of the phase equation. Its physical meaning is very transparent: It describes the accumulation of the phase shift due to the potential. The phase function vanishes in the origin and is built up by the potential as one moves away from the origin, until it reaches its asymptotic value; the asymptotic value is obviously attained as soon as one gets out of the range of the potential, and it yields directly the value of the scattering phase shift. If the potential does not change sign, the asymptotic value is reached monotonically. Attractive potentials yield positive phase shifts, and repulsive potentials, negative phase shifts; more generally, the fact that $V(r) \geqslant \bar{V}(r)$ for $r \leqslant \bar{r}$ implies that $\delta_l(\bar{r}) \leqslant \bar{\delta}_l(\bar{r})$. The fact that the term multiplying the potential vanishes as r^{2l+2} near the origin represents vividly the centrifugal screening of the innermost part of the potential. The value $\delta_l(r)$ of the phase function at the distance r from the origin is the scattering phase shift that would be produced by the potential if it were amputated of its part extending beyond r.

Before discussing the numerical computation of the phase shift, we insert two additional remarks. The first is that obviously the definition of the scattering phase shift through the phase equation does not suffer from any mod(π) ambiguity. It is easily seen that this definition agrees with the conventional one, introduced in Chapter 2 through Eq. (2.14). In fact, it follows from the presence of the factor k^{-1} in the r.h.s. of the phase equation that the phase function (and therefore also the phase shift) vanishes as k diverges (see also Appendix III). Incidentally, we note that this result, which is obtained almost by inspection from the phase equation, is a nontrivial one to prove on the basis of the traditional formulation. We also note that the phase equation is seen by inspection to imply that the phase shift—or, for that matter, the phase function—is a continuous function of the potential strength and vanishes identically if the potential disappears. We thus confirm what had been anticipated in Chapter 2, namely, that the requirement that the phase shift has this property is, for the purpose of lifting the mod(π) ambiguity inherent in its original definition, tantamount to the condition that the phase shift be a continuous function of k and vanish as k diverges (for regular potentials).

The second remark concerns the formal symmetry of the phase equation under the exchange $k \leftrightarrow -k$. This follows from the symmetry properties, Eqs. (I.9) [or, equivalently, Eqs. (I.22)], of the Riccati–Bessel functions given in Appendix I, and it implies the formal relation $\delta_l(k, r) = -\delta_l(-k, r)$, where we have indicated explicitly the dependence of the phase function on k. In terms of the S matrix, this becomes the well-known equation

$$S_l(k, r) = S_l^{-1}(-k, r). \tag{4}$$

We now consider the problem of the numerical computation of the phase shift. This is accomplished through the numerical integration of the phase equation, starting from the origin. The Eq. (3.14a) or (3.14b) may be used. The integration need be carried only so far that the effect of the potential may be neglected thereafter. If one wants to repeat the calculation for several values of k, it may be convenient to use $x = kr$ as integration variable. Obviously the nonlinearity of the equation is of no difficulty as far as the numerical integration is concerned. It should be emphasized that the simplicity of the phase equation, especially in the S-wave case, makes it quite feasible to undertake a desk computation, at least to get an approximate result. This is much less feasible if one adopts the traditional approach.

It is also worthwhile to consider the possibility of using the

equation for the tangent function, Eq. (3.10), for the computation
of the scattering phase shift. However, as we already noted, the
solution of this equation need not be bounded; in fact, we know that
the tangent function $t_l(r)$ has a pole whenever the phase function
$\delta_l(r)$ goes through an odd multiple of $\pi/2$. This fact seems to make
this equation unsuitable for a numerical computation unless the
phase function always stays less than $\pi/2$ in magnitude. But this
difficulty may be gotten around as follows.

We introduce the "cotangent function" $ct_l(r)$, defined by

$$ct_l(r) = 1/t_l(r) = \cot \delta_l(r), \tag{5}$$

which satisfies the Riccati equation

$$ct_l'(r) = k^{-1}V(r)[ct_l(r)\hat{j}_l(kr) - \hat{n}_l(kr)]^2. \tag{6}$$

We then integrate the equation for the tangent function $t_l(r)$,
Eq. (3.10), starting from the origin, until we obtain, at $r = r_1$, a
value larger in modulus than unity for $t_l(r)$. From there on, we
integrate Eq. (6) for the cotangent function, assuming as starting
value at r_1 the value given by Eq. (5). The same procedure is used
again as soon as the modulus of the cotangent function exceeds unity
to switch back to the tangent function, and it is repeated until we
get out of the range of the potential, where the functions become
asymptotically constant. For a potential that does not change sign
(say, an attractive potential) in the succeeding intervals, the tangent
and cotangent functions alternate between -1 and 1. The final value
of the phase shift is obtained in an obvious manner, from the
asymptotic values of the tangent or cotangent functions, whichever
obtains, and the number of intervals necessary to reach the asymptotic
region. We conclude therefore that it is possible to base the computation of the phase shift on the integration of the equations for the
tangent and cotangent functions. These are both Riccati equations,
and the fact that they are simpler in their dependence on the dependent
variable may provide an incentive to use them rather than the phase
equation.

We end this discussion of the phase equation by giving a very
simple example of the actual behavior of the phase function. We
consider here a case that may be easily solved analytically, namely,
S-wave scattering on a square well potential. Other numerical
examples are presented in the following chapter.

Let V_0 be the strength of the potential, and let us assume that it is negative, so that we have an attractive potential well. The momentum of the particle within the well is p,

$$p = (k^2 - V_0)^{1/2}, \tag{7}$$

and because V_0 is negative, p is certainly real. The phase function may then be computed easily, if we recall that $\delta_l(r)$ is the phase shift produced by the potential truncated at r. For the S-wave phase function produced by a well of range $\bar{r}$, we find

$$\delta_0(r) = \tan^{-1}\left\{\frac{k \cos kr \sin pr - p \sin kr \cos pr}{k \sin kr \sin pr + p \cos kr \cos pr}\right\} \quad \text{for} \quad r \leqslant \bar{r},$$

$$\delta_0(r) = \tan^{-1}\left\{\frac{k \cos k\bar{r} \sin p\bar{r} - p \sin k\bar{r} \cos p\bar{r}}{k \sin k\bar{r} \sin p\bar{r} + p \cos k\bar{r} \cos p\bar{r}}\right\} \quad \text{for} \quad r \geqslant \bar{r}. \tag{8}$$

The mod(π) ambiguity of the inverse tangent function is lifted by the condition that the phase function vanish in the origin and that it be a continuous function of r (for $k \neq 0$; the zero-energy limit is discussed below). Of course, $\delta_0(\infty) = \delta_0(\bar{r})$ and, more generally, $\delta_0(r)$ is, for $r \leqslant \bar{r}$, the S-wave phase shift produced by a square well of range r.

The behavior of the phase function $\delta_0(r)$ is shown in Fig. 1 for various values of k and for $V_0 = -9$. Obviously from this figure

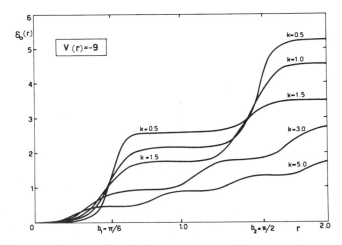

FIG. 1. The S-wave phase function for an attractive square well potential of depth $|V_0| = 9$. $b_1 = \pi/6$ and $b_2 = \pi/2$ are the minimum radii of square wells of the same depth possessing, respectively, one and two S-wave bound states.

one may read the S-wave phase shift produced by a square well of strength $V_0 = -9$ and of any range $\bar{r} \leqslant 2$. Of course the phase shift depends only on the two dimensionless quantities $k\bar{r}$ and $V_0\bar{r}^2$, so that the phase shift produced by a potential of different strength may also be obtained by appropriate scaling.

From these graphs one sees clearly that at small r (which implies small kr) the phase shift increases with increasing k, a fact in agreement with what has been discussed above. Another feature to which we draw attention is the steplike behavior of the phase function, which is more pronounced the smaller k is. This behavior may be understood recalling Levinson's theorem [27], which states that at $k = 0$,

$$\delta_l = n\pi, \tag{9}$$

where n is the number of bound states with angular momentum l possessed by the potential. (The $2l + 1$ degeneracy connected with the spherical symmetry of the problem is not taken into account; bound states differing only in their overall spatial orientation are not counted as different.) In fact, Levinson's theorem may be proved on the basis of this approach, as will be shown in Chapter 22; but for the moment let us assume its validity in order to understand the behavior of the phase function at small energy. Then, because we know that the phase function itself is, for all values of r, the scattering phase shift corresponding to a certain potential, we conclude that Levinson's theorem holds for the phase function itself; namely, we have, at $k = 0$,

$$\delta_l(r) = \pi n_i \quad \text{for} \quad b_i < r < b_{i+1}, \tag{10}$$

where the distances b_i are defined by the condition that the potential, if amputated immediately after b_i, can support n_i bound states. (Notice that we have not committed ourselves as to the value of the phase function at the points b_i. This point will be settled in Chapter 22; it is connected with the more accurate version of Levinson's theorem that also takes into account the marginal situation of a bound state or resonance occurring at zero energy.) Of course, the quantities b_i and n_i depend on the angular momentum, beside the potential. In the case of an everywhere attractive potential, instead of Eq. (10) we may write

$$\delta_l(r) = \pi \sum_i \theta(r - b_i), \tag{11}$$

the number of terms in the sum being equal to the number of bound states with angular momentum l, and the distances b_i being defined by the condition that the potential, amputated immediately before b_i, has $i - 1$ bound states, but amputated immediately after b_i, has i bound states. (The potential obtained when the amputation is performed exactly at b_i has $i - 1$ bound states and, in addition, one zero-energy resonance or bound state.) Of course in the case of a repulsive potential, just as in the case of an attractive potential too weak to possess bound states, the zero-energy phase function vanishes identically.

In conclusion, we see that at zero energy the phase function may cease to be a continuous function of r and may instead develop jumps of magnitude π. Of course if the energy is very small but different from zero, the phase function is a continuous function of r, but it tends to resemble the discontinuous function into which it goes in the $k \to 0$ limit. This explains the occurrence of the steplike behavior in the example considered.

It should be emphasized that these considerations apply to any potential, not only to the example at hand. In this particular example we may obtain explicitly the zero-energy phase shift by taking the limit of Eq. (8) as k vanishes. We find

$$\delta_0(r) = \pi \sum_i \theta(r - b_i) \qquad \text{for} \quad r < \bar{r} \quad (k = 0),$$

$$\delta_0(r) = \pi n \qquad \text{for} \quad r > \bar{r} \quad (k = 0), \tag{12}$$

where the distances b_i are given by the formula

$$b_i = \tfrac{1}{2}(2i - 1)\pi |V_0|^{-1/2}, \qquad i = 1, 2, 3, ..., \tag{13}$$

and n is the number of solutions of this equation which are smaller than $\bar{r}$.

One should keep the steplike behavior of the phase function in mind while performing a numerical integration of the phase equation at low energy, to avoid the large numerical imprecision that might be caused by the abrupt changes of the dependent variable. The phenomenon had already been noted by Morse and Allis [2], who performed a numerical integration of the phase equation using a primitive computer. This is probably the main reason that they did not pursue this approach any further, which in turn probably has resulted in the phase method's being less widely known and used than it deserves to be.

5

The phase function. Examples

In this chapter we discuss some explicit examples of phase functions, which have been evaluated by numerical integration of the phase equation.

The first case considered is the attractive Yukawa potential

$$V(r) = -(10/r)e^{-r}. \tag{1}$$

The phase function associated with this potential is plotted in Figs. 1–4, for various values of l and k. In the first three figures the phase function corresponding to a given value of l is plotted for several values of k. From Fig. 1 and the discussion of the preceding chapter we infer that the potential of Eq. (1) possesses two S-wave bound states; it would possess only one S-wave bound state if it were amputated of its part extending beyond $\bar{r}$, with $0.15 \lesssim \bar{r} \lesssim 1.15$, and no bound state if $\bar{r} \lesssim 0.15$. (For a check of these results, see Fig. 21.2) Similarly, we infer from Figs. 2 and 3 that the potential of Eq. (1) possesses one P-wave and no D-wave bound states. (Incidentally, the phase function for $k = 0.1$ has not been plotted in Fig. 3 because it turns out to be too small.) Note that for lower partial waves the phase function increases with k for small r and decreases with k for large r. The former behavior corresponds to the dominance of the centrifugal barrier, which is better pierced by more energetic particles; the latter, to the attractive nature of the potential, as represented by Levinson's theorem. For $l = 2$ the centrifugal repulsion is sufficient to forbid any bound state, and accordingly the asymptotic values of the phase function do not increase monotonically with k; they must, in fact, vanish at both small and large k. It should of course be kept in mind that the asymptotic value of the phase function is determined by a scattering experiment at best only up to a mod (π) ambiguity. Thus it is not

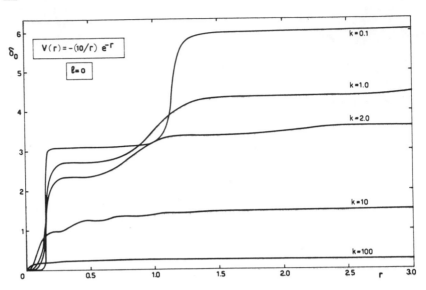

FIG. 1. S-Wave phase function for an attractive potential. Note that this potential possesses two S-wave bound states.

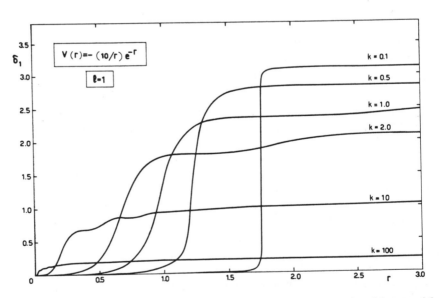

FIG. 2. P-Wave phase function for an attractive potential. Note that this potential possesses one P-wave bound state.

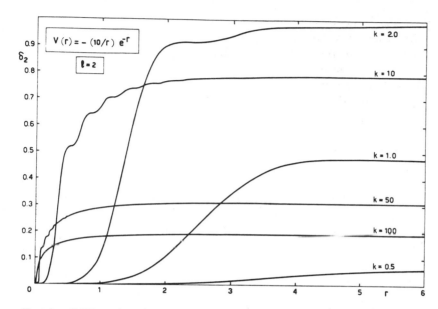

FIG. 3. D-Wave phase function for an attractive potential. Note that this potential possesses no D-wave bound state.

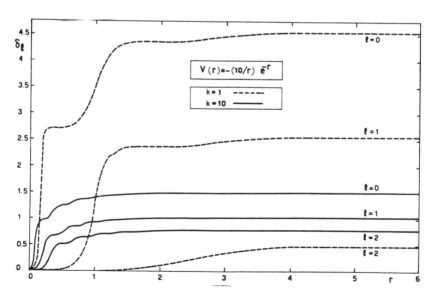

FIG. 4.   Phase function for an attractive potential.

possible, in general, to infer from the values of the scattering phase shift whether a bound state does or does not exist. However, by examining the behavior of the phase shift as a function of k and of l and by comparing it with graphs such as those discussed here and below, one may try to build up a rough image of the potential. In comparing the results for different values of the angular momentum l it should be noted that different scales have been used in Figs. 1–3; a more convenient comparison is afforded by Fig. 4, where the phase functions corresponding to different values of l are plotted on the same graph.

In conclusion, we may abstract the following qualitative rules for the energy dependence of the phase shift produced by an attractive potential. If the energy is small so that $k\bar{r} \ll (l + 1)$, where $\bar{r}$ is some measure of the range of the potential, the centrifugal effect dominates the behavior of the phase shift, which therefore increases with energy. The more energetic the scattering particles, the more they penetrate into the potential region, and therefore the larger the scattering phase shift. This rule, however, applies only if the potential is not strong enough to possess bound states; otherwise it is Levinson's theorem that dominates the low-energy behavior of the phase shift. This may be physically interpreted as being due to a sort of tunnel effect, by which the particles penetrate into the inner region and are kept there by the attractive interaction, when the attraction is strong enough to bind one or more bound states. On the other hand, if the energy is large, so that $k\bar{r} \gg (l + 1)$, then the dominant factors in determining the phase shift are the time spent by the particle in the potential region (which is longer the slower the particle moves) and the ratio of the potential to kinetic energy; both factors collaborate in increasing the phase shift as k decreases.

We consider next the repulsive Yukawa potential

$$V(r) = (20/r)e^{-2r}. \qquad (2)$$

The phase function associated with this potential is plotted in Figs. 5–8 for various values of l and k. In the first three of these figures the phase function corresponding to a given l is plotted for several values of k; in the last one, the phase function is plotted on the same graph for different values of l and k. Of course the repulsive nature of the potential is reflected by the fact that the phase function is negative and vanishes for both large and small values of k. This potential is

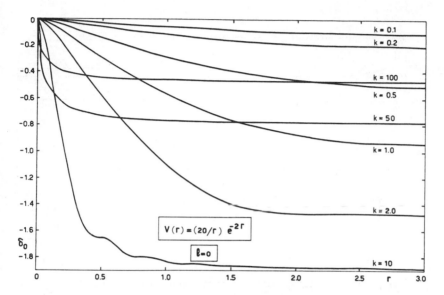

FIG. 5. *S*-Wave phase function for a repulsive potential.

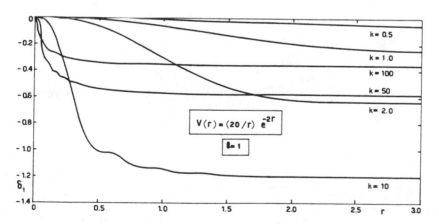

FIG. 6. *P*-Wave phase function for a repulsive potential.

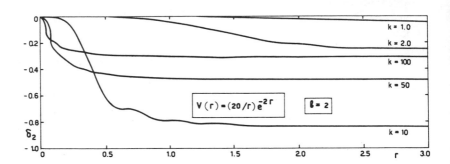

FIG. 7. *D*-Wave phase function for a repulsive potential.

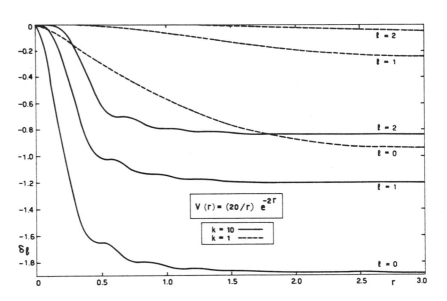

FIG. 8. Phase function for a repulsive potential.

similar in shape to the attractive one discussed above, except that its range is shorter and its strength greater; but of course the behavior of the phase function is very different, especially at small k, because the interaction has changed from attractive to repulsive. However, there are certain common features, notably that at short distances the phase function increases with k and that the accumulation of the phase begins at larger values of r the larger the value of l and the smaller the value of k. In fact, both these effects are due to the centrifugal barrier and are therefore essentially independent of the nature of the potential.

Finally, we consider the potential that obtains by adding the two potentials previously considered:

$$V(r) = (20/r)e^{-2r} - (10/r)e^{-r}. \tag{3}$$

This potential is repulsive at short distances and attractive at great distances; it changes sign in the neighborhood of $r = 0.7$. The phase function associated with it is, of course, decreasing and negative for $r < 0.7$, and increasing for $r > 0.7$; it is plotted in Figs. 9–12 for various values of l and k. It is apparent from the first three of these figures that this potential possesses only one S-wave bound state and no P-wave (or, of course, D-wave) bound states. For a given value of l, the asymptotic value of the phase function is positive for small k and negative for large k; this corresponds to the fact, already noted above and clearly displayed by the behavior of the phase function in all cases, that at large k it is the inner part of the potential that plays a dominant role in the growth of the phase function, with the converse happening at small k.

In conclusion, let us summarize the main qualitative features of the behavior of the phase function. Its growth begins at a value of r that is larger, the larger l is and the smaller k is; this is a centrifugal effect, with an obvious semiclassical interpretation. For large values of k, the accumulation of the phase shift occurs mostly at small values of r; thus the values of the phase shift for large energies are probes of the inner potential region. (From the point of view of the phase equation, this is an effect of the factor k^{-1} in the r.h.s., which makes the derivative $\delta_l'(r)$ small for large k as soon as the potential is not large.) For small values of k, the accumulation of the phase shift occurs mostly for larger values of r, the more so the larger l is. (This is again an effect of the factor k^{-1} in the r.h.s. of the phase

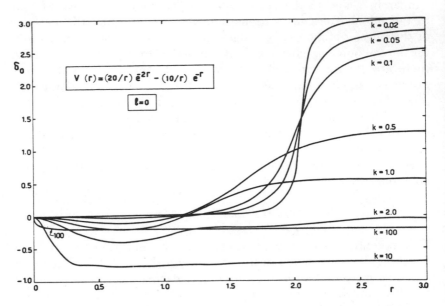

FIG. 9.   S-Wave phase function for a potential that is repulsive at short distances and attractive at large distances.

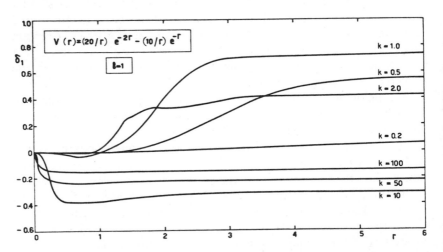

FIG. 10.   P-Wave phase function for a potential that is repulsive at short distances and attractive at large distances.

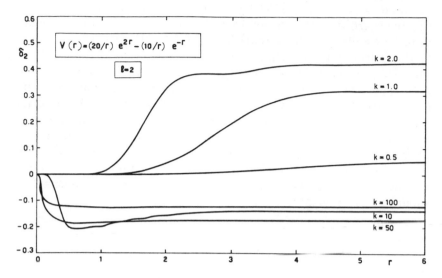

FIG. 11.   *D*-Wave phase function for a potential that is repulsive at short distances and attractive at large distances.

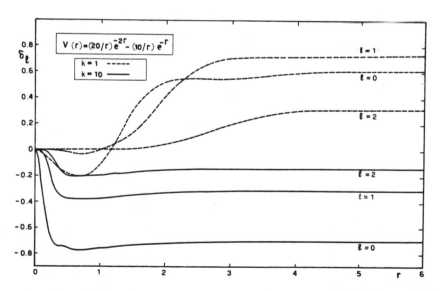

FIG. 12.   Phase function for a potential that is repulsive at short distances and attractive at large distances.

equation, which makes $\delta_l'(r)$ large when k is small, except near the origin, where the other factor that multiplies the potential is small, of order $(kr)^{2l+2}$.) Another remarkable effect at large k is the wiggles in the behavior of the phase function; their width is of order π/k (in fact, somewhat less for attractive potentials, more for repulsive potentials), and their origin is clearly related to the periodic vanishing of the factor that multiplies the potential in the r.h.s. of the phase equation. (This is particularly evident in the S-wave case, but is valid in general as soon as $kr \gg l + 1$, so that the Riccati–Bessel functions may be replaced by their asymptotic expressions.) Finally the major role played by Levinson's theorem, for attractive interactions, in affecting the behavior of the phase function for small k, should be mentioned.

6

Connection between phase function and radial wave function. The amplitude function

In this chapter we investigate the relationship between the radial wave function and the phase function, and in so doing we introduce another auxiliary function of remarkable physical relevance, the "amplitude function." In particular, we show that once the phase function is known, the radial wave function may be obtained with one quadrature. We also give a derivation of the phase equation different from that given in Chapter 3, which also clarifies further the significance of the phase method.

We introduce an "amplitude function" $\alpha_l(r)$, beside the phase function $\delta_l(r)$, setting

$$u_l(r) = \alpha_l(r)[\cos \delta_l(r)\hat{j}_l(kr) - \sin \delta_l(r)\hat{n}_l(kr)], \tag{1a}$$

$$u_l'(r) = k\alpha_l(r)[\cos \delta_l(r)\hat{j}_l'(kr) - \sin \delta_l(r)\hat{n}_l'(kr)]. \tag{1b}$$

Here $u_l(r)$ is the radial wave function, and the prime indicates, as usual, differentiation with respect to the argument. It is shown below that the phase function $\delta_l(r)$ introduced through these equations is identical with that previously introduced.

These relationships may be solved for $\alpha_l(r)$ and $\delta_l(r)$, and we find

$$\delta_l(r) = \tan^{-1} \left\{ \frac{\hat{j}_l(kr)u_l'(r) - k\hat{j}_l'(kr)u_l(r)}{\hat{n}_l(kr)u_l'(r) - k\hat{n}_l'(kr)u_l(r)} \right\}, \tag{2a}$$

$$\alpha_l(r) = k^{-1}\{[\hat{n}_l(kr)u_l'(r) - k\hat{n}_l'(kr)u_l(r)]^2 + [\hat{j}_l(kr)u_l'(r) - k\hat{j}_l'(kr)u_l(r)]^2\}^{1/2}. \tag{2b}$$

31

The expression for $\alpha_l(r)$ simplifies in the S-wave case, for in that case Eq. (2b) becomes

$$\alpha_0(r) = k^{-1}[u_0'^2(r) + k^2 u_0^2(r)]^{1/2}. \tag{3}$$

Note that these equations imply, for the functions $\alpha_l(r)$ and $\delta_l(r)$, the boundary conditions

$$\delta_l(0) = 0, \tag{4a}$$

$$\alpha_l(0) = 1, \tag{4b}$$

which are easily obtained by remembering that near the origin the radial wave function $u_l(r)$ becomes identical to the Riccati–Bessel function $\hat{\jmath}_l(kr)$.

We now differentiate Eq. (1a) and compare the result with Eq. (1b), obtaining

$$\alpha_l'(r)[\cos \delta_l(r)\hat{\jmath}_l(kr) - \sin \delta_l(r)\hat{n}_l(kr)]$$
$$= \delta_l'(r)\alpha_l(r)[\sin \delta_l(r)\hat{\jmath}_l(kr) + \cos \delta_l(r)\hat{n}_l(kr)]. \tag{5}$$

On the other hand, differentiating Eq. (1b) and using the radial Schrödinger equation (2.6) and the Riccati–Bessel equation (I.1) we find

$$V(r)u_l(r) = k\alpha_l'(r)[\cos \delta_l(r)\hat{\jmath}_l'(kr) - \sin \delta_l(r)\hat{n}_l'(kr)]$$
$$- k\alpha_l(r)\delta_l'(r)[\sin \delta_l(r)\hat{\jmath}_l'(kr) + \cos \delta_l(r)\hat{n}_l'(kr)]. \tag{6}$$

We now multiply both sides by

$$\frac{u_l(r)}{\alpha_l^2(r)} = \frac{\cos \delta_l(r)\hat{\jmath}_l(kr) - \sin \delta_l(r)\hat{n}_l(kr)}{\alpha_l(r)}, \tag{7}$$

and we use Eq. (5), to eliminate the ratio $\alpha_l'(r)/\alpha_l(r)$, and the Wronskian relation equation (I.6). In this manner we obtain

$$\delta_l'(r) = -k^{-1}V(r)[u_l(r)/\alpha_l(r)]^2, \tag{8}$$

which we recognize as the phase equation. This demonstrates that the function $\delta_l(r)$, introduced through Eqs. (1), is identical with the phase function previously introduced, because they are both solutions of the same first-order differential equation with the same boundary condition in the origin.

Having shown that the function $\delta_l(r)$ is the phase function, we now return to Eq. (5), and we rewrite it using the phase equation to eliminate $\delta_l'(r)$. We find

$$\alpha_l'(r) = -k^{-1}\alpha_l(r)V(r)[\cos\delta_l(r)\hat{j}_l(kr) - \sin\delta_l(r)\hat{n}_l(kr)]$$
$$\times [\sin\delta_l(r)\hat{j}_l(kr) + \cos\delta_l(r)\hat{n}_l(kr)], \qquad (9a)$$

or, equivalently,

$$\alpha_l'(r) = (2k)^{-1}\alpha_l(r)V(r)\hat{D}_l^2(kr)\sin 2[\hat{\delta}_l(kr) + \delta_l(r)]. \qquad (9b)$$

This is now a linear first-order differential equation for $\alpha_l(r)$, and it is easily solved. Taking into account also the boundary condition (4b), we find

$$\alpha_l(r) = \exp\left\{(2k)^{-1}\int_0^r ds\, V(s)\hat{D}_l^2(ks)\sin 2[\hat{\delta}_l(ks) + \delta_l(s)]\right\}. \qquad (10)$$

Therefore, once the phase function $\delta_l(r)$ is known, the amplitude function may also be obtained with one quadrature, as shown by this equation. When both the phase function $\delta_l(r)$ and the amplitude function $\alpha_l(r)$ are determined, the radial wave function is also obtained through Eq. (1a), and its derivative through Eq. (1b). On the other hand, the knowledge of the radial wave function and of its first derivative determines the phase function and the amplitude function through Eqs. (2). It should be noted that while the phase function depends only on the ratio $u_l'(r)/u_l(r)$—i. e., only on the logarithmic derivative of the radial wave function—the amplitude function depends separately on the radial wave function and on its derivative.

As is apparent from the *Ansatz* equations (1), the present approach is based on a separation of the radial wave function into an amplitude part (which never vanishes) and an oscillating part with a variable phase. It is thus to a certain extent possible to separate the two effects of the potential, to produce a scattering phase shift and to deform the radial wave function. Only the first effect is relevant in the study of elastic scattering, and it is a merit of the phase method that it allows attention to be focused separately on this effect; the second effect is also important, however, in many physical instances. A qualitative feature of this kind of influence of the potential may be read directly from Eq. (9), which implies that $\alpha_l'(r)$ in the neighborhood of the origin is negative or positive depending on

whether the potential there is attractive or repulsive. This displays
the effect of the potential, to attract or repel the wave function (we
recall that the amplitude function is always normalized to unity in
the origin). It is therefore reasonable to introduce a quantity that
provides a measure of the deformation induced by the potential into
the radial wave function near the origin, just as the phase shift
measures its effect at large distances. Such a quantity is the factor G_l,
which we introduce as follows. We set

$$\tilde{u}_l(r) = u_l(r)/\alpha_l(\infty). \tag{11}$$

This is the radial wave function, renormalized so that it becomes
asymptotically a sine function:

$$\tilde{u}_l(r) \xrightarrow[r \to \infty]{} \sin\left(kr - l\frac{\pi}{2} + \delta_l\right). \tag{12}$$

The G_l factor is then defined by

$$G_l = \lim_{r \to 0}[\tilde{u}_l(r)/\hat{j}_l(kr)] = 1/\alpha_l(\infty). \tag{13}$$

This definition implies that when there is no potential, G_l is unity.
In general, from Eq. (10) we obtain for it the closed expression in
terms of the phase function

$$G_l = \exp\left\{-(2k)^{-1}\int_0^\infty dr\, V(r)\hat{D}_l^2(kr) \sin 2[\hat{\delta}_l(kr) + \delta_l(r)]\right\}. \tag{14}$$

From this expression we may obtain approximate evaluations of
G_l, substituting in the r.h.s. the approximate expressions for $\delta_l(r)$
to be discussed later. The simpler (Born) approximation G_l^B is
obtained simply by setting $\delta_l(r)$ equal to zero in the r.h.s. There
results the formula

$$G_l^B = \exp\left\{k^{-1}\int_0^\infty dr\, V(r)\hat{j}_l(kr)\hat{n}_l(kr)\right\}. \tag{15}$$

We emphasize that the evaluation of G_l, especially in the S-wave
case, is of importance in several physical problems (beta decay, etc.).
    Finally, we give the relationships between the radial wave function

and the S-matrix function $S_l(r)$ introduced at the end of Chapter 3. We find that

$$u_l(r) = (i/2)\alpha_l(r)[S_l^{-1/2}(r)\hat{h}_l^{(2)}(kr) - S_l^{1/2}(r)\hat{h}_l^{(1)}(kr)], \tag{16a}$$

$$u_l'(r) = k(i/2)\alpha_l(r)[S_l^{-1/2}(r)\hat{h}_l^{(2)\prime}(kr) - S_l^{1/2}(r)\hat{h}_l^{(1)\prime}(kr)]. \tag{16b}$$

These equations may be solved for $S_l(r)$, to obtain

$$S_l(r) = \frac{\hat{h}_l^{(2)}(kr)u_l'(r) - k\hat{h}_l^{(2)\prime}(kr)u_l(r)}{\hat{h}_l^{(1)}(kr)u_l'(r) - k\hat{h}_l^{(1)\prime}(kr)u_l(r)}. \tag{17}$$

We also record the expressions of the tangent function and the sine and cosine of the phase function in terms of the radial wave function. We find from Eqs. (3.1) and (3.6) that

$$\tan \delta_l(r) = \frac{-k^{-1} \int_0^r ds\, V(s)\hat{j}_l(ks)u_l(s)}{1 - k^{-1} \int_0^r ds\, V(s)\hat{n}_l(ks)u_l(s)}. \tag{18}$$

On the other hand, as is well known, the sine of the scattering phase shift is given by the equation

$$\sin \delta_l = -k^{-1} \int_0^\infty dr\, V(r)\hat{j}_l(kr)\tilde{u}_l(r). \tag{19}$$

We emphasize that while both the function $u_l(r)$ and the function $\tilde{u}_l(r)$ are solutions of the radial Schrödinger equation and vanish in the origin, the first one is normalized in the origin by Eq. (2.16), while the second one is normalized asymptotically by Eq. (12).

Note that Eq. (19) implies for the sine of the phase function the expression

$$\sin \delta_l(r) = -k^{-1}\alpha_l^{-1}(r) \int_0^r ds\, V(s)\hat{j}_l(ks)u_l(s). \tag{20}$$

Of course, Eqs. (18) and (20) also imply the relation

$$\cos \delta_l(r) = \alpha_l^{-1}(r) \left[1 - k^{-1} \int_0^r ds\, V(s)\hat{n}_l(ks)u_l(s)\right]. \tag{21}$$

We end this chapter noting that the amplitude function $\alpha_l(r)$ coincides with the modulus of the "Jost function" [28] produced by the potential truncated at r, as may be easily verified. This remark, together with Eq. (10) and Eq. (5.21) of Ref. 28, implies the relationship

$$-\pi^{-1}P \int_{-\infty}^{+\infty} dp\,(p-k)^{-1}\,\delta_l(p,r) + \sum_{j=1}^{n_l(r)} \ln[1 + k^{-2}q_j{}^2(r)]$$

$$= (2k)^{-1} \int_0^r ds\, V(s)\, \hat{D}_l{}^2(ks) \sin 2[\hat{\delta}_l(ks) + \delta_l(ks)]. \qquad (22)$$

Here P stands for principal value, and we have explicitly indicated the dependence of the phase function on the momentum. The quantity $n_l(r)$ is the number of l-wave bound states possessed by the potential V cut off at r, and the corresponding binding energies are $-q_j{}^2(r)$ (we have omitted to indicate explicitly their l-dependence); these functions are considered in detail in Chapter 20 and 21.

This equation holds of course also for $r = \infty$, in which case it becomes a relationship between an integral of the phase function over all values of the coordinate, an integral of the scattering phase shift over all values of the momentum, and a sum over the binding energies of bound states. Differentiating this equation with respect to r and using the phase equation we obtain the remarkable relation

$$\pi^{-1}P \int_{-\infty}^{+\infty} dp\, p^{-1}(p-k)^{-1} \sin^2[\hat{\delta}_l(pr) + \delta_l(p,r)]$$

$$= (2k)^{-1} \hat{D}_l{}^2(kr) \sin 2[\hat{\delta}_l(kr) + \delta_l(k,r)]. \qquad (23)$$

This equation, from which the potential has dropped out, holds provided the potential $V(r')\,\theta(r-r')$ possesses no l-wave bound state. Otherwise it must be substituted by the equation

$$\pi^{-1}P \int_{-\infty}^{+\infty} dp\, p^{-1}(p-k)^{-1}V(r)\, \hat{D}_l{}^2(pr) \sin^2[\hat{\delta}_l(pr) + \delta_l(p,r)]$$

$$+ \sum_{j=1}^{n_l(r)} 2q_j{}'(r)q_j(r)[1 + k^{-2}q_j{}^2(r)]^{-1}$$

$$= (2k)^{-1}V(r)\, \hat{D}_l{}^2(kr) \sin 2[\hat{\delta}_l(kr) + \delta_l(k,r)] \qquad (24)$$

where, as usual, the prime indicates differentiation with respect to r.

7

Bounds on the scattering phase shift and on its variation with energy

The simplicity of the phase equation, and especially the straight-forward way in which it displays the dependence of the phase shift on the potential, makes it an ideal tool for deriving general properties of the scattering phase shift. In this chapter we indicate how bounds may be established for the scattering phase shift and its variation with energy. Because our main purpose is to illustrate the method rather than to obtain results, we restrict our consideration to the simpler case of the S-wave phase shift. More general results may be found in the literature, and also bounds on other quantities, such as the variation of the phase shift with angular momentum [13]. But we emphasize that the simplicity of the procedure and the possibility of exploiting special features of the potential (such as the fact that it does not change sign, that its derivative does not change sign, etc.) suggest that whenever confronted with a specific problem, one should derive its own bounds, exploiting the techniques exemplified here.

A bound for the S-wave phase shift is immediately obtained from the corresponding phase equation (3.15):

$$\delta'(r) = -k^{-1}V(r) \sin^2[kr + \delta(r)].$$

(In this chapter we drop the S-wave subscript 0.) In fact, integrating both sides of this equation, we obtain for the scattering phase shift

$$\delta = -k^{-1} \int_0^\infty dr \, V(r) \sin^2[kr + \delta(r)], \qquad (1)$$

and from this we immediately obtain

$$k^{-1} \int_0^\infty dr \, V(r)\theta[-V(r)] \leqslant \delta \leqslant k^{-1} \int_0^\infty dr \, V(r)\theta[V(r)]. \qquad (2)$$

37

Of course, this equation does not provide a very stringent bound. On the other hand, there is no difficulty in improving it in special cases. For instance, for a nowhere attractive potential, from Eqs. (4.3) and (1) we easily (see below) obtain

$$0 \geqslant \delta > -k \int_0^R dr\, r^2 V(r) - k^{-1} \int_R^\infty dr\, V(r), \qquad (3)$$

where R may be chosen arbitrarily.

We now proceed to derive a bound on the derivative of the phase shift with respect to linear momentum. First we set

$$r = k^\alpha y \qquad (4)$$

and

$$\delta(r) = \Delta(k, y). \qquad (5)$$

Here α is an arbitrary real constant. In the new dependent variable $\Delta(k, r)$ we have indicated explicitly the dependence on k. This function satisfies the differential equation

$$\Delta'(k, y) = -k^{\alpha-1} V(k^\alpha y) \sin^2[k^{\alpha+1} y + \Delta(k, y)] \qquad (6)$$

(the prime indicates differentiation with respect to the last variable, y), with boundary condition

$$\Delta(k, 0) = 0. \qquad (7)$$

The scattering phase shift is still defined by

$$\delta(k) = \Delta(k, \infty). \qquad (8)$$

Here we have written $\delta(k)$ for the scattering phase shift, to emphasize its dependence on k.

We now differentiate Eq. (6) with respect to k. We obtain

$$\begin{aligned}
\Delta_k'(k, y) = &-(\alpha - 1)k^{\alpha-2} V(k^\alpha y) \sin^2[k^{\alpha+1} y + \Delta(k, y)] \\
&-\alpha k^{2\alpha-2} y V'(k^\alpha y) \sin^2[k^{\alpha+1} y + \Delta(k, y)] \\
&-[(\alpha + 1)k^\alpha y + \Delta_k(k, y)]k^{\alpha-1} V(k^\alpha y) \sin 2[k^{\alpha+1} y + \Delta(k, y)].
\end{aligned} \qquad (9)$$

Here the subscript k indicates differentiation with respect to k, while the prime indicates differentiation with respect to the last argument. Note that because the boundary condition equation (7) is independent of k, we have for $\Delta_k(k, y)$ the boundary condition

$$\Delta_k(k, 0) = 0. \qquad (10)$$

Similarly, from Eq. (8) we infer

$$\delta_k(k) = \Delta_k(k, \infty).\tag{11}$$

Therefore, to get a bound on the derivative with respect to k of the phase shift, it is sufficient to establish a bound on $\Delta_k(k, \infty)$. This is easily obtained from Eq. (9), which may be considered a linear first-order equation for $\Delta_k(k, y)$, and which may be solved to yield

$$\Delta_k(k, \infty) = k^{-2} \int_0^\infty dr \{-[(\alpha - 1)V(r) + \alpha r V'(r)] \sin^2[kr + \delta(r)]$$

$$- k(\alpha + 1)r V(r) \sin 2[kr + \delta(r)]\}$$

$$\times \exp\left\{k^{-1} \int_r^\infty ds\, V(s) \sin 2[ks + \delta(s)]\right\}.\tag{12}$$

We have reverted, within the integrand, to the original variables r and $\delta(r)$.

From this equation we obtain immediately the following theorem:

The derivative with respect to k of the S-wave phase shift is not larger than

$$k^{-2} \int_0^\infty dr \{-(\alpha - 1)V(r)\theta[-(\alpha - 1)V(r)] - r\alpha V'(r)\theta[-\alpha V'(r)]$$

$$+ kr|\,(\alpha + 1)V(r)\,|\} \exp\left\{k^{-1} \int_r^\infty ds\, |V(s)|\right\},$$

and it is not smaller than

$$k^{-2} \int_0^\infty dr \{-(\beta - 1)V(r)\theta[(\beta - 1)V(r)] - r\beta V'(r)\theta[\beta V'(r)]$$

$$- kr|\,(\beta + 1)V(r)\,|\} \exp\left\{k^{-1} \int_r^\infty ds\, |V(s)|\right\},$$

where α and β are arbitrary real constants.

These expressions appear complicated but may be greatly simplified in certain cases. For instance, for an attractive potential with positive slope, by setting $\beta = -1$ and performing the remaining integral, we secure the simple lower bound

$$\delta_k \geqslant 2k^{-1}\left(1 - \exp\left[k^{-1} \int_0^\infty dr|\,V(r)\,|\right]\right) \qquad (V'(r) \geqslant 0,\, V(r) \leqslant 0),\tag{13}$$

while by setting $\alpha = 1$ we obtain

$$\delta_k \leqslant 2\bar{r} \left(\exp\left[k^{-1} \int_0^\infty dr \, |V(r)| \right] - 1 \right) \qquad (V'(r) \geqslant 0, \, V(r) \leqslant 0), \qquad (14)$$

where the distance $\bar{r}$ is defined by

$$\bar{r} = \frac{\int_0^\infty dr \, r |V(r)| \exp[k^{-1} \int_r^\infty ds| \, V(s) \, |]}{\int_0^\infty dr \, |V(r)| \exp[k^{-1} \int_r^\infty ds| \, V(s) \, |]} . \qquad (15)$$

Similarly, for a repulsive potential with negative slope, by setting $\alpha = -1$ we obtain

$$\delta_k \leqslant 2k^{-1} \left(\exp\left[k^{-1} \int_0^\infty dr \, |V(r)| \right] - 1 \right) \qquad (V'(r) \leqslant 0, \, V(r) \geqslant 0), \qquad (16)$$

and by setting $\beta = 1$ we obtain

$$\delta_k \geqslant 2\bar{r} \left(1 - \exp\left[k^{-1} \int_0^\infty dr \, |V(r)| \right] \right) \qquad (V'(r) \leqslant 0, \, V(r) \geqslant 0), \qquad (17)$$

with $\bar{r}$ defined as in Eq. (15).

All these bounds become trivial if the integral $\int_0^\infty dr \mid V(r)|$ diverges. In such a case, a more stringent version of the theorem has to be used, which may be obtained from Eq. (12) by majorizing the circular functions more carefully. This is particularly easy in the case of a repulsive potential because we know from Chapter 4 that the quantity $kr + \delta(r)$ is positive and smaller than kr. Thus in majorizing the r.h.s. of Eq. (12), we may substitute in place of $\sin^2[kr + \delta(r)]$ either 1 or $(kr)^2$, whichever is more convenient, and in place of $\sin 2[kr + \delta(r)]$, either 1 or $2kr$. For instance, in this manner we may obtain, instead of Eq. (16), the upper bound

$$\delta_k \leqslant k^{-1} \left(\exp\left[2 \int_0^\infty dr \, rV(r) \right] - 1 \right) \qquad (V'(r) \leqslant 0, \, V(r) \geqslant 0), \qquad (18)$$

and, in place of Eq. (17), the lower bound

$$\delta_k \geqslant 2k^{-1} \left(1 - \exp\left[2 \int_0^\infty dr \, rV(r) \right] \right) \qquad (V'(r) \leqslant 0, \, V(r) \geqslant 0). \qquad (19)$$

These bounds may be compared with that provided by Wigner's theorem [29],

$$\delta_k \geqslant -R, \tag{20}$$

which is valid, however, only for potentials that vanish identically beyond the range R and only at high energy (if bound states are present; otherwise it holds at all energies [30]). Moreover, Wigner's theorem provides only a lower bound on the phase shift; this bound depends on the range of the potential, not on its strength. The bounds given here also depend on the strength of the potential, and are obviously more stringent than Wigner's bound if the energy is sufficiently large. An advantage of Wigner's bound is its simple physical interpretation.

In this chapter we have indicated how to obtain simple bounds for the phase shifts directly from the phase equation. A more powerful but perhaps less simple approach that also yields bounds for the scattering phase shifts will be introduced in Chapters 9 and 14.

We end this chapter mentioning that the recent results by Chadan previously quoted [30] imply the formula

$$\frac{\partial \delta_l(k, r)}{\partial k} = -\bar{r} - \pi^{-1} \int_{-\infty}^{+\infty} dk' \, (k' - k)^{-2}$$

$$\times \ln| \cos[(k' - k)\bar{r} + \delta_l(k', r) - \delta_l(k, r)] |, \qquad \bar{r} \geqslant r. \tag{21}$$

Here $\delta_l(k, r)$ is the phase function for angular momentum l and linear momentum k; the values of the phase function for negative k, which enter in the integral, are given by the symmetry property $\delta_l(k, r) = -\delta_l(-k, r)$ (see the end of Chapter 4). This equation holds for all values of r such that the potential $V(r')\theta(r - r')$ has no (l wave) bound states. Otherwise it must be replaced by the more general formula

$$\frac{\partial \delta_l(k, r)}{\partial k} = -\bar{r} - 2 \sum_{j=1}^{n_l(r)} q_j(r)[k^2 + q_j^2(r)]^{-1}$$

$$- \pi^{-1} \int_{-\infty}^{+\infty} dk' \, (k' - k)^{-2} \ln| \cos[(k' - k)\bar{r} + \delta_l(k', r)$$

$$- \delta_l(k, r) + \theta(k', r) - \theta(k, r)] |, \qquad \bar{r} \geqslant r, \tag{22}$$

where

$$\theta(k, r) = \sum_{j=1}^{n_l(r)} \arg\{[k - iq_j(r)]/[k + iq_j(r)]\}$$

$$= -2 \sum_{j=1}^{n_l(r)} \tan^{-1}[q_j(r)/k]. \tag{23}$$

In these equations $n_l(r)$ is the number of l-wave bound states possessed by the potential V cutoff at r, and the corresponding binding energies are $-q_j^2(r)$ (see Chapter 20). (Note that the quantities $q_j(r)$ and $\theta(k, r)$ depend also on l, although we have not explicitly indicated this dependence.)

These equations express the quantity $\partial\delta_l(k, r)/\partial k$ as an integral over the values of $\delta_l(k', r')$ for all k' and $r' = r$. It is interesting to compare these formulas with that which follows directly from the phase method, and which expresses the same quantity $\partial\delta_l(k, r)/\partial k$ as an integral over the values of $\delta_l(k', r')$ for $k' = k$ and all $r' \leqslant r$:

$$\partial\delta_l(k, r)/\partial k = k^{-2} \int_0^r ds\, V(s)\{\hat{D}_l(ks)[\hat{D}_l(ks) - 2ks\hat{D}_l'(ks)]$$

$$\times \sin^2[\hat{\delta}_l(ks) + \delta_l(k, s)] - ks \sin 2[\hat{\delta}_l(ks) + \delta_l(k, s)]\}$$

$$\times \exp\left\{-k^{-1} \int_s^r dt\, V(t)\hat{D}_l^2(kt) \sin 2[\hat{\delta}_l(kt) + \delta_l(k, t)]\right\}. \tag{24}$$

This equation is derived applying the same method used previously in this chapter, namely, performing a partial differentiation with respect to k on the phase equation and then solving formally the resulting linear first-order differential equation satisfied by the quantity $\partial\delta(k, r)/\partial k$ (considered as a function of r for fixed k).

8

Born approximation
and improved Born approximation

In this chapter we assume that the interaction is "weak," and we introduce and discuss approximate expressions for the evaluation of the scattering phase shifts. We take as definition of a "weak" potential the condition that the corresponding phase function always stays small, and, in particular, never reaches $\pi/2$ in modulus. Of course a potential may be weak at certain energies, but strong at other energies; in fact, all (regular) potentials become weak at sufficiently large energies.

Under this condition on the potential, we now derive approximate expressions for the phase shifts. It is actually more convenient to work with the tangent function rather than the phase function because it satisfies a simpler differential equation. We accordingly focus attention on the tangent of the scattering phase shift, rather than on the phase shift itself.

We recall the differential equation and boundary conditions satisfied by the tangent function. They are

$$t_l'(r) = -k^{-1}gV(r)[\hat{j}_l^2(kr) - 2\hat{j}_l(kr)\hat{n}_l(kr)t_l(r) + \hat{n}_l^2(kr)t_l^2(r)], \qquad (1)$$

$$t_l(0) = 0, \qquad (2)$$

$$t_l(\infty) = \tan \delta_l . \qquad (3)$$

We have introduced explicitly for convenience a "coupling constant" g. The assumed weakness of the potential guarantees that the function $t_l(r)$ is continuous.

This differential equation may be approached by iteration; in fact, several iterative schemes are possible. We indicate only two of these

43

possibilities, without delving into the question of their convergence, but restricting our consideration to the two approximate expressions obtained by stopping the iteration process after the first cycle.

The first iteration scheme is obtained by setting

$$t_l^{(n+1)\prime}(r) = -k^{-1}g V(r)[\hat{j}_l^2(kr) - 2\hat{j}_l(kr)\hat{n}_l(kr)t_l^{(n)}(r) + \hat{n}_l^2(kr)t_l^{(n)2}(r)], \qquad (4)$$

with

$$t_l^{(0)}(r) = 0. \qquad (5)$$

After the first cycle it yields the "Born approximation" for the tangent of the phase shift

$$(\tan \delta_l)_B = -k^{-1}g \int_0^\infty dr\ V(r)\hat{j}_l^2(kr). \qquad (6)$$

(Incidentally, although the terms that we have eliminated from the r.h.s. of the tangent equation (1) in order to obtain the Born approximation have coefficients diverging in the origin, we may assert from the known behavior of the tangent function in the origin, Eq. (3.7), that these terms not only do not diverge at the origin, but in fact vanish there faster than the remaining term.) After n cycles, the tangent of the phase shift appears as a polynomial of degree $2^n - 1$ in the "potential strength" or "coupling constant" g; the first n terms of this polynomial are not modified by the subsequent cycles and represent the first terms of the power expansion in g of the tangent of the phase shift.

It may be amusing to prove this explicitly, which may be done by induction, as follows. First, the recursion relation (4) implies that

$$t_l^{(n+1)\prime}(r) - t_l^{(n)\prime}(r) = -k^{-1}g V(r)\hat{n}_l(kr)[t_l^{(n)}(r) - t_l^{(n-1)}(r)]$$
$$\times\{-2\hat{j}_l(kr) + \hat{n}_l(kr)[t_l^{(n)}(r) + t_l^{(n-1)}(r)]\}. \qquad (7)$$

We then prove that

$$t_l^{(n)}(r) - t_l^{(n-1)}(r) = g^n d_l^{(n)}(r) + O(g^{n+1}). \qquad (8)$$

This equation is equivalent to our previous statement because it means that all the terms of lower order in g than g^n are the same in $t_l^{(n)}(r)$ and $t_l^{(n-1)}(r)$. To prove this equation, we note first of all that it is certainly true for $n = 1$; we then show that the assumption of its being true for n implies that it is true for $n + 1$. In fact, inserting it in the r.h.s. of Eq. (7), we obtain

$$t_l^{(n+1)\prime}(r) - t_l^{(n)\prime}(r) = -k^{-1}gV(r)\hat{n}_l(kr)[g^n d_l^{(n)}(r) + O(g^{n+1})]$$

$$\times\{-2\hat{j}_l(kr) + O(g)\}. \tag{9}$$

We have also used the fact that both $t_l^{(n)}(r)$ and $t_l^{(n-1)}(r)$ are of order g. From this equation we see that $t_l^{(n+1)}(r) - t_l^{(n)}(r)$ is of order g^{n+1}. Q.E.D. We also obtain the recursion relation

$$d_l^{(n+1)}(r) = 2k^{-1}\int_0^r ds\ V(s)\hat{j}_l(ks)\hat{n}_l(ks)\,d_l^{(n)}(s), \tag{10}$$

with

$$d_l^{(1)}(r) = -k^{-1}g\int_0^r ds\ V(s)\hat{j}_l{}^2(ks). \tag{11}$$

It should be emphasized, however, that knowledge of all the functions $d_l^{(n)}(r)$ is not sufficient for reconstructing the functions $t_l^{(n)}(r)$ and the tangent function $t_l(r)$. This is because, to know $t_l^{(n)}(r)$ to order g^n, we need not only $d_l^{(n)}(r)$, but also $t_l^{(n-1)}(r)$ to order g^n (*not* to order g^{n-1}).

The second iteration process obtains by setting

$$t^{(n+1)\prime}(r) = -k^{-1}gV(r)[\hat{j}_l{}^2(kr) - 2\hat{j}_l(kr)\hat{n}_l(kr)t_l^{(n+1)}(r)$$

$$+ \hat{n}_l{}^2(kr)(2t_l^{(n+1)}(r)t_l^{(n)}(r) - t_l^{(n)2}(r))], \tag{12}$$

$$t_l^{(0)}(r) = 0. \tag{13}$$

The reason for choosing this type of iteration scheme is that the term $2t_l^{(n+1)}(r)t_l^{(n)}(r) - t_l^{(n)2}(r)$ always provides an approximation *by defect* of $[t_l^{(n+1)}(r)]^2$, which is the corresponding term in the exact equation. This point is very important in certain cases because it implies that the successive approximations approach monotonically the exact value. This also implies that the approximate expressions provide rigorous bounds for the exact result, as will be discussed below. A general discussion of such an iteration scheme for differential equations has been given by Kalaba [31]. However, here we restrict ourselves to the discussion of the result obtained after the first cycle. Obviously the same result would also obtain with many other iteration schemes, the point being that we now neglect only the last term in the r.h.s. of Eq. (1), not the second one (or, of course, the first one). In this manner we obtain an approximate expression for the tangent of the phase shift, which we term "improved Born approximation." It reads

$$(\tan \delta_l)_{\text{BB}} = -k^{-1}g \int_0^\infty dr \, V(r)\hat{\jmath}_l^2(kr) \exp\left[2k^{-1}g \int_r^\infty ds \, V(s)\hat{\jmath}_l(ks)\hat{n}_l(ks)\right]. \quad (14)$$

Note that already after the first cycle the tangent of the phase shift does not appear as a polynomial in g. However, if it is expanded in powers of g, it yields a result correct up to the second order, as is obviously implied by its derivation.

This formula, which has also been independently rederived by Rosendorff and Tani [32], resembles the "high energy approximation" first introduced by Molière [33] and subsequently investigated by Glauber [34], inasmuch as in both cases an exponential correction term appears within the Born integral, to take approximately into account the deformation of the wave function in the potential region. (It may be easily verified that at least if the range $\bar{r}$ of the potential is small relative to k^{-1}, the exponential is larger than one for attractive potentials and smaller than one for repulsive potentials.) An advantage of the present derivation is that it makes more clear the limits of validity of this approximation and it allows a straightforward evaluation by iteration of subsequent correction terms. However, the Molière–Glauber approach yields an expression for the full scattering amplitude, which is more useful especially at high energy when many partial waves contribute.

Summarizing, we repeat that the Born approximation for the tangent of the phase shift, Eq. (6), is obtained by neglecting the second and third terms in the r.h.s. of the tangent equation (1), while the improved Born approximation (14) is obtained by neglecting only the third term. We therefore expect the latter to be more accurate generally than the former. Further support for this opinion is given in the following chapter, where we show that the improved Born approximation may also be obtained from a variational approach. Moreover, we shall prove that *it is an approximation by defect (or excess) for potentials that are nowhere repulsive (or attractive)*. (Equivalent statement: Under the conditions stated, *the improved Born approximation has the same sign and a smaller modulus than the tangent of the phase shift*.) The sign of the error of the Born approximation, instead, is not known *a priori*. However, there may be situations in which the Born approximation turns out to be more accurate than the improved Born approximation. Also, the improved Born approximation requires a double integration, and it is therefore sufficiently complicated to exclude in most cases the possibility of an evaluation in closed form. Specific examples of the results obtained with these approximations are given in Chapter 10.

This is probably a good place to comment also on the possibility of solving the phase equation, rather than the tangent equation, by iteration, namely, by setting

$$\delta_l^{(n+1)}(r) = -k^{-1}g \int_0^r ds\, V(s)[\cos \delta_l^{(n)}(s)\hat{j}_l(ks) - \sin \delta_l^{(n)}(s)\hat{n}_l(ks)]^2, \quad (15)$$

with

$$\delta_l^{(0)}(r) = 0. \tag{16}$$

Of course, after the first cycle, one again obtains the Born formula, this time for the phase shift itself—a reminder of the fact that the validity of the Born formula requires that the phase shift be small, so that the tangent does not differ appreciably from its argument. But now it is easy to prove that irrespective of the strength of the potential, this iteration scheme converges to the correct solution. However, because of the strong nonlinearity of the phase equation, the resulting expressions already become unmanageably complicated by the second cycle. The iteration scheme, however, may be successfully tested numerically.

9

Variational and extremum principles for evaluating scattering phase shifts

In this chapter we derive variational and extremum principles for evaluating scattering phase shifts. This we do by a straightforward application of the results of Appendix II to the phase equation and to the equation satisfied by the tangent function. Numerical examples are discussed in the following chapter.

Applying the variational principle equation (II.9) to the phase equation (3.14b), we secure

$$\delta_l = \operatorname*{stat}_{v} \left\{ -k^{-1} \int_0^\infty dr \; V(r) \hat{D}_l{}^2(kr) \right.$$

$$\times \left[\sin^2(\hat{\delta}_l(kr) + v(r)) - v(r) \sin 2(\hat{\delta}_l(kr) + v(r)) \right]$$

$$\left. \times \exp\left[-k^{-1} \int_r^\infty ds \; V(s) \hat{D}_l{}^2(ks) \sin 2(\hat{\delta}_l(ks) + v(s)) \right] \right\}. \tag{1}$$

The exact value of the phase shift is obtained by setting in the r.h.s.

$$v_{\text{opt}}(r) = \delta_l(r), \tag{2}$$

where $\delta_l(r)$ is the phase function.

An approximate expression for the phase shift, which is presumably superior to the Born approximation, is obtained by inserting the simple trial function $v(r) = 0$ in the variational expression given above, Eq. (1). We find in this manner the formula

$$\delta_l = -k^{-1} \int_0^\infty dr \; V(r) \hat{D}_l{}^2(kr) \sin^2 \hat{\delta}_l(kr)$$

$$\times \exp\left[-k^{-1} \int_r^\infty ds \; V(s) \hat{D}_l{}^2(ks) \sin 2\hat{\delta}_l(ks) \right]. \tag{3}$$

The r.h.s. of this expression is nothing but the "improved Born approximation" for the tangent of the phase shift, derived in the preceding chapter. There is a consistency in this coincidence because only if the phase function is quite small may we have confidence in this expression, which has been obtained by setting $v(r) = 0$ while we know that the correct result requires that $v(r)$ coincide with the phase function, Eq. (2). But if the phase function is small, the phase shift is also small, and therefore it does not differ appreciably from its tangent. On the other hand, we may take this coincidence as an indication that the improved Born approximation, as well as the Born approximation itself, is unreliable unless the phase shift is small. Further support for this indication is given below. We emphasize, however, one important difference between the improved Born approximation for the tangent of the phase shift, Eq. (8.14), and the "improved Born approximation" for the phase shift, Eq. (3): While the sign of the error associated with Eq. (3) is unknown *a priori*, the sign of the error associated with Eq. (8.14) is, in certain cases, known *a priori* (see below).

The variational principle of Appendix II may also be applied to the equation for the tangent of the phase function, Eq. (3.10). We thus obtain the following variational expression for the tangent of the phase shift:

$$\tan \delta_l = \underset{v}{\mathrm{stat}} \left\{ -k^{-1} \int_0^\infty dr\, V(r)[\hat{j}_l^2(kr) - v^2(r)\hat{n}_l^2(kr)] \right.$$

$$\left. \times \exp\left[2k^{-1} \int_r^\infty ds\, V(s)\hat{n}_l(ks)(\hat{j}_l(ks) - v(s)\hat{n}_l(ks)) \right] \right\}. \qquad (4)$$

The optimal trial function is now

$$v_{\mathrm{opt}}(r) = t_l(r), \qquad (5)$$

where $t_l(r)$ is the tangent function. Insertion of the simple trial function $v(r) = 0$ yields, as we expect by now, simply the improved Born approximation (8.14).

If the potential never changes sign—say, it is attractive everywhere—and provided it is weak in the sense of the previous chapter (the potential being everywhere attractive, this assumption corresponds simply to the requirement that the phase shift itself be smaller than $\pi/2$), we may apply to the equation for the tangent function, Eq. (3.10), the maximum principle of Appendix II, Eq. (II.25). We obtain

$$\tan \delta_l = \max_w \left\{ -k^{-1} \int_0^\infty dr \ V(r) \hat{j}_l^2(kr)[2 - w(r)]w(r) \right.$$

$$\left. \times \exp\left[2k^{-1} \int_r^\infty ds \ V(s) \hat{j}_l(ks) \hat{n}_l(ks) w(s) \right] \right\}. \qquad (6)$$

(The difference between this expression and Eq. (4), other than the substitution of *max* in place of *stat*, results from our use of the form (II.25) of the maximum principle, rather than Eq. (II.24). This difference is therefore only apparent because it corresponds to a redefinition of the trial functions, as is also clear from comparing Eqs. (5) and Eq. (7a), below.) The corresponding optimal trial function is

$$w_{\mathrm{opt}}(r) = 1 - t_l(r) \hat{n}_l(kr)/\hat{j}_l(kr), \qquad (7a)$$

or, equivalently, in terms of the radial wave function, the phase function and the amplitude function of Chapter 6,

$$w_{\mathrm{opt}}(r) = u_l(r)/[\alpha_l(r) \cos \delta_l(r) \hat{j}_l(kr)]. \qquad (7b)$$

The improved Born approximation is obtained with the choice $w(r) = 1$. It is therefore proved that under these conditions, the improved Born approximation is an approximation by defect.

Note that in the case now considered of a "weak" attractive potential, we have by definition

$$0 \leqslant \delta_l \leqslant \tan \delta_l < \infty. \qquad (8)$$

We emphasize that while we have now learned that the improved Born approximation—i. e., the r.h.s. of Eq. (3), for instance—provides an approximation by defect to $\tan \delta_l$, we do not know *a priori* whether it provides an approximation of δ_l by defect or by excess. A completely similar situation occurs in the case of a "weak" repulsive potential, except for the fact that all the inequalities are reversed, and *max* is replaced by *min*.

The advantages of an extremum principle such as Eq. (6) over a variational principle such as Eq. (4) are so important that we wish to draw attention to this point once more. In fact, while a variational principle often yields more accurate results than a first-order approximation such as the Born approximation, it has the disadvantage of giving no clue as to how to improve the accuracy (whereas the first-order approximation may be improved by computing the higher-order corrections, provided, of course, the situation is such that the series does converge). An extremum principle, on the other hand, while providing, with respect to accuracy, all the advantages connected with the stationary property of the functional, also yields a criterion for improving the approximation because it provides information for selecting the best one of several different trial functions. Moreover, it provides rigorous bounds on the quantity to be computed. Let us therefore repeat once more the two conditions required for the validity of Eq. (6): The potential must be nowhere repulsive, and the phase shift must be smaller than $\pi/2$. If the potential were nowhere attractive and the corresponding phase shift were larger than $-\pi/2$, we would have, in place of the maximum principle, a minimum principle obtained simply by substituting *min* for *max* in Eq. (6).

Finally, we comment on the choice of the trial function to feed into these principles. We know how the optimal trial functions are related to the (unknown) phase function or tangent function. On the other hand, we have given, in Chapter 4, considerable information on the qualitative behavior of these functions, which may be easily translated into information concerning the optimal trial function. The final decision on how to use all this information to construct a trial function resembling as much as possible the optimal one has to be tailored to the specific problem, with computing availability also kept in mind.

One disadvantage of the variational expressions derived above is the fact that they involve a double integration, which may only seldom be performed in closed form. This difficulty is also a feature of the improved Born approximation of the preceding chapter. It is, however, always possible to choose the trial function in the variational principle so as to trivialize one integration; equivalently, one may use the inequality given at the end of Appendix II. There results the following lower bound in modulus to the tangent of the scattering phase shift:

$$|\tan \delta| \geqslant \left| \frac{\int_0^\infty dr\, V(r)\hat{j}_l(kr)\hat{n}_l(kr)}{\int_0^\infty dr\, V(r)\hat{n}_l^2(kr)} L \left[k^{-1} \int_0^\infty dr\, V(r)\hat{j}_l(kr)\hat{n}_l(kr) \right] \right|. \quad (9)$$

The universal function $L(t)$ is defined, tabulated, and plotted in Appendix II. The usual conditions are required for the validity of Eq. (9): semidefiniteness of the potential and continuity of $\tan \delta(r)$, which is equivalent (for semidefinite potentials) to the requirement that $|\delta| < \pi/2$. Of course the result becomes trivial if the integral $\int_0^\infty dr\, V(r)\hat{n}_l^2(kr)$ diverges. Beside yielding a rigorous lower bound in modulus to the value of $\tan \delta$, which depends only on the two integrals $\int_0^\infty dr\, V(r)\hat{j}_l(kr)\hat{n}_l(kr)$ and $\int_0^\infty dr\, V(r)\hat{n}_l^2(kr)$, the expression in the r.h.s. of Eq. (9) may be useful for quick estimates of the value of $\tan \delta$; it may, but it need not, provide a better approximation to it than the Born approximation $(\tan \delta)_B$ or the improved Born approximation $(\tan \delta)_{BB}$ of the preceding chapter. To gauge its reliability, it may be recalled that the r.h.s. of Eq. (9) is obtained by inserting in the r.h.s. of Eq. (6) the trial function

$$w(r) = 2 - c\hat{n}_l(kr)/\hat{j}_l(kr), \tag{10}$$

and then adjusting the constant c to majorize the result. Because this trial function is rather different from the optimal one, Eq. (7), we do not expect this estimate to be generally accurate. For one example (which confirms this expectation), see the end of the following chapter.

10

Born approximation, improved Born approximation, variational and extremum principles. Examples

In this chapter we give some explicit examples of calculations using the approximate and variational methods discussed in the two preceding chapters. We discuss first a case that is as simple as possible, in order to be able to study it by analytical methods. We then consider some examples that have been computed numerically.

To be able to obtain some results in closed form we consider the very simple potential

$$V(r) = gR^{-1}\delta(r - R), \qquad R > 0, \tag{1}$$

where $\delta(x)$ is the Dirac distribution. To be sure, this is an idealized potential, but, as we shall see, it is good enough to provide an illustration of the main features of the approximate and variational expressions under discussion. We emphasize that the potential of Eq. (1) should be considered the limit of a finite potential that is very large but all concentrated in a narrow region, e.g., the limit of the "square well" potential

$$V_\epsilon(r) = gR^{-1}(2\epsilon)^{-1}\theta(r - R - \epsilon)\theta(r - R + \epsilon) \tag{2}$$

as ϵ vanishes. The dimensionless "coupling constant" g is a measure of the strength of the potential.

There is no difficulty in evaluating the Born approximation $(\tan \delta)_B$ to the tangent of the S-wave scattering phase shift, and its exact value $\tan \delta$. (We omit the subscript 0 or l whenever it may be done without ambiguity.) We find

$$(\tan \delta)_B = -g(kR)^{-1} \sin^2(kR), \tag{3}$$

$$\tan \delta = -g(kR)^{-1} \sin^2(kR)[1 + G]^{-1}, \tag{4}$$

53

with
$$G = g(2kR)^{-1} \sin 2kR. \tag{5}$$

The Born approximation, Eq. (3), is computed from Eq. (8.6); the exact value, Eq. (4), is computed from Eqs. (2.15) and (6.18). It is also possible, but nontrivial, to obtain the exact value from the phase equation, using the procedure applied below to compute the improved Born approximation.

To evaluate the improved Born approximation for the tangent of the phase shift, $(\tan \delta)_{BB}$, we insert in its definition, Eq. (8.14), the potential $V_\epsilon(r)$, Eq. (2), and after having performed the integrations we take the limit $\epsilon \to 0$. In this manner we obtain

$$(\tan \delta)_{BB} = -g(kR)^{-1} \sin^2(kR)[(2G)^{-1}(1 - e^{-2G})]. \tag{6}$$

It should be emphasized that a direct insertion of the deltalike potential equation (1) into Eq. (8.14) results in an ambiguous expression; the same happens if we introduce the deltalike potential in the phase equation.

Let us now compare these expressions. First of all it is verified that the Born approximation is correct up to the order g, while the improved Born approximation is correct up to the order g^2; in fact, an expansion around $G = 0$ yields

$$(2G)^{-1}[1 - e^{-2G}] = 1 - G + \tfrac{2}{3}G^2 + O(G^3), \tag{7}$$

while, of course,

$$(1 + G)^{-1} = 1 - G + G^2 + O(G^3). \tag{8}$$

(This implies that the condition of convergence of the Born series with this potential is $|G| < 1$.) Also, whenever $kR = n\pi$, n being a nonvanishing integer (which implies $G = 0$), the Born and improved Born approximations yield the correct result. The physical justification of this fact is that in such a case the potential acts just where the wave function vanishes, and therefore no nonlinear effects arise. We exclude this case from consideration in the discussion below.

A more interesting phenomenon occurs for very large $|g|$, which implies very large $|G|$. Of course, in this case the Born approximation is completely inadequate; in fact, it diverges, while the exact result tends to a constant value

$$\tan \delta = -\tan(kR)[1 + O(g^{-1})], \tag{9}$$

or, equivalently,

$$\delta = -kR[1 + O(g^{-1})], \qquad \text{mod } (\pi). \qquad (10a)$$

In the following we assume that g diverges through positive values, to avoid the ambiguous physical meaning of diverging attractive potentials (cf. the discussion in Chapter 15). We note, however, that depending on the value of kR, G may diverge to plus infinity, or it may diverge to minus infinity. There is a very significant difference between these two cases: In the former, as g increases from the value zero to infinity, $\tan \delta$ does not present any discontinuity; in the latter, it presents one discontinuity, which occurs at $G = -1$. Thus, recalling that one way to define the phase shift uniquely (i. e., without mod (π) ambiguity) is to assume that it vanishes at $g = 0$ and that it is a continuous function of g (see Chapters 2 and 4), we conclude that

$$-\pi/2 < \delta < 0 \qquad \text{if } G > -1, \qquad (11a)$$

$$-\pi < \delta < -\pi/2 \qquad \text{if } G < -1. \qquad (11b)$$

These equations are valid generally, and also in particular in the limit of large g, in which case they eliminate the mod (π) ambiguity of Eq. (10a).

Let us now investigate the validity of the improved Born approximation for very large g. We find

$$(\tan \delta)_{BB} = -\tfrac{1}{2} \tan(kR)[1 + O(g^{-1})] \qquad \text{for } G \gg -1, \qquad (10b)$$

$$(\tan \delta)_{BB} = \tfrac{1}{2} \tan(kR)e^{-2G}[1 + O(g^{-1})] \qquad \text{for } G \ll -1. \qquad (10c)$$

We thus see that in the latter case, the improved Born approximation gives a completely wrong result, which diverges exponentially with g; in the former, it gives one half of the correct result. Both of these findings can be easily understood, as indicated below; and on the basis of this interpretation we infer that they are of general validity, not merely limited to the very special potential under consideration.

The first thing to understand is the origin of the exact limiting result (9) or (10a). Recalling the discussion of Chapter 4, we see that this is simply the maximum negative value that the phase shift may achieve, if it is produced by a potential that vanishes identically beyond R. It is, in fact, simply the value of the phase shift produced by an infinitely repulsive potential of range R; the physical situation it represents is that of perfect reflection on a sphere of radius R. Thus it is quite obvious that this should be the limiting result, as the "coupling constant" g diverges, of the phase shift produced by a repulsive potential of any shape, provided it vanishes identically beyond R.

(Actually precisely the case we are considering is an exception because, as we have seen, the magnitude of the phase shift can never exceed π, even for large kR and g; while for a general (repulsive) potential of range R, the limiting value of the phase shift as g diverges is exactly kR. This feature has to do with the peculiar nature of a deltalike potential. At any rate, the important distinction is between the case when the modulus of the phase shift exceeds $\pi/2$ and the case when it is smaller than $\pi/2$, and a deltalike potential is adequate to illustrate this difference.)

We have understood the physical significance of the limiting value of the phase shift, Eq. (9) or (10a). It is also instructive to see how this comes about in the framework of the tangent equation

$$t'(r) = -k^{-1}V(r)[\sin^2 kr + 2t(r)\sin kr \cos kr + t^2(r)\cos^2 kr]. \quad (12)$$

We then see that as the potential becomes very large and positive, the tangent function is pushed close to the value $-\tan kr$, so that, by making the square bracket small in the r.h.s., it can reduce the derivative $t'(r)$ to a reasonable value, counterbalancing the effect of the large $V(r)$. (For a further analysis and a fruitful exploitation of this point of view see Chapter 15, where the case of singular potentials is discussed.)

Now that we have analyzed the exact value of the tangent of the phase shift for large g, let us return to the discussion of the improved Born approximation to it, Eqs. (10b) and (10c). The second case, $G \ll -1$, is easily understood: Because the exact phase shift is larger in modulus than $\pi/2$, Eq. (11b), the improved Born approximation does not work (recall its derivation, in Chapter 8 and especially in Chapter 9). The best it can do is yield a very large result, as an indication that the tangent has gone through an infinity.

The first case, $G \gg -1$, is more interesting. We recall that the improved Born approximation is derived neglecting the last term in the r.h.s. of the tangent equation (12), namely, reducing it to

$$t'_{\mathrm{BB}}(r) = -k^{-1}V(r)[\sin^2 kr + 2t_{\mathrm{BB}}(r)\sin kr \cos kr]. \quad (13)$$

Let us now use the same argument exploited before to obtain the limiting value of the function $t_{BB}(r)$, as $V(r)$ becomes very large. We require that the square bracket in the r.h.s. become very small and eventually vanish. We immediately obtain for $t_{BB}(r)$ the value $-\frac{1}{2} \tan kr$. The origin of the factor $\frac{1}{2}$ is thus understood. As previously remarked, the arguments used are sufficiently general to hold for any potential, not only for the deltalike one used as explicit example.

We conclude that the improved Born approximation is more accurate than the Born approximation for very weak potentials and also for very strong potentials, provided the corresponding phase function never exceeds $\pi/2$ in modulus. For very strong potentials, the improved Born approximation is off by a factor of $\frac{1}{2}$. (These potentials must be repulsive and of limited range $R < (\pi/2)k^{-1}$, to satisfy the previous condition. In the terminology of Chapter 8, such potentials are always weak.)

Having discussed our explicit example of a deltalike potential for very small and very large g, we consider it finally for all values of g, as given by Eq. (6). We see that the difference between the exact result and the improved Born approximation is the presence of the term $(2G)^{-1}[1 - \exp(-2G)]$ in the latter, in place of $(1 + G)^{-1}$ in the former. (The corresponding value for the Born approximation is unity.) These functions are compared in Fig. 1. It is of course verified that so long as the phase shift is smaller than $\pi/2$—i. e., for $G > -1$—the modulus of the improved Born approximation is smaller than that of the exact result. It should be emphasized that the present comparison includes cases of both repulsive and attractive potentials. Note that Fig. 1 also contains the result of a variational calculation, which is discussed immediately below.

Let us now turn to a discussion of the variational expressions (9.4) and (9.6) for the tangent of the phase shift. For the moment we restrict our discussion to the case $G > -1$; this condition, as we have seen, implies that the modulus of the phase shift is smaller than $\pi/2$, so that we are entitled to apply the extremum principle equation (9.6).

Let us investigate what we obtain if we substitute a constant in place of the trial function $w(r)$ in Eq. (9.6). We then secure, by performing the integrations as explained above, the variational result

$$(\tan \delta)_V = -g(kR)^{-1} \sin^2 kR \max_{w}[(2 - w)(2G)^{-1}(1 - e^{-2Gw})], \quad (14a)$$

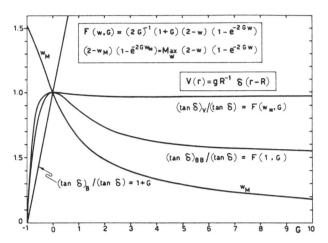

FIG. 1. Approximate evaluations of the tangent of the S-wave phase shift, for a delta-like potential. See text for explanation.

and we may assert that

$$| \tan \delta | \geqslant | (\tan \delta)_V | \geqslant | (\tan \delta)_{BB} |. \tag{15}$$

It is easily seen that the result (14) applies both in the attractive and in the repulsive cases.

(Incidentally, because of the peculiar nature of the potential we are considering, the result (14) obtains for any choice of the trial function $w(r)$ (with $w = w(R)$), provided it is a *continuous* function of r. For instance, it is easily verified that the result obtained by applying the procedure indicated at the end of Chapter 9,

$$| (\tan \delta)_V | = | \tan(kR)L(-G) |, \tag{14b}$$

coincides with Eq. (14a). On the other hand, the optimal trial function $w_{\mathrm{opt}}(r)$, Eq. (9.7a), is certainly not continuous here because the tangent function $t(r)$ is discontinuous at the distance R, where it jumps from the value zero to its final value, Eq. (4). This justifies the fact that, even by inserting an arbitrary (but continuous) function $w(r)$ in the extremum principle, we do not obtain the exact result.)

The function $\max_w \{(2 - w)(2G)^{-1}[1 - \exp(-2Gw)]\}$ has been computed numerically and its ratio to the corresponding function for the exact result, $(1 + G)^{-1}$, is plotted in Fig. 1. It is thus seen that the variational expression (14) provides a very good approximation (by defect in modulus) to tan δ for all values of G such that the phase shift δ is, in modulus, neither larger nor very close to $\pi/2$; and, in particular, it reproduces the exact result as G becomes very large. The optimal values w_M that correspond to the maximum in Eq. (14) are also plotted in Fig. 1. Note that as G diverges, w_M vanishes: in fact, it is easily seen that for large G, $w_M = (4G)^{-1} \ln(4G)$, which implies $(\tan \delta)_V = (\tan \delta)\{1 - (4G)^{-1}[\ln(4G) - 3]\}$. It may be recalled that the choice $w = 0$ corresponds simply to the elimination of the factor 2 in the second term in the bracket in the r.h.s. of Eq. (13), which, as discussed above, was the origin of the discrepancy at large G between the improved Born approximation and the exact result. This concludes our discussion of the deltalike potential of Eq. (1).

Let us return now to more ordinary potentials—in fact, just the same examples considered in Chapter 5—for which the Born approximation $\delta_B(r)$ and the improved Born approximation $\delta_{BB}(r)$ to the phase function $\delta(r)$ have been computed numerically. The corresponding results are plotted in Figs. 2–9 and are tabulated in Tables I and II. It should be emphasized that, while for convenience in the graphs and tables we have given the phase functions themselves rather than their tangents, the approximate phase functions are obtained by taking the inverse tangent of the approximate expressions for the tangent:

$$\delta_B(r) = \tan^{-1}\left[-k^{-1} \int_0^r ds\, V(s)\hat{j}_l^2(ks)\right], \tag{15a}$$

$$\delta_{BB}(r) = \tan^{-1}\left\{-k^{-1} \int_0^r ds\, V(s)\hat{j}_l^2(ks) \exp\left[2k^{-1} \int_s^r dt\, V(t)\hat{j}_l(kt)\hat{n}_l(kt)\right]\right\}. \tag{16}$$

The first case considered is the attractive Yukawa potential

$$V(r) = -(10/r)e^{-r}. \tag{17}$$

The corresponding results are plotted in Figs. 2–4 for various values of l and k. It is seen from these examples, which have been selected to exclude those cases in which the phase function becomes too large (see Chapter 5), that the improved Born approximation is almost always more accurate than the Born approximation. Note that both, by definition, can never exceed $\pi/2$. For very large k they become extremely accurate; e.g., for $l = 1$ and $k = 100$, they are so close to the exact values that they cannot be resolved in Fig. 4. A sample of the

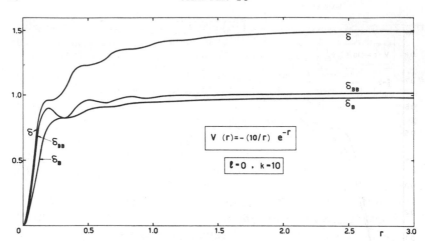

FIG. 2. Approximate and exact S-wave phase functions for an attractive potential. See text for explanation.

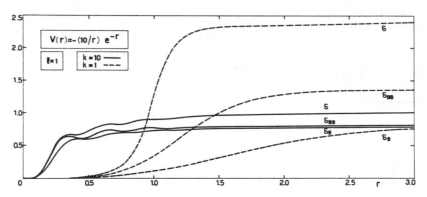

FIG. 3. Approximate and exact P-wave phase functions for an attractive potential. See text for explanation.

corresponding data is given in Table I; from these data it can be seen just how accurate these approximations become. It is remarkable that in this case the Born approximation turns out to be more accurate than the improved Born approximation. Of course in all the cases considered the improved Born approximation provides an approximation by defect; this also happens to the Born approximation. In fact it is easy to prove that at least for small kr, in the case of a nowhere repulsive potential the conditions $\delta(r) \geqslant \delta_{BB}(r) \geqslant \delta_B(r)$ hold (see Chapter 11).

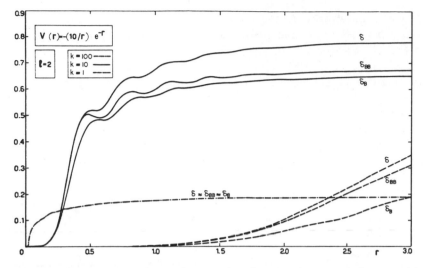

FIG. 4. Approximate and exact D-wave phase functions for an attractive potential. See text for explanation.

TABLE I

APPROXIMATE AND EXACT D-WAVE PHASE FUNCTIONS FOR AN
ATTRACTIVE POTENTIAL[a]

r	Born approximation[b] $\delta_B(r)$	Exact phase function $\delta(r)$	Improved Born approximation[c] $\delta_{BB}(r)$
0.1	0.125	0.125	0.124
0.5	0.182	0.184	0.182
1.0	0.200	0.201	0.198
3.0	0.211	0.213	0.2095
5.0	0.211	0.214	0.210

[a] For the attractive Yukawa potential $V(r) = -(10/r)\,e^{-r}$ for $l = 2$ and $k = 100$. These data are plotted in Fig. 4. The last digit shown may be in error by one unit.
[b] From Eq. (15).
[c] From Eq. (16).

We consider next the repulsive Yukawa potential

$$V(r) = (20/r)e^{-2r}. \qquad (18)$$

The corresponding results are plotted in Figs. 5–7, for various values of l and k. In this case, of course, the improved Born approximation provides an approximation by excess (by defect in modulus), while the Born approximation provides for small kr an approximation by defect (by excess in modulus). This phenomenon is easily accounted for by inspection of the phase equation; see the analogous discussion in Chapter 11. As regards accuracy, again we find that generally the

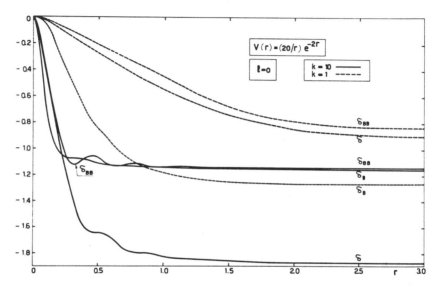

FIG. 5. Approximate and exact S-wave phase functions for a repulsive potential. See text for explanation.

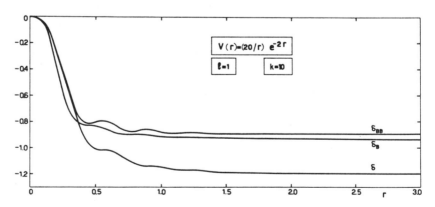

FIG. 6. Approximate and exact P-wave phase functions for a repulsive potential. See text for explanation.

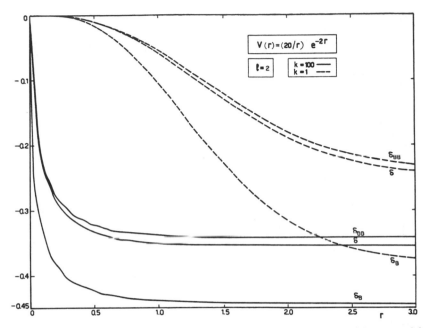

FIG. 7. Approximate and exact D-wave phase functions for a repulsive potential.
See text for explanation.

improved Born approximation is more accurate than the Born
approximation, although there are exceptions to this rule. Of course
a necessary condition for the approximate expressions to represent
accurately the exact phase function is that the latter do not exceed
$\pi/2$ in modulus.

Finally, we consider the potential obtained by superposition of the
two potentials discussed above:

$$V(r) = (20/r)e^{-2r} - (10/r)e^{-r}. \qquad (19)$$

This potential is repulsive at short distances and attractive at large
distances; it vanishes at $r \approx 0.7$. The corresponding approximate and
exact phase functions are plotted in Figs. 8 and 9 for various values
of l and k. Some of the corresponding data are collected in Table II.
In this case, because the potential does change sign, the improved
Born approximation need not be smaller in modulus than the exact
result; see, e. g., the $l = 0, k = 1$ case in Fig. 8. Of course, when r is
small, the features of the repulsive case are reproduced; at large

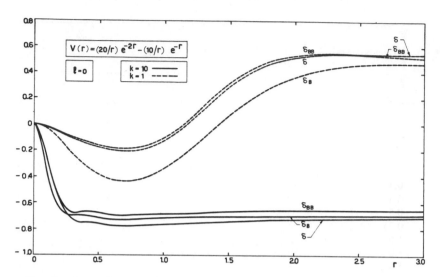

FIG. 8. Approximate and exact S-wave phase functions for a potential which is repulsive at short distances and attractive at large distances. See text for explanation.

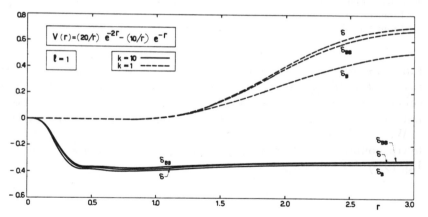

FIG. 9. Approximate and exact P-wave phase functions for a potential which is repulsive at short distances and attractive at large distances. See text for explanation.

values of r, the features of the repulsive case are still dominant if k is large, because in this case the phase function is mainly built up at small r (see, e. g., the $l = 0$, $k = 10$ case in Fig. 8). On the other hand, at values of l and k such that the phase function is mainly built up in the attractive region, the features of the approximate

TABLE II

APPROXIMATE AND EXACT P-WAVE PHASE FUNCTIONS FOR A POTENTIAL
THAT IS REPULSIVE AT SHORT DISTANCES AND
ATTRACTIVE AT LARGE DISTANCES[a]

r	Born approximation[b] $\delta_B(r)$	Exact phase function $\delta(r)$	Improved Born approximation[c] $\delta_{BB}(r)$
0.1	−0.0197	−0.0174	−0.0173
0.3	−0.329	−0.285	−0.2835
0.5	−0.385	−0.375	−0.364
0.75	−0.396	−0.382	−0.372
1.0	−0.385	−0.379	−0.365
3.0	−0.340	−0.319	−0.315
5.0	−0.334	−0.314	−0.309

[a] For the potential $V(r) = (20/r)\,e^{-2r} - (10/r)\,e^{-r}$ for $l = 1$ and $k = 10$. These data are plotted in Fig. 9. The last digit shown may be in error by one unit.

[b] From Eq. (15).

[c] From Eq. (16).

functions are those of the attractive case (see, e. g., the $l = 1$, $k = 1$ case in Fig. 9). Some of the data for the $l = 1$, $k = 10$ case are collected in Table II because the corresponding graphs in Fig. 9 are not sufficiently separated for a clear reading.

We end this chapter with one example of application of the simple lower bound in modulus $(\tan\delta)_L$ to the tangent of the phase shift, Eq. (9.9). We take as an example the "square well" potential

$$V(r) = V_0\theta(R - r); \qquad (20)$$

we recall that $(\tan\delta)_L$ vanishes for a potential singular as r^{-1} in the origin, so that an application to the cases considered above would yield a trivial result. The exact and approximate S-wave phase functions are given, for $r \leqslant R$, by the expressions

$$\delta(r) = -kr + \tan^{-1}[(k/p)\tan(kr)\tan pr], \qquad \text{if } k^2 \geqslant V_0,$$

$$= -kr + \tan^{-1}[(k/p)\tan(kr)\tanh pr], \qquad \text{if } k^2 \leqslant V_0, \qquad (21)$$

where

$$p = | k^2 - V_0 |^{1/2}, \tag{22}$$

$$\delta_B(r) = -\tan^{-1}\{[V_0/(2k^2)][kr - \tfrac{1}{2}\sin(2kr)]\}, \tag{23}$$

$$\delta_{BB}(r) = -\tan^{-1}\left\{[V_0/k^2]\int_0^{kr} dx\ \sin^2 x\ \exp[(V_0/2k^2)(\cos 2kr - \cos 2x)]\right\}, \tag{24}$$

$$\delta_L(r) = \tan^{-1}\{\sin^2(kr)[kr + \tfrac{1}{2}\sin(2kr)]^{-1}L[-(V_0/2k^2)\sin^2(kr)]\}. \tag{25}$$

The universal function L is defined, tabulated, and plotted in Appendix II.

These functions are plotted in Fig. 10 for the $V_0 = -1$, $k = 1$

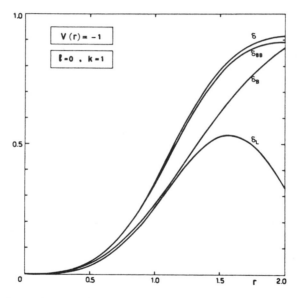

Fig. 10. Approximate and exact S-wave phase functions for an attractive square well potential. See text for explanation.

case. While it is easily verified that $\delta_L(r)$ provides a lower bound to $\delta(r)$, it turns out that the approximation is rather poor for all but very small values of r. This result—which would also be confirmed with other values of V_0 and k—might have been anticipated because the trial function that had to be inserted in the maximum principle to derive the bound of Eq. (9.9) provided a poor approximation to the optimal one, as already emphasized in Chapter 9.

11

Low-energy expansion.
Scattering length and effective range.
Bounds on the zero-energy cross section

In this chapter we discuss the low-energy behavior of scattering phase shifts. We pay special attention to the S wave, in which case we introduce, as is customary, the "scattering length" and the "effective range." The scattering length is discussed in detail; approximate and variational expressions are obtained and discussed and rigorous bounds are established. These bounds imply bounds on the zero-energy cross section: For nowhere attractive potentials we exhibit both upper and lower bounds; for nowhere repulsive potentials we exhibit only lower bounds, and only if the potential is not sufficiently attractive to possess bound states. Numerical examples are considered in the following chapter.

We assume in this chapter that the potential vanishes asymptotically at least as an exponential. As is well known, this implies that the partial wave scattering amplitude or, for that matter, the scattering phase shift, is an analytic function of k in the neighborhood of $k = 0$. We are therefore allowed to introduce a (convergent) power expansion in k of the scattering quantities, as a convenient tool for the study of their low-energy behavior. It should be mentioned, however, that Levy and Keller [10] have found it convenient to use this same approach to discuss the low-energy behavior of the scattering phase shift in the case of long-range potentials (in particular, potentials vanishing at infinity as inverse powers of r), namely, in the case when the phase shifts are not analytic functions of k at $k = 0$.

We concentrate our attention on the tangent function $t_l(r)$, and we set

$$t_l(r) = k^{2l+1}[a_l(r) + k^2 b_l(r) + O(k^4)]. \tag{1}$$

(Incidentally, this expansion is always convergent for finite r and sufficiently small k, independent of the asymptotic behavior of the potential because $t_l(r)$ is the tangent of the phase shift for a potential that vanishes identically beyond r. What happens in the case of potentials that vanish slowly at infinity is that the radius of convergence of this power expansion vanishes as r diverges; this is usually manifested by the lack of convergence of some or all of the coefficients $a_l(r)$, $b_l(r)$, etc., as r diverges. See below and, for a complete discussion, see Ref. [10].)

Inserting this expansion in the equation satisfied by the tangent function, Eq. (3.10), and equating the coefficients of equal powers of k, we find the differential equations

$$a_l'(r) = -V(r)\left[\frac{r^{l+1}}{(2l+1)!!} + r^{-l}(2l-1)!!a_l(r)\right]^2, \qquad (-1)!! = 1, \quad (2)$$

$$b_l'(r) = -V(r)\left[\frac{r^{l+1}}{(2l+1)!!} + r^{-l}(2l-1)!!a_l(r)\right]$$

$$\times \left[\frac{-r^{l+3}}{(2l+3)!!} + r^{-l}(2l-1)!!\left(\frac{r^2 a_l(r)}{(2l-1)} + 2b_l(r)\right)\right]. \qquad (3)$$

On the other hand, the boundary condition equation (3.7) implies for $a_l(r)$ and $b_l(r)$ the conditions

$$a_l(r) \xrightarrow[r\to0]{} -\frac{V_0 r^{2l+3-m}}{(2l+3-m)[(2l+1)!!]^2} \xrightarrow[r\to0]{} 0, \qquad (4)$$

$$b_l(0) = 0. \qquad (5)$$

It is interesting to note that the equation satisfied by $b_l(r)$ is linear, so that $b_l(r)$ may be obtained by quadrature, once the function $a_l(r)$ is known. This is also true for all the subsequent terms in the expansion of Eq. (1); they all satisfy linear first-order differential equations, and each may therefore be evaluated by quadrature once the previous terms have been obtained.

The only functions that satisfy nonlinear equations—in fact, Riccati equations—are the leading coefficients $a_l(r)$. It is convenient to renormalize them (for $l \neq 0$) by the substitution

$$\alpha_l(r) = (2l+1)!!(2l-1)!!a_l(r). \qquad (6)$$

(These $\alpha_l(r)$, however, have nothing to do with the amplitude functions of Chapter 6.) We find for these functions the differential equations

$$\alpha_l'(r) = -(2l+1)^{-1}V(r)[r^{l+1} + r^{-l}\alpha_l(r)]^2, \tag{7}$$

with boundary conditions

$$\alpha_l(r) \xrightarrow[r\to 0]{} -\frac{V_0 r^{2l+3-m}}{(2l+3-m)(2l+1)} \xrightarrow[r\to 0]{} 0. \tag{8}$$

We recall that, as implied by Eq. (1), the dimensions of $\alpha_l(r)$ are those of a length raised to the power $2l+1$. Note that the existence of $\alpha_l(\infty)$ is implied by our assumption on the asymptotic vanishing of the potential.

Particularly interesting is the case $l = 0$, because in this case the function $a(r)$ yields asymptotically the "scattering length" a, whose square multiplied by 4π equals the total zero-energy cross section σ. (We drop the subscript zero on this function.) This function satisfies the remarkably simple equation

$$a'(r) = -V(r)[r + a(r)]^2, \tag{9}$$

with boundary condition

$$a(r) \xrightarrow[r\to 0]{} -\frac{V_0 r^{3-m}}{3-m} \xrightarrow[r\to 0]{} 0. \tag{10}$$

Incidentally, if we relax for a moment the restriction on the asymptotic vanishing of the potential, it will be noticed that from this equation we can read off immediately a condition on the asymptotic behavior of the potential sufficient to guarantee the existence of a finite scattering length (unless a zero-energy resonance occurs; see below), and therefore also of a finite zero-energy total cross section. This condition is

$$\int^R dr\, r^2|\,V(r)\,| \xrightarrow[R\to\infty]{} \text{finite}, \tag{11a}$$

for whose validity it is sufficient that the potential vanish asymptotically faster than r^{-3}:

$$\lim_{r\to\infty} r^3 V(r) = 0. \tag{11b}$$

More generally, we may infer from Eq. (7) the condition that the potential is required to satisfy in order to have a finite limit $\alpha_l(\infty)$:

$$\int^R dr \, r^{2l+2} V(r) \xrightarrow[R\to\infty]{} \text{finite},$$

(11c)

or, equivalently,

$$\lim_{r\to\infty} r^{2l+3} V(r) = 0.$$

(11d)

If this condition is satisfied, the dominant term in the low-energy behavior of the phase shift δ_l is $a_l(\infty)k^{2l+1}$. (In this discussion we have disregarded the possibility that a zero-energy bound state or resonance exists, in which case $\alpha_l(\infty)$ diverges; see below.)

The functions $\alpha_l(r)$, solutions of Eq. (7), need not be bounded. It is easily seen, however, that they are bounded if the potential is nowhere attractive, because in this case the same argument as that used in Chapter 4 yields the restriction

$$-r^{2l+1} \leqslant \alpha_l(r) \leqslant 0.$$

(12)

In fact, from this inequality and from the differential equation (7), we also infer in this case the restriction

$$\alpha_l(r) \geqslant \alpha_l^B(r) = -(2l+1)^{-1} \int_0^r ds \, s^{2l+2} V(s),$$

(13)

where $\alpha_l^B(r)$ is obviously the Born approximation. Combining Eq. (13) with Eq. (12), we may also write

$$\alpha_l(r) \geqslant -R^{2l+1} - (2l+1)^{-1} \int_R^r ds \, s^{2l+2} V(s), \qquad r \geqslant R,$$

(14)

where R is an arbitrary distance. This relationship may be more stringent than Eq. (13) in the case of strongly repulsive potentials and, in particular, in the case of potentials strongly singular in the origin (in which case it remains valid; see Chapter 15).

From Eq. (13) we obtain the upper bound for the zero-energy cross section,

$$\sigma \leqslant \sigma_B = 4\pi \left| \int_0^\infty dr \, r^2 V(r) \right|^2.$$

(15)

We emphasize that this upper bound holds for a nowhere attractive-potential. A more general bound is obtained from Eq. (14):

$$\sigma \leqslant 4\pi \left| R + \int_R^\infty dr\, r^2 V(r) \right|^2, \tag{16}$$

which is reduced to the previous one by setting the arbitrary constant R at zero. In particular, for any repulsive potential that vanishes identically beyond the range $\bar{r}$, we obtain from this inequality, by setting $R = \bar{r}$, the bound

$$\sigma \leqslant 4\pi\bar{r}^2. \tag{17}$$

This corresponds to the simple statement that any repulsive potential of range $\bar{r}$ yields a zero-energy cross section smaller than a hard sphere of radius $\bar{r}$ (i. e., an infinitely repulsive potential of range $\bar{r}$).

On the other hand, if the potential is attractive, the solution $\alpha_l(r)$ of Eq. (7) need not be continuous. Actually, as will be shown later, the number of discontinuities of $\alpha_l(r)$ in the interval from zero to infinity equal the number of bound states with angular momentum l —a fact closely linked with Levinson's theorem [27], as will be shown in Chapter 22.

However, if the potential is nowhere repulsive but so weak as to have no bound states, so that the functions $\alpha_l(r)$ are continuous, then by inspection from Eq. (7) and the fact that $\alpha_l(r)$ is positive, we obtain the lower bound

$$\alpha_l(r) \geqslant \alpha_l^B(r) = -(2l+1)^{-1} \int_0^r ds\, s^{2l+2} V(s). \tag{18}$$

This implies for the zero-energy cross section the bound

$$\sigma \geqslant 4\pi \left| \int_0^\infty dr\, r^2 V(r) \right|^2. \tag{19}$$

We repeat that this lower bound holds for a nowhere repulsive potential, provided it does not possess any bound state.

Much better bounds and approximations are of course obtained using the extremum principle of Appendix II. In the case of a nowhere attractive potential we thus find, from Eq. (II.25),

$$\alpha_l(r) = \min_w \left\{ -(2l+1)^{-1} \int_0^r ds\ s^{2l+2} V(s)[2-w(s)]w(s) \right.$$

$$\left. \times \exp\left[-2(2l+1)^{-1} \int_s^r dt\ t V(t)w(t) \right] \right\}. \tag{20}$$

The optimal trial function is

$$w_{\text{opt}}(r) = 1 + \alpha_l(r)/r^{2l+1}, \tag{21}$$

and from the inequality (12) we may conclude that

$$0 \leqslant w_{\text{opt}}(r) \leqslant 1. \tag{22}$$

Moreover, the behavior of $\alpha_l(r)$ in the origin, Eq. (8) and the fact that it tends asymptotically to a constant imply that

$$w_{\text{opt}}(0) = w_{\text{opt}}(\infty) = 1. \tag{23}$$

In particular, for the scattering length a, we obtain from Eq. (20) the representation

$$a = \min_w \left\{ -\int_0^\infty dr\ r^2 V(r)[2-w(r)]w(r)\ \exp\left[-2\int_r^\infty ds\ s V(s)w(s) \right] \right\}. \tag{24}$$

Setting $w(s) = 1$, we secure a lower bound for the scattering length, which is recognized as the "improved Born approximation," namely,

$$a \leqslant a_{\text{BB}} = -\int_0^\infty dr\ r^2 V(r) \exp\left[-2\int_r^\infty ds\ s V(s) \right]. \tag{25}$$

Thus, for the zero-energy cross section σ on a nowhere attractive potential, we have the upper and lower bounds

$$4\pi \left| \int_0^\infty dr\ r^2 V(r) \exp\left\{ -2\int_r^\infty ds\ s V(s) \right\} \right|^2 \leqslant \sigma \leqslant 4\pi \left| R + \int_R^\infty dr\ r^2 V(r) \right|^2, \tag{26}$$

where R is an arbitrary nonnegative constant. These inequalities imply the less stringent but simpler condition

$$4\pi I_2^2 e^{-4I_1} \leqslant \sigma \leqslant 4\pi I_2^2 = \sigma_{\text{B}}, \tag{27}$$

where we define

$$I_p = \int_0^\infty dr\, r^p V(r). \tag{28}$$

(The dimensions of I_p are those of a length raised to the power $p - 1$; I_1 is dimensionless.) It should be emphasized that Eq. (27) provides a controlled approximation for the zero-energy cross section on a nowhere attractive potential that requires the knowledge of only the first two moments of the potential.

Another interesting lower bound in modulus for the scattering length follows immediately from Eq. (II.35). It reads

$$|a| \geqslant |(I_1/I_0)L(-I_1)|, \tag{29}$$

where the universal function $L(t)$ is defined, tabulated, and plotted in Appendix II (Eq. (II.36), Table II.I, and Fig. II.1). This lower bound for $|a|$ requires only the knowledge of the first two moments of the potential; it becomes completely trivial, however, if the potential diverges in the origin as r^{-1} or faster, because in such a case I_0 diverges. It implies for the zero-energy cross section the lower bound

$$\sigma \geqslant 4\pi(I_1/I_0)^2[L(-I_1)]^2. \tag{30}$$

If the potential is nowhere repulsive but not attractive enough to possess bound states, we may apply again the extremum principle of Appendix II—in this case, a maximum principle—to the differential equation (7). We do not write the results obtained in this manner because they are identical with those for the repulsive case, except for the substitution of *max* in place of *min* and for the reversal of some inequalities. But we emphasize that in this case we obtain from the improved Born approximation a lower bound for the zero-energy cross section that is more stringent than that previously given (Eq. (19)), namely,

$$\sigma \geqslant 4\pi \left| \int_0^\infty dr\, r^2 V(r) \exp\left[-2\int_r^\infty ds\, s V(s)\right] \right|^2. \tag{31}$$

However, in this case we are not entitled to extend the integration in the exponent from zero to infinity; thus to obtain this bound it is necessary to perform a double integration. On the other hand, a simpler bound, which requires only the knowledge of the first two moments of the potential, is provided by Eqs. (29) and (30), which remain valid in this case. In certain cases, however, this bound is less stringent than that provided by the Born approximation, Eq. (19); there are also cases in which it is *more* stringent than either the Born approximation, Eq. (19), or the improved Born approximation, Eq. (31). For one example, see the following chapter.

It should be emphasized that in the case of attractive potentials we do not obtain any upper bound for the zero-energy cross section.

If the potential is sufficiently attractive to possess bound states, the solutions $\alpha_l(r)$ of Eq. (7) are not continuous (see Chapters 20 and 22 and Appendix IV). It is then convenient to adopt the usual trick, namely, to introduce new functions $\mu_l(r)$ through

$$\alpha_l(r) = R^{2l+1} \tan \mu_l(r). \tag{32}$$

Here R is an arbitrary positive constant, with the dimensions of a length. This equation defines the functions $\mu_l(r)$ only $\mathrm{mod}(\pi)$; an absolute definition obtains if we require their continuity, together with the boundary condition

$$\mu_l(0) = 0. \tag{33}$$

That we may require these functions to be continuous follows from the form of the equations they satisfy, which are derived by substitution in Eq. (7). The equations are

$$\mu_l'(r) = -(2l+1)^{-1}RV(r)[(r/R)^{l+1}\cos\mu_l(r) + (r/R)^{-l}\sin\mu_l(r)]^2. \tag{34}$$

Of course, whenever the value of $\mu_l(r)$ is an odd multiple of $\pi/2$, the corresponding $\alpha_l(r)$ suffers a discontinuity. Equation (32) implies that the distances b_i at which $\mu_l(b_i)$ has values that are multiples of $\pi/2$ are independent of the choice of the scale constant R, although the value of $\mu_l(r)$ at all other points does depend on it. The use of the variables $\mu_l(r)$ and of the equation (34) that they satisfy is obviously the most convenient approach for evaluating the quantities $\alpha_l(r)$ whenever the potential is attractive and strong; the variables $\mu_l(r)$ may prove useful in all cases. Approximate and variational calculations of the coefficients $\alpha_l(r)$ may be performed on the basis of Eq. (34), with the advantage of not having to worry about divergences. Because by now the procedure for obtaining such results has been repeatedly illustrated, we leave it to the interested reader to derive the explicit expressions. But we emphasize that the methods of Appendix II produce now, even for semidefinite potentials, only variational expressions, because the extremum principle can not be applied to this equation.

As a matter of curiosity we mention the possibility of casting Eq. (34) into a form that is formally identical to the phase equation in the S-wave case. This is achieved by the substitutions

$$r = R(\tan ks)^{\lambda}, \qquad \lambda = (2l+1)^{-1}, \tag{35a}$$

$$\mu_l(r) = \nu_l(s), \tag{35b}$$

which transform Eqs. (34) and (33) into the form

$$\nu_l'(s) = -k^{-1}W_l(k, s) \sin^2[ks + \nu_l(s)], \tag{36a}$$

$$\nu_l(0) = 0, \tag{36b}$$

with

$$W_l(k, s) = \lambda^2 kR^2(\sin ks)^{2(\lambda-1)}(\cos ks)^{-2(\lambda+1)} V[R(\tan ks)^{\lambda}] \tag{37a}$$

$$= (2l+1)^{-2}kR^{-2}[R^2(r/R)^{-2l} + r^2(r/R)^{2l}]^2 V(r). \tag{37b}$$

The quantities α_l are then given by the equation

$$\alpha_l = \alpha_l(\infty) = R^{2l+1} \tan[\nu(\tfrac{1}{2}\pi/k)]. \tag{38}$$

Finally, we mention the possibility of using the differential equation (3) to obtain information on the second coefficient of the expansion equation (1). In particular, in the S-wave case, $b_0(\infty) \equiv b$ is simply connected to the so-called effective range parameter. A closed expression for b in terms of the "scattering length function" $a(r)$, obtained by solving the differential equation, is

$$b = \int_0^{\infty} dr\, V(r)r^2[r + a(r)][a(r) + r/3] \exp\left\{-2\int_r^{\infty} ds\, V(s)[s + a(s)]\right\}. \tag{39}$$

Approximate expressions and bounds for b may be obtained from this expression, using the information on $a(r)$ previously discussed. For instance, setting $a(r)$ at zero within the integral we obtain a kind of improved Born approximation for b:

$$b_{\mathrm{BB}} = \frac{1}{3}\int_0^{\infty} dr\, r^4 V(r) \exp\left[-2\int_r^{\infty} ds\, s V(s)\right]. \tag{40}$$

Note, however, that only in the case of a nowhere repulsive potential which does not possess bound states do we know *a priori* the sign of the error associated with this approximation; in fact, in this case, Eq. (40) provides an upper bound to b (lower bound in modulus; b is negative). On the other hand, for nowhere attractive potentials it is easy to derive directly from Eqs. (39) and (12) the upper and lower bounds

$$-\frac{1}{9}\int_0^\infty dr\, r^4 V(r) \leqslant b \leqslant \frac{1}{3}\int_0^\infty dr\, r^4 V(r). \tag{41}$$

12

The scattering length and its approximate and variational expressions. Examples

In this chapter we discuss some explicit instances of approximate calculations of the scattering length. We limit our discussion to very simple examples, which may be treated almost completely by analytical methods, without recourse to numerical computations. We also mention that another example of approximate evaluation of the scattering length is given, for a singular potential, in Chapter 15.

We recall the definitions of the Born and improved Born approximations for the scattering length:

$$a_{\rm B} = - \int_0^\infty dr\, r^2 V(r), \tag{1}$$

$$a_{\rm BB} = - \int_0^\infty dr\, r^2 V(r) \exp\left[-2\int_r^\infty ds\, s V(s)\right]. \tag{2}$$

We shall also discuss the variational approximation, defined by

$$a_{\rm V} = \min_w \left\{ -(2-w)w \int_0^\infty dr\, r^2 V(r) \exp\left[-2w\int_r^\infty ds\, s V(s)\right] \right\}. \tag{3}$$

This is obtained from the exact expression, Eq. (11.24), by inserting a constant w in place of the trial function $w(r)$. The expression as it is written here applies to a nowhere attractive potential, in which case it provides an approximation by excess (by defect in modulus) to the exact value a. In the case of attractive potentials, *max* should be inserted in place of *min*; in this case, the approximation is by defect if the potential has no bound states. (This condition is also necessary for the approximation to be of any validity; see below.) At the end we provide one example of the lower bound in modulus

77

to the scattering length, which requires only the evaluation of the first two moments of the potential, Eq. (11.29).

The first potential we consider is the cut-off Coulomb potential

$$V(r) = [g/(rR)]\theta(R - r).\qquad(4)$$

For dimensional reasons the scattering length in this case is a function of the dimensionless coupling constant g times the dimensional quantity R. We will assume that R is unity; this merely fixes the scale.

The exact value of the scattering length produced by the potential equation (1) is easily evaluated, and we find

$$a = -\frac{J_2(2\sqrt{-g})}{g J_0(2\sqrt{-g})}\qquad(5a)$$

$$= -\frac{\sum_{k=1}^{\infty} g^k/[(k + 1)!(k - 1)!]}{\sum_{k=0}^{\infty} g^k/(k!)^2}.\qquad(5b)$$

In Eq. (5a), the functions $J_p(x)$ are standard Bessel functions. Of course for a repulsive potential, $g > 0$, the scattering length is negative; for an attractive potential, $g < 0$, the scattering length is positive if $g > -1.446$, i. e., if the potential is too weak to possess a bound state. At $g = -1.446$, the scattering length has a pole.

We now consider the Born approximation, the improved Born approximation, and the variational approximation to the scattering length, which in this case are also easily evaluated. We find

$$a_B = -g/2,\qquad(6)$$

$$a_{BB} = -\tfrac{1}{2}[1 - (2g)^{-1}(1 - e^{-2g})],\qquad(7)$$

$$a_V = \tfrac{1}{2}(-|g|/g)\max_{w}\{(2 - w)[1 - (2gw)^{-1}(1 - e^{-2gw})]\}.\qquad(8)$$

The maximum operation in the last equation must be performed numerically.

Equations (6)–(8) have been plotted in Fig. 1, together with the exact result, Eq. (5). Some of the corresponding numerical data are also displayed in Table I because the accuracy of the approximation a_V is so good that for most of the values of g in the figure the plots of a_V and a cannot be resolved. In fact, for all positive values of g, a_V approximates a within 0.5 percent or better. Note that in Table I

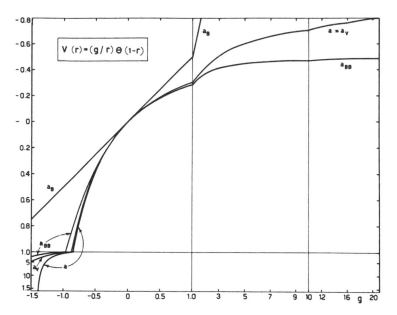

Fig. 1.   Scattering length for the potential $V(r) = (g/r)\, \theta(1 - r)$.

we have also recorded, for each value of g, the value of w that corresponds to the maximum in Eq. (8).

From these results we conclude that the Born approximation is applicable only if the coupling constant is small; for $|g| \sim 1$ it has already broken down completely. The improved Born approximation is applicable over a much larger range; of course, for negative g (attractive potential), it also breaks down completely as we approach the pole, and it is very accurate only for very small values of g owing to the rapid change of a with g; while for positive values of g, it remains accurate over a wide range, and it is reasonable for all values of g (see below). It should be emphasized that, although at small g the improved Born approximation reproduces the expansion of a in powers of g (Born expansion) to order g^2, for large positive values of g it is much better, because any approximation consisting of a finite number of terms of the Born expansion diverges as g diverges. Moreover, for positive values of g, it provides an approximation by excess while the Born approximation provides an approximation by defect. These properties remain true for any repulsive potential, as was already noted in the preceding chapter. They are, however, not

TABLE I

EXACT AND APPROXIMATE VALUES OF THE
SCATTERING LENGTH FOR THE POTENTIAL $V(r) = (g/r)\theta(1 - r)$ [a]

Coupling constant g	Born approxi-mation[b] a_B	Improved Born approxi-mation[c] a_{BB}	Exact scattering length[d] a	Variational approxi-mation[e] a_V	Optimal value of w
20	−10	−0.4875	−0.7893	−0.7889	0.2235
15	−7.5	−0.4833	−0.7591	−0.7585	0.2578
10	−5	−0.4750	−0.7100	−0.7090	0.3144
5	−2.5	−0.4500	−0.6066	−0.6049	0.4342
2	−1	−0.3773	−0.4368	−0.4351	0.6224
1	−0.5	−0.2838	−0.3022	−0.3013	0.7568
0.5	−0.25	−0.1839	−0.1880	−0.1877	0.8586
0.1	−0.05	−0.04683	−0.046881	−0.046875	0.9678
−0.1	0.05	0.05351	0.053580	0.053571	1.0345
−0.5	0.25	0.3591	0.3771	0.3734	1.1945
−1.0	0.5	1.097	1.576	1.136	1.420
−1.3	0.65	1.897	6.201	2.861	1.537
−1.4	0.7	2.258	21.18	3.704	1.570
−1.45	0.725	2.461	−238.6	4.223	1.585

[a] As a function of the coupling constant g. The exact scattering length has a pole at $g = -1.446$. The data in this table are plotted in Fig. 1.
[b] From Eq. (6). [c] From Eq. (7). [d] From Eq. (5). [e] From Eq. (8).

shared by the second-order Born approximation, which in this case, for instance, is

$$a_B^{(2)} = -\tfrac{1}{2}g + \tfrac{1}{3}g^2; \qquad (9)$$

therefore for $g = 0.1$ it yields the value $a_B^{(2)} = -0.04667$, which is an approximation by excess, while for $g = 0.5$ it yields the value $a_B^{(2)} = -0.1889$, which is an approximation by defect (see Table 12.I). As regards the variational approximation, we have already noted that it is very accurate for all positive values of g; for negative g it breaks down as the pole is approached. Of course, the variational approximation is, by its very definition, always more accurate than the improved Born approximation, at least for $g > -1.446$.

Finally, as g diverges to negative infinity, both a_{BB} and a_V diverge exponentially; while as g diverges to positive infinity, a_V converges to -1 (i. e., to the correct value) while a_{BB} tends to $-1/2$. In fact, we have, for positive g,

$$a = -1 + g^{-1/2} + O(g^{-1}), \tag{10}$$

$$a_V = -1 + g^{-1/2} + O(g^{-1}), \tag{11}$$

$$a_{BB} = -\tfrac{1}{2} + \tfrac{1}{4}g^{-1} + O(g^{-2}). \tag{12}$$

We do not expand on the explanation of this behavior, because it already has been clarified at the beginning of Chapter 10, and the discussion given there applies here without modification. Again we emphasize the general validity of these conclusions for any cut-off potential.

The second example that we consider is the cut-off "centrifugal" potential

$$V(r) = gr^{-2}\theta(R - r). \tag{13}$$

Because this potential is singular, and singular attractive potentials lead to ambiguities (see Chapter 15), we shall restrict our discussion to the repulsive case, $g > 0$.

It is very easy to evaluate the exact function $a(r)$ apposite to this potential. In fact, setting

$$a(r) = rA(r) \tag{14}$$

in Eq. (11.9), we find

$$rA'(r) = -g[1 + A(r)]^2 - A(r), \tag{15}$$

which admits two constant solutions,

$$A_\pm = -1 - (2g)^{-1}[1 \pm (1 + 4g)^{1/2}]. \tag{16}$$

It is easy to convince oneself (see also Chapter 15) that the physical solution $a(r)$ corresponds to the "minus" solution A_-. Thus we have

$$a(r) = -r\{1 + (2g)^{-1}[1 - (1 + 4g)^{1/2}]\}, \tag{17}$$

and the scattering length is the value of this function for $r = R$.

On the other hand, for the Born and improved Born approximations, we find

$$a_B(r) = -rg, \tag{18}$$

$$a_{BB}(r) = -rg/(1 + 2g). \tag{19}$$

A comparison of these approximate results with the exact one leads to the same conclusions as in the previous case. Of course, the fact that in this case all the expressions for the scattering length function are proportional to r could have been anticipated on dimensional grounds because the potential of Eq. (13) contains no dimensional constant other than the cutoff R.

A remarkable property of this example is that the variational approximation, Eq. (3), yields the exact result, Eq. (17), as is discovered by a simple calculation. This phenomenon is easily understood on the basis of Eqs. (11.21) and (17), which imply that in this case the optimal trial function is a constant, so that the transition from the exact equation (11.24) to Eq. (3) does not entail any approximation.

In conclusion, we emphasize that the remarks extracted from the analysis of these explicit examples presumably point out qualitative features that apply in general. The more noteworthy one is the applicability of the improved Born and variational approximations in the case of repulsive interactions, even if they are quite strong.

Finally, to test the lower bound in modulus provided by Eq. (11.29), we consider the simple case of the "square well" potential

$$V(r) = V_0 \theta(R - r). \tag{20}$$

The exact scattering length for this potential is

$$a = -R[1 - (2I)^{-1/2} \tanh(2I)^{1/2}], \qquad I \geqslant 0,$$

$$= -R[1 - |2I|^{-1/2} \tan|2I|^{1/2}], \qquad I \leqslant 0, \tag{21}$$

with

$$I = \tfrac{1}{2} R^2 V_0. \tag{22}$$

On the other hand, Eq. (11.29) yields the inequality

$$|a| \geqslant \tfrac{1}{2} R |L(-I)| = |a_M|. \tag{23}$$

Of course this inequality holds only if the potential does not possess bound states, i. e., provided

$$I > -\pi^2/8. \tag{24}$$

The exact scattering length a, Eq. (21), and its lower bound in modulus a_M, Eq. (23), are plotted in Fig. 2 as functions of I, together with the Born and improved Born approximations

$$a_B = -\tfrac{2}{3} RI, \tag{25}$$

$$a_{BB} = -2RIe^{-2I} \int_0^1 dy\, y^2 \exp(2Iy^2). \tag{26}$$

The corresponding data are tabulated in Table II. We have set the scale constant R equal to unity. It may be noted that the improved Born approximation is, in this case, more accurate than the approximation a_M for repulsive interaction, but less accurate for attractive interaction, except in a small range of values of I (see Table II).

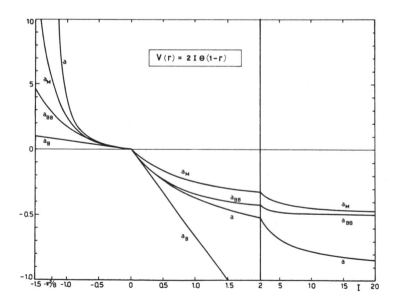

FIG. 2.   Approximate and exact scattering length for square well potential.

TABLE II

EXACT AND APPROXIMATE VALUES OF THE SCATTERING LENGTH
FOR THE POTENTIAL $V(r) = 2I\theta(1 - r)$ [a]

I	Born approximation[b] a_B	Improved Born approximation[c] a_{BB}	Exact scattering length[d] a	Lower bound in modulus[e] a_M
20	−13.333	−0.494	−0.842	−0.467
15	−10	−0.492	−0.817	−0.458
10	−6.667	−0.487	−0.776	−0.443
5	−3.333	−0.473	−0.685	−0.404
2	−1.333	−0.425	−0.518	−0.329
1	−0.667	−0.340	−0.372	−0.246
0.5	−0.333	−0.231	−0.238	−0.165
0.3	−0.2	−0.159	−0.161	−0.115
0.2	−0.133	−0.114	−0.115	−0.083
0.1	−0.067	−0.0616	−0.0617	−0.0454
−0.1	0.067	0.0723	0.0725	0.0556
−0.2	0.133	0.157	0.159	0.124
−0.3	0.2	0.257	0.263	0.211
−0.4	0.267	0.376	0.393	0.323
−0.5	0.333	0.515	0.557	0.467
−0.6	0.4	0.680	0.773	0.659
−0.7	0.467	0.876	1.070	0.915
−0.8	0.533	1.107	1.503	1.262
−0.9	0.6	1.383	2.196	1.736
−1.0	0.667	1.710	3.479	2.389
−1.1	0.733	2.099	6.681	3.293
−1.2	0.8	2.56	28.88	4.55
−1.3	0.87	3.12	−15.88	6.32
−1.4	0.93	3.78	−6.81	8.79
−1.5	1	4.57	−4.55	12.32

[a] As a function of I. The exact scattering length has a pole at $I = -\pi^2/8$. The data in this table are plotted in Fig. 2.

[b] From Eq. (25).

[c] From Eq. (26).

[d] From Eq. (21).

[e] $a_M = -\frac{1}{2}L(-I)$ (see Eq. (23)) is obtained from Table II.I.

13

Generalized formulation of the phase method. Other types of phase equations

In this chapter we discuss a more general formulation of the variable phase method, and thereby obtain other types of basic equations for the evaluation of scattering phase shifts, which may in certain cases be more convenient than the standard phase equation (3.14).

Let the function $u(r)$ be defined, up to a multiplicative constant, by the differential equation

$$u''(r) + [k^2 - W(r) - \overline{W}(r)]u(r) = 0 \tag{1}$$

and the boundary condition

$$u(0) = 0. \tag{2}$$

The two real functions $W(r)$ and $\overline{W}(r)$ are arbitrary, but they are required to satisfy the same restrictions as a potential in scattering theory, namely, they must vanish asymptotically faster than r^{-1} and be less singular in the origin than r^{-2}. In fact we may allow the function $\overline{W}(r)$ to be more singular in the origin, provided it is positive in that neighborhood. In addition, the final results may be valid and useful when $W(r)$ is more singular, as will be discussed later in this chapter and in Chapter 15.

These restrictions on the functions $W(r)$ and $\overline{W}(r)$ are sufficient to guarantee that the boundary condition equation (2) identifies up to a multiplicative constant the function $u(r)$, and that this function becomes asymptotically proportional to a circular function:

$$u(r) \xrightarrow[r\to\infty]{} \text{const} \times \sin(kr + \Delta). \tag{3}$$

It is the purpose of the present discussion to introduce a method for evaluating the "phase shift" Δ defined by this equation. With the present method it is also possible to reconstruct the whole function $u(r)$. However, because the procedure is completely analogous to that displayed in Chapter 6, we limit ourselves to mentioning this possibility and leave it to the interested reader to derive explicitly the relevant formulas.

We now introduce two independent solutions $\bar{u}_{1,2}(r)$ of the differential equation

$$\bar{u}''(r) + [k^2 - \overline{W}(r)]\bar{u}(r) = 0, \tag{4}$$

identified by the boundary conditions in the origin

$$\bar{u}_1(0) = 0, \tag{5}$$

and at infinity

$$\bar{u}_1(r) \xrightarrow[r \to \infty]{} \sin(kr + \bar{\Delta}), \tag{6a}$$

$$\bar{u}_2(r) \xrightarrow[r \to \infty]{} \cos(kr + \bar{\Delta}). \tag{6b}$$

These boundary conditions, together with the differential equation (4), are sufficient to specify completely the two functions $\bar{u}_{1,2}(r)$ and also to define the quantity $\bar{\Delta}$ (which is simply the S-wave scattering phase shift produced by the potential $\overline{W}(r)$). In fact, the boundary condition in the origin, Eq. (5), characterizes the function $\bar{u}_1(r)$ up to a multiplicative constant, which is then fixed by the asymptotic boundary condition equation (6a); this condition defines, at the same time, the phase shift $\bar{\Delta}$. Finally, once $\bar{\Delta}$ has been defined, the second boundary condition, Eq. (6b), characterizes the function $\bar{u}_2(r)$ completely.

We now assume that the two "comparison functions" $\bar{u}_{1,2}(r)$ are known, and we write for the unknown $u(r)$ the *Ansatz*

$$u(r) = \alpha(r)[\cos \gamma(r)\bar{u}_1(r) + \sin \gamma(r)\bar{u}_2(r)], \tag{7}$$

thereby introducing the "amplitude function" $\alpha(r)$ and the "phase function" $\gamma(r)$ of the function $u(r)$ relative to the comparison function $\bar{u}_1(r)$. Assuming that these functions tend asymptotically to well-defined limits $\alpha(\infty)$ and $\gamma(\infty)$ (this is proved below), we infer from comparison of Eqs. (7), (6), and (3) the result

$$\Delta = \bar{\Delta} + \gamma(\infty). \tag{8}$$

Therefore the knowledge of the asymptotic value $\gamma(\infty)$ is all that is required to determine the phase shift Δ, since the phase shift $\bar{\Delta}$ of the comparison function $\bar{u}_1(r)$ is considered known.

Thus far there is a large amount of arbitrariness in the choice of $\alpha(r)$ and $\gamma(r)$ because we have two functions at our disposal to manufacture only one (see Eq. (7)). A convenient choice obtains when we supplement Eq. (7) with the equation

$$u'(r) = \alpha(r)[\cos \gamma(r)\bar{u}_1'(r) + \sin \gamma(r)\bar{u}_2'(r)]. \tag{9}$$

Now the two equations (7) and (9) may be solved for $\alpha(r)$ and $\gamma(r)$, and, in particular, we obtain for $\gamma(r)$

$$\gamma(r) = -\tan^{-1} \frac{u(r)\bar{u}_1'(r) - u'(r)\bar{u}_1(r)}{u(r)\bar{u}_2'(r) - u'(r)\bar{u}_2(r)}. \tag{10}$$

This equation, together with the boundary condition equation (5), implies for $\gamma(r)$ the boundary condition

$$\gamma(0) = 0. \tag{11}$$

On the other hand, from Eqs. (7) and (9), proceeding in close analogy to the treatment of Chapter 6, we secure for $\gamma(r)$ the phase equation

$$\gamma'(r) = -k^{-1}W(r)[\cos \gamma(r)\bar{u}_1(r) + \sin \gamma(r)\bar{u}_2(r)]^2. \tag{12}$$

This first-order equation, together with the boundary condition equation (11), allows the evaluation of the function $\gamma(r)$ and therefore also the evaluation of its asymptotic value $\gamma(\infty)$, which, through Eq. (8), determines the phase shift Δ.

Obviously the development of this chapter is a straightforward generalization of the treatment given in Chapter 6, to which it becomes identical with the special choice

$$\overline{W}(r) = l(l+1)r^{-2} \tag{13}$$

and

$$W(r) = V(r) \tag{14}$$

because this choice also implies

$$\bar{u}_1(r) = \hat{j}_l(kr), \qquad \bar{u}_2(r) = -\hat{n}_l(kr). \tag{15}$$

More generally, the present treatment provides a method for the evaluation of the scattering phase shift δ_l, provided we set

$$W(r) + \overline{W}(r) = l(l+1)r^{-2} + V(r) \qquad (16)$$

because we then have

$$\delta_l = \varDelta + l\pi/2. \qquad (17)$$

This is therefore a generalized phase method, and most of our previous remarks remain valid (see, in particular, Chapters 4 and 6), so we shall not repeat them here. We emphasize that the generalization allows, roughly speaking, hiding one part of the potential and (or) the centrifugal term in the comparison functions, and exposing only the effect of the remaining part by means of the phase equation. This freedom is, of course, very useful for gaining understanding of the qualitative features of the scattering phase shift. For instance, it implies immediately that if the potential $V_-(r)$ never exceeds the potential $V_+(r)$,

$$V_+(r) \geqslant V_-(r), \qquad (18)$$

then the corresponding scattering phase shift satisfies the inequality

$$\delta_+ \leqslant \delta_-, \qquad (19)$$

a fact already noted in Chapter 4. This statement is now demonstrated noting that the difference $\delta_- - \delta_+$ is the asymptotic value $\gamma_{-+}(\infty)$ of a phase function $\gamma_{-+}(r)$, which is positive semidefinite, being the solution of the differential equation

$$\gamma'_{-+}(r) = -k^{-1}[V_-(r) - V_+(r)][\cos\gamma_{-+}(r)\bar{u}_1^{(+)}(r) + \sin\gamma_{-+}(r)\bar{u}_2^{(+)}(r)]^2, \quad (20)$$

with boundary conditions

$$\gamma_{-+}(0) = 0. \qquad (21)$$

The two comparison functions $\bar{u}_1^{(+)}(r)$ and $\bar{u}_2^{(+)}(r)$ are now properly chosen solutions of the radial Schrödinger equation for the potential $V_+(r)$. Incidentally, this same conclusion could also be reached by considering the phase function $\gamma_{+-}(r)$, which satisfies an equation similar to Eq. (20), except for a change in the sign of the r.h.s. and for the fact that the comparison functions $\bar{u}_{1,2}^{(+)}(r)$ must be replaced by $\bar{u}_{1,2}^{(-)}(r)$, i. e., by the appropriate solutions of the radial Schrödinger equation with potential $V_-(r)$. The asymptotic value $\gamma_{+-}(\infty)$ would then yield directly the difference $\delta_+ - \delta_-$. This implies that $\gamma_{+-}(\infty) = -\gamma_{-+}(\infty)$. However, it is not true that $\gamma_{+-}(r) = -\gamma_{-+}(r)$ for all r; in fact, $\gamma_{+-}(\bar{r})$ gives the difference between the phase shift due to the potential $\theta(\bar{r} - r)V_+(r) + \theta(r - \bar{r})V_-(r)$ and the phase shift due to the potential $V_-(r)$, while $\gamma_{-+}(r)$ gives the difference between the phase shift due to the potential $\theta(\bar{r} - r)V_-(r) + \theta(r - \bar{r})V_+(r)$ and the phase shift due to the potential $V_+(r)$.

The generalized phase method may also be useful computationally or for obtaining approximate expressions for the phase shift, especially when the radial Schrödinger equation for a comparison potential $\bar{V}(r)$ not very different from the actual potential $V(r)$ is solvable in closed form. For instance, this might be the case if one were to evaluate the scattering phase shift due to a Yukawa potential $V(r) = gr^{-1} \exp(-\mu r)$, in which case a convenient potential to use might be $\bar{V}(r) = gr^{-1}\theta(R - r)$, with R of the order of μ^{-1}.

Another case when the use of the generalized phase method appears to be appropriate is that of a short-range potential superimposed over the Coulomb potential, a situation often met in nuclear physics. Then one would absorb the Coulomb part of the potential in the comparison functions, which would then become the (properly normalized) regular and irregular Coulomb functions, and would thus set up a phase equation that contains explicitly only the short-range potential and that yields directly only the additional phase shift due to this potential. Note that in this fashion all the problems connected with the long-range character of the Coulomb potential are bypassed. Therefore this procedure may prove useful both for numerical computations and for theoretical investigations of the scattering phase shifts.

Another important possibility is that of exhibiting the dependence on the centrifugal potential, in addition to the scattering potential, i. e., of setting

$$\bar{W}(r) = 0, \tag{22a}$$

$$W(r) = l(l+1)r^{-2} + V(r). \tag{22b}$$

Note, however, that the potential $W(r)$ is now singular because it also contains the centrifugal part. This situation requires some extra care, as we now show.

First of all, the comparison functions corresponding to the choice of Eq. (22a) are simply

$$\bar{u}_1(r) = \sin kr, \qquad \bar{u}_2(r) = \cos kr. \tag{23}$$

Thus the generalized phase equation becomes simply

$$\gamma_l'(r) = -k^{-1}[l(l+1)r^{-2} + V(r)] \sin^2[kr + \gamma_l(r)], \tag{24}$$

and the scattering phase shift δ_l is given by

$$\delta_l = \gamma_l(\infty) + l\pi/2. \tag{25}$$

The significance of these equations is quite obvious; the phase equation yields the phase shift due both to the centrifugal and to the external potential, and the scattering phase shift is obtained by subtracting the centrifugal part $-l\pi/2$ from the total phase shift $\gamma_l(\infty)$. Note incidentally that it is no longer true that $\gamma_l(\bar{r})$ is directly connected with the scattering phase shift produced by the potential $V(r)\theta(\bar{r} - r)$; but, rather, $\gamma_l(\bar{r})$ is the (S-wave) phase shift due to the potential $[l(l+1)r^{-2} + V(r)]\theta(\bar{r} - r)$.

We have not yet written the boundary condition in the origin satisfied by the function $\gamma_l(r)$. This is obviously

$$\gamma_l(0) = 0, \tag{26a}$$

as is also implied by the physical meaning of the function $\gamma_l(r)$, just mentioned. However, because of the singular nature of the differential equation (24) in the origin, this boundary condition is not sufficient to identify the solution of the differential equation; in fact, as we now show, there are infinite different solutions of Eq. (24), which all vanish in the origin.

To discuss this point, it is sufficient to consider the simpler problem without external potential because, in the neighborhood of the origin, the centrifugal part dominates. We accordingly focus attention on the differential equation

$$\beta_l'(x) = -l(l+1)x^{-2} \sin^2[x + \beta_l(x)]. \tag{27}$$

We have shifted to the independent variable $x = kr$, and we have called $\beta_l(x)$ the phase function for this case. It is now very easy to write down the most general (real) solution of this differential equation:

$$\beta_l(x) = \tan^{-1} \frac{[j_l(x) + A\hat{n}_l(x)] \cos x - [j_l'(x) + A\hat{n}_l'(x)] \sin x}{[j_l(x) + A\hat{n}_l(x)] \sin x + [j_l'(x) + A\hat{n}_l'(x)] \cos x}. \tag{28}$$

This equation follows, for instance, from Eq. (10) and the fact that $u_l(x) = \hat{\jmath}_l(x) + A\hat{n}_l(x)$ is a solution of the corresponding second-order linear differential equation; here A is an arbitrary constant. Obviously $\beta_l(x)$ is the phase of $u_l(x) = \hat{\jmath}_l(x) + A\hat{n}_l(x)$ relative to $\sin x$, and the solution that we wish to single out is that corresponding to $A = 0$, i. e., the case in which u_l vanishes in the origin, and $\beta_l(\infty) = -l\pi/2$. But we now see that, although for $A = 0$ it is true that $\beta_l(x)$ vanishes in the origin, the requirement that $\beta_l(x)$ vanish in the origin does not imply that A vanishes because, in fact, $\beta_l(x)$ vanishes in the origin for all values of A:

$$\beta_l(x) = \begin{cases} -x[l/(l+1)][1 + O(x^2)], & A = 0, \\ -x[(l+1)/l][1 + O(x^2)], & A \neq 0. \end{cases} \qquad (29)$$

(In this discussion we assume $l > 0$; the case $l = 0$ is trivial.)

In conclusion, we see that to single out the physical case $A = 0$, we must assign, in addition to the boundary condition $\beta_l(0) = 0$, the condition $\beta_l{}'(0) = -l/(l+1)$. Also, in the case $A \neq 0$, to distinguish between different values of A it would be necessary to assign the derivative of order n, with $n = 2l + 2$, because all the derivatives of lower order are also independent of the value of A.

(Incidentally, it is easy to check explicitly that this phenomenon does not happen in the case of a regular potential. In this case, the most general solution of the radial Schrödinger equation behaves near the origin as $u_l(r) = \hat{\jmath}_l(kr) + A\hat{n}_l(kr)$, and now, inserting this expression in Eq. (6.2a), we see that the condition $\delta_l(0) = 0$ implies $A = 0$.)

Returning now to our general case, we may conclude that to identify the physical solution of Eq. (24)—i. e., the solution whose asymptotic value yields the scattering phase shift through Eq. (25)—it is necessary to supplement the boundary condition equation (26a) with the additional condition

$$\gamma_l{}'(0) = -kl/(l+1). \qquad (26b)$$

All other solutions satisfy instead the condition

$$\gamma_l{}'(0) = -k(l+1)/l. \qquad (26c)$$

The phase equation (24) may be useful to desk-compute the phase shifts whenever the Riccati–Bessel functions are not available. On a computer, the use of this equation in place of the standard phase equation (3.14) may result in a time gain because it does not require the evaluation of the Riccati–Bessel functions at every integration step. However, it is necessary to integrate from the origin to a large distance even for short-range potentials because of the slow asymptotic vanishing of the centrifugal term. Moreover, for large l, one has to build up quite a large centrifugal phase shift. A procedure that may be more convenient, and requires only the knowledge of the Riccati– Bessel functions at one point, consists in the integration of Eq. (24) up to a distance $\bar{r}$, such that the potential $V(r)$ is negligible beyond it. Then, using the known solutions of the equation in the region where $V(r)$ is not present, we find with some algebra that

$$\delta_l = \tan^{-1} \frac{\cos[k\bar{r} + \gamma_l(\bar{r})]\hat{j}_l(k\bar{r}) - \sin[k\bar{r} + \gamma_l(\bar{r})]\hat{j}_l{}'(k\bar{r})}{\cos[k\bar{r} + \gamma_l(\bar{r})]\hat{n}_l(k\bar{r}) - \sin[k\bar{r} + \gamma_l(\bar{r})]\hat{n}_l{}'(k\bar{r})}. \tag{30}$$

This formula allows the evaluation of the scattering phase shift from the knowledge of $\gamma_l(\bar{r})$ only, besides the Riccati–Bessel functions of argument $k\bar{r}$.

Of course, rather than integrating the phase equation (24), one may use the Riccati equations for the tangent and cotangent of $\gamma_l(r)$, as discussed in Chapter 4. The relevant equations are

$$[\tan \gamma_l(r)]' = -k^{-1}[l(l+1)r^{-2} + V(r)][\sin kr + \cos kr \tan \gamma_l(r)]^2, \tag{31a}$$

$$[\cot \gamma_l(r)]' = k^{-1}[l(l+1)r^{-2} + V(r)][\sin kr \cot \gamma_l(r) + \cos kr]^2, \tag{31b}$$

with boundary conditions

$$\tan \gamma_l(0) = 0, \tag{32a}$$

$$[\tan \gamma_l(0)]' = -kl/(l+1). \tag{32b}$$

Finally, we mention that the phase equation (24) is also a convenient starting point for deriving general properties of the phase shifts, such as bounds, approximate expressions, etc. For these we refer the reader to the literature [13].

14

Simultaneous maximum and minimum principles for the evaluation of scattering phase shifts

In this chapter we exploit the results of the previous chapter and of Appendix II to establish simultaneous maximum and minimum principles for the evaluation of scattering phase shifts.

The first step consists in manufacturing two potentials, $V_+(r)$ and $V_-(r)$, such that

$$V_-(r) \leqslant V(r) \leqslant V_+(r) \tag{1}$$

and the radial Schrödinger equations corresponding to these potentials are exactly solvable. We do not discuss here the procedure to produce such potentials; the interested reader may find a detailed description in the literature [16]. We also note that while the potentials described there are energy independent, such a restriction may be relaxed without modifying any of the following results.

Let $u_{1,2}^{(+)}(r)$ and $u_{1,2}^{(-)}(r)$ be the comparison solutions corresponding, respectively, to the potentials $V_+(r)$ and $V_-(r)$. (We recall that these comparison functions are solutions of the corresponding radial Schrödinger equations, the functions $u_1^{(+,-)}(r)$ being characterized by the condition that they vanish in the origin, Eq. (13.5), and normalized by the asymptotic condition

$$u_1^{(+,-)}(r) \xrightarrow[r \to \infty]{} \sin[kr - l\pi/2 + \beta_{+,-}], \tag{2a}$$

while the functions $u_2^{(+,-)}(r)$ are identified by the condition that asymptotically

$$u_2^{(+,-)}(r) \xrightarrow[r \to \infty]{} \cos[kr - l\pi/2 + \beta_{+,-}]. \tag{2b}$$

Here, of course, the quantities β_+ and β_- are simply the scattering phase shifts corresponding to the potentials $V_+(r)$ and $V_-(r)$, respectively.)

We know already that Eq. (1) implies that

$$\beta_+ \leqslant \delta_l \leqslant \beta_- , \tag{3}$$

where δ_l is the scattering phase shift. Moreover, we assume that the potentials $V_+(r)$ and $V_-(r)$ are chosen sufficiently close so that

$$\beta_- - \beta_+ < \pi/2. \tag{4}$$

(Needless to say, the phase shifts $\beta_{+,-}$ also depend on l and k, and the condition of Eq. (4) is required to hold for those values of l and of k for which one wishes to evaluate the scattering phase shift.)

We now introduce the functions $\tau_{+,-}(r)$ through the equations

$$\tau_{+,-}(0) = 0, \tag{5}$$

$$\tau'_{+,-}(r) = -k^{-1}[V(r) - V_{+,-}(r)][u_1^{(+,-)}(r) + \tau_{+,-}(r)u_2^{(+,-)}(r)]^2. \tag{6}$$

It then follows from the discussion of the preceding chapter that

$$\delta_l = \gamma_+ + \beta_+ = \gamma_- + \beta_- , \tag{7}$$

where γ_+ and γ_- are defined by

$$\gamma_{+,-} = \tan^{-1}[\tau_{+,-}(\infty)]. \tag{8}$$

Of course, $\gamma_{+,-}$ also depend on l and k. Moreover, their definition through Eq. (8) suffers a $\mathrm{mod}(\pi)$ ambiguity, as does the definition of $\beta_{+,-}$ through Eq. (2a); this ambiguity should be disposed of in the usual way (see also Eq. (9)). At any rate, we disregard this trivial point in the following, with the understanding that some of the inequalities and equations derived hold only up to such ambiguities.

But now the differences $V(r) - V_{+,-}(r)$ appearing in Eq. (6) are semidefinite. Moreover, the condition of Eq. (4) guarantees that

$$|\gamma_{+,-}| < \pi/2, \tag{9}$$

which in turn implies that the functions $\tau_{+,-}(r)$ are continuous. We may therefore apply to Eq. (6) the extremum principle of Appendix II (Eq. (II.25)), and we obtain in this manner the following two relations:

$$\tan \gamma_+ = \max_{w_+} \left\{ -k^{-1} \int_0^\infty dr [V(r) - V_+(r)][u_1^{(+)}(r)]^2 [2 - w_+(r)] w_+(r) \right.$$

$$\left. \times \exp\left[-2k^{-1} \int_r^\infty ds [V(s) - V_+(s)] u_1^{(+)}(s) u_2^{(+)}(s) w_+(s) \right] \right\}, \qquad (10)$$

$$\tan \gamma_- = \min_{w_-} \left\{ -k^{-1} \int_0^\infty dr [V(r) - V_-(r)][u_1^{(-)}(r)]^2 [2 - w_-(r)] w_-(r) \right.$$

$$\left. \times \exp\left[-2k^{-1} \int_r^\infty ds [V(s) - V_-(s)] u_1^{(-)}(s) u_2^{(-)}(s) w_-(s) \right] \right\}. \qquad (11)$$

From these equations and Eq. (7), we obtain the simultaneous maximum and minimum principles for the scattering phase shifts

$$\delta_l = \max_{w_+} \left\{ \beta_+ - \tan^{-1}\left(k^{-1} \int_0^\infty dr [V(r) - V_+(r)][u_1^{(+)}(r)]^2 [2 - w_+(r)] w_+(r) \right. \right.$$

$$\left. \left. \times \exp\left[-2k^{-1} \int_r^\infty ds [V(s) - V_+(s)] u_1^{(+)}(s) u_2^{(+)}(s) w_+(s) \right] \right) \right\}, \qquad (12)$$

$$\delta_l = \min_{w_-} \left\{ \beta_- - \tan^{-1}\left(k^{-1} \int_0^\infty dr [V(r) - V_-(r)][u_1^{(-)}(r)]^2 [2 - w_-(r)] w_-(r) \right. \right.$$

$$\left. \left. \times \exp\left[-2k^{-1} \int_r^\infty ds [V(s) - V_-(s)] u_1^{(-)}(s) u_2^{(-)}(s) w_-(s) \right] \right) \right\}. \qquad (13)$$

To obtain these equations, we also use Eq. (9).

By substituting two trial functions $w_+(r)$ and $w_-(r)$ in these equations, we obtain a controlled approximation for the scattering phase shift, i. e., we may assert that its actual value must lie within a certain interval, which is the smaller the better the trial functions approximate the optimal ones. These functions are connected to the (unknown) functions $\tau_{+,-}(r)$ by the relations

$$w_{+,-}^{opt}(r) = 1 + \tau_{+,-}(r) u_2^{(+,-)}(r) / u_1^{(+,-)}(r). \qquad (14)$$

Of course, these maximum and minimum principles imply Eq. (3), as is found by inserting $w_{+,-}(r) = 0$ in their r.h.s. Usually a better choice for the trial functions is $w_{+,-}(r) = 1$; this corresponds to the improved Born approximation for the difference between actual and comparison potentials.

In conclusion, we remark that the idea exploited is that of introducing auxiliary potentials, which are exactly solvable and which approximate by defect and by excess the potential whose phase shift is to be evaluated. It is then a trivial fact that the corresponding phase shifts approximate by excess and by defect the unknown phase shift. What is less trivial is the validity of the exact expressions that we have given, Eqs. (12) and (13), which have the form of simultaneous maximum and minimum principles. From these expressions, the phase shift may be determined in principle with arbitrary accuracy. It should be emphasized, however, that these expressions are not simple and are therefore not very convenient for practical computations.

15

Scattering on singular potentials. High-energy behavior and approximate expression of the scattering phase shift in this case

In this chapter we discuss the problem of scattering on a potential that is more singular in the origin than the centrifugal term. This problem is interesting per se as a mathematical problem, and because in several physical applications one is confronted by phenomenological potentials that are strongly singular in the origin. Another motivation for discussing scattering on singular potentials is the analogy of this problem with that of the infinities occurring in renormalizable and unrenormalizable field theories. We begin with an outline of the situation from the traditional point of view, namely, that based on the radial Schrödinger equation. Next we consider the phase approach, and we discuss the phase equation in this case. We find that the behavior of the phase function is susceptible of a clear physical interpretation. Finally, we exploit the simplicity of the phase equation and the transparent behavior of the phase function to ascertain the behavior of the scattering phase shift as the energy diverges and to derive an approximate expression for the scattering phase shift—a sort of modified Born approximation [19].

In the following we refer for definiteness to potentials that diverge in the origin as inverse powers of r, and we write

$$V(r) = gr^{-m}C(r) = r_0^{-2}(r_0/r)^m C(r), \qquad C(0) = 1, \quad m > 2. \qquad (1a)$$

We have introduced here the two constants g and r_0; the first is the "coupling constant," the second is the length that establishes the scale of the singular region. These are related by

$$r_0^{m-2} = g. \tag{1b}$$

Of course the potential is also required to vanish asymptotically as r diverges, as is usual in scattering theory. We emphasize that most of our final results are generally valid for any singular potential, i. e., for any potential such that $r^2V(r)$ diverges in the origin. We shall mention explicitly which results must be modified and how, if the behavior of the potential near the origin is not of the power type.

In our discussion we refer for simplicity to the S-wave case. The extension of the results to all partial waves presents no difficulty; we shall simply write the relevant final formulas [19].

The most important fact to keep in mind while considering the problem of scattering on a singular potential is that there is a major qualitative difference between the case when the singular part of the potential is positive, and therefore represents strong repulsive forces at short distances, and when it is negative, i. e., when it represents attractive forces. In fact, only in the former case is the problem susceptible to a straightforward physical interpretation; the case of strong attractive forces gives rise instead to an unphysical behavior, which may be interpreted as the "fall" of the scattering particles into the origin. Although a physical reinterpretation of the results in this case might be attempted, our point of view is to consider physically sound only those situations in which the singular part of the potential is repulsive.

(Incidentally, these remarks do not apply in the relativistic cases, namely, when the behavior of the particles is governed by the Klein–Gordon or Dirac equations rather than the Schrödinger equation. In fact, although these problems may be reduced to equivalent Schrödinger problems, with an (energy dependent) effective potential, it turns out that this contains terms that are quadratic in the original potential. These terms dominate in the neighborhood of the origin, and obviously their sign does not depend on the original sign of the potential, but on the way in which the potential enters in the original equation; this, in turn, depends on its relativistic transformation properties—e.g., whether it is a relativistic scalar or the fourth component of a relativistic vector. Moreover, because the effective potential contains the square of the original potential, the border line between regular and singular potentials corresponds to the behavior r^{-1} rather than r^{-2}. At any rate, in the following we restrict our consideration to the nonrelativistic (Schrödinger) case.)

We now discuss how the physical difference between the cases of attractive and repulsive singular forces at short distances appears in the mathematical formalism, first in the framework of the Schrödinger equation and then in the framework of the phase equation. In the neighborhood of the origin, the Schrödinger equation becomes

$$u''(r) - gr^{-m}u(r) = 0 \qquad (2)$$

because in that neighborhood we may substitute in place of the potential its behavior at short distances, given by Eq. (1a), and we may neglect the kinetic energy term k^2 with respect to the potential. For simplicity of presentation we now consider the special case $m = 4$, but the argument could be repeated for any m—in fact, for any singular potential—with the same conclusions.

The Schrödinger equation in the neighborhood of the origin, Eq. (2), admits for $m = 4$ the two independent real solutions

$$u_{+,-}(r) = r \exp(\pm \mid g \mid^{1/2}/r), \qquad \text{if } g > 0, \qquad (3)$$

$$u_{+,-}(r) = r \sin(\mid g \mid^{1/2}/r \pm \pi/4), \qquad \text{if } g < 0. \qquad (4)$$

The difference between the two cases is now evident. In the first case, $g > 0$, we have one solution, $u_{+}(r)$, which diverges in the origin, and a second solution, $u_{-}(r)$, which vanishes exponentially there. Clearly this second solution is the physical wave function; its fast vanishing corresponds to the physical fact that the strong repulsive forces acting at short distances prevent the scattering particles from getting close to the origin. On the other hand, in the second case, $g < 0$, all solutions of the differential equation vanish in the origin, and we have no criterion for selecting the physical wave function. Moreover, all solutions have an infinite number of zeros, which accumulate at the origin—a fact suggesting the existence of an infinite number of bound states without any lower limit to their energies.

From now on, we consider only the physically reasonable case of singular potentials that are repulsive near the origin. It is then generally true that there is one and only one solution that vanishes in the origin, while all other solutions diverge there. Thus the usual boundary condition requiring the radial wave function to vanish in the origin, Eq. (2.5), is sufficient to identify it up to a multiplicative constant; the radial wave function then defines the phase shift in the usual way, Eq. (2.9). Note, however, that the radial wave function vanishes now near the origin faster than would be implied by Eq. (2.8), and its behavior there is independent of the angular momentum l because, in the neighborhood of the origin, the centrifugal term is now dominated by the potential. We also emphasize that in general the behavior of the radial wave function in the origin depends on the coupling constant g in a form that is not analytic at $g = 0$. This is displayed explicitly in the special case $m = 4$ in Eq. (3), and it is true in general. Such lack of analyticity carries over to the asymptotic behavior of the radial wave function, and it is therefore also a property of the scattering phase shift (although the nature of the singularity need not be the same).

The fact that the scattering phase shift, or, for that matter, the scattering matrix, is not an analytic function of the coupling constant g at $g = 0$ may also be inferred on the basis of the following heuristic argument. Suppose *per absurdum* that it were analytic. Then, if we pass from a small positive g to a small negative g, the scattering matrix should not change much. But this is inconsistent with the physics of the problem because the change from positive to negative g entails, as we have seen, a drastic modification. We emphasize that this argument is not rigorous; it is, however, very illuminating, and its conclusions are correct. Note that the fact that the scattering quantities are not analytic in g at $g = 0$ implies that they cannot be expanded in powers of g, so that the perturbative approach is doomed to failure. In fact, the first term of that expansion, i. e., the Born approximation, already yields a divergent result if $m \geqslant 3$. Later in this chapter we develop and discuss a modified Born approximation, which yields convergent results for singular potentials.

We turn now to a discussion of the phase equation. First of all, we note that it is still valid, as the derivation given in Chapter 6 implies. (In fact, the derivation of Chapter 3 also remains valid, but this is less evident.) We emphasize, however, that in this case the boundary condition in the origin, Eq. (6.4a), although valid, is not sufficient to identify the phase function. In fact, as we now show, all solutions of the phase equation vanish in the origin. In this respect the situation is analogous to that already encountered in Chapter 13, when we treated the centrifugal term as an ordinary potential. We

SCATTERING ON SINGULAR POTENTIALS

found there that a more careful analysis of the behavior of the phase function in the origin was in order and that it yielded a prescription for selecting the actual phase function; this prescription consisted in assigning the value of the first derivative of the phase function in the origin. We follow the same procedure. However, as we shall presently see, the required prescription is now a more detailed one; in fact, all solutions of the phase equation also have the first derivative in the origin identical.

To investigate the behavior of the phase function near the origin, we may choose between two procedures: We may either concentrate on the phase equation, or use the explicit expression of the phase function in terms of the radial wave function, Eq. (6.2a), and our knowledge of the behavior of the wave function in the origin. We follow the first procedure, which is also more instructive, and we subsequently also indicate how the second procedure would work, to verify the consistency of our approach.

Let us recall here the phase equation

$$\delta'(r) = -k^{-1}V(r)\sin^2[kr + \delta(r)].$$ (5)

It is well to remember that $\delta(\bar{r})$ is the phase shift due to the potential $V(r)\theta(\bar{r} - r)$. Thus we must also have the boundary condition

$$\delta(0) = 0$$ (6)

because if the potential is cut off completely, the phase shift must vanish. Moreover, the function $\delta(r)$ must be finite for all r. But the potential in the phase equation diverges in the origin as gr^{-m} with $m > 2$. Therefore the behavior of the phase function (or, more generally, of any bounded solution of the phase equation) in the neighborhood of the origin must be just such as to keep $\delta'(r)$ finite in spite of the potential. It is immediately seen that the only behavior satisfying these specifications is

$$\delta(r) = -kr + \epsilon(r),$$ (7)

with $\epsilon(r)$ vanishing fast near the origin. Just how fast? This we easily ascertain by substituting this *Ansatz* in the phase equation itself and considering the situation near the origin. We find

$$\epsilon(r) = \pm k[V(r)]^{-1/2} + \eta(r),$$ (8)

where $\eta(r)$ must vanish faster than the first term, which behaves as $r^{m/2}$. Again we may ask, Just how fast? And again we find the answer by substituting Eqs. (7) and (8) in the phase equation. In this manner we obtain the behavior

$$\delta(r) = -kr \pm k[V(r)]^{-1/2} + \tfrac{1}{4}kV'(r)V^{-2}(r) + O[(r/r_0)^{\tfrac{1}{2}(3m-4)}]. \qquad (9)$$

We emphasize that this equation is valid for any bounded solution of the phase equation that is required to vanish in the origin.

This is an interesting equation, and it is worthwhile to pause a moment to consider it. First of all we note that the first term behaves as r to the first power, the second (near the origin) as r to the power $m/2$, the third as r to the power $m - 1$, etc. In general, the nth term behaves as r to the power $1 + \tfrac{1}{2}(n - 1)(m - 2)$. The condition $m > 2$ guarantees that the successive terms vanish faster near the origin. Of course this behavior obtains only for potentials that diverge at the origin as an inverse power; but if the behavior of the potential is different (provided it is more singular than r^{-2}), Eq. (9) still provides an expansion of the phase function near the origin, in the sense that each successive term vanishes faster than the preceding one. (The reader may verify this explicitly both for a potential that diverges in the origin barely more than the centrifugal term, say,

$$V(r) = gr^{-2} \ln^\beta(r), \qquad \beta > 0, \qquad (10)$$

and for a potential that diverges more than any power, say,

$$V(r) = g \exp(\beta/r), \qquad \beta > 0.) \qquad (11)$$

Continuing our scrutiny of Eq. (9), we note that the first term, $-kr$, is simply the scattering phase shift produced by a hard sphere of radius r, i. e., an infinitely repulsive potential of range r. This may be seen from the phase equation itself; if the potential is divergent in the region 0 to r, the only way for the phase function to remain finite and satisfy the phase equation is for it to be exactly equal to $-kr$, so as to cancel the divergent potential. Physically this means that the wave function is pushed away from the forbidden region, so that the condition that it vanish in the origin is now maintained all the way to the distance r. The phase shift thus gained is $-kr$, which is also, as we already noted in Chapter 4, the maximum negative phase shift that a potential of range r can produce.

We now go on to consider the second term in the r.h.s. of Eq. (9). This is most interesting. First of all, it contains the square root of the potential. Thus, if we have a potential that is repulsive, i. e., positive, in the neighborhood of the origin, this term is real; but the term becomes imaginary if the potential is attractive near the origin. Therefore at this point the restriction to singular *repulsive* interactions appears relevant in the framework of the phase approach; in the attractive singular case, the phase equation has no real solution vanishing in the origin. (With some imagination one might wish to interpret the complex phase shift thus obtained as representing the absorption of the incident beam due to the potential hole; this interpretation would also fix the sign of the imaginary part of the phase shift. We prefer, however, to maintain our conservative viewpoint, according to which an attractive singular potential does not correspond to a physically reasonable situation.) We also note that the appearance of the square root of the potential is a clear indication of the nonanalyticity in the coupling constant of the phase function, and therefore also of the phase shift.

Finally, we come to the point constituting the original motivation of this discussion; this point is the ambiguity inherent in the double sign in front of the second term in the r.h.s. of Eq. (9). It appears that two solutions of the phase equation (5) exist, both satisfying the boundary condition equation (6): the first, for which we maintain the notation $\delta(r)$, is characterized by the small r behavior

$$\delta(r) = -kr + k[V(r)]^{-1/2} + \tfrac{1}{4}kV'(r)V^{-2}(r) + O[(r/r_0)^{\frac{1}{2}(3m-4)}]; \quad (12)$$

the other, which we indicate by the notation $\bar{\delta}(r)$, is characterized by the small r behavior

$$\bar{\delta}(r) = -kr - k[V(r)]^{-1/2} + \tfrac{1}{4}kV'(r)V^{-2}(r) + O[(r/r_0)^{\frac{1}{2}(3m-4)}]. \quad (13)$$

Which one is the physical solution, i. e., the actual phase function whose asymptotic value yields the scattering phase shift? It is the first one, as is implied by the following physical remark: The phase function must be less negative than $-kr$ because this value corresponds to a potential that is infinitely repulsive all the way from 0 to r, whereas $\delta(r)$ is the phase shift due to the actual potential cutoff at r, i. e., due to a potential that is singular only at the origin.

In conclusion, we summarize our analysis of the behavior of the phase function near the origin, given by Eq. (12). The dominant term is negative and it represents the phase shift due to an infinitely repulsive potential; the subsequent term is positive, to take into account the fact that the potential is less strong than an infinitely repulsive potential. Note that this term is more important, the less singular and large the potential, implying that the actual phase function is quite different from the saturation value $-kr$, apposite to the completely singular potential. The restriction to singular *repulsive* interactions is essential in order to obtain a real answer. The nonanalyticity in the coupling constant is also directly implied.

In fact, as we might have expected by analogy with the discussion of the phase equation for the centrifugal potential in Chapter 13, there is an infinity of solutions, and not just two, of the phase equation, all vanishing in the origin. One of them is uniquely characterized by the behavior of Eq. (12), and it is the physical solution, i. e., the actual phase function. All the others, instead, behave near the origin according to Eq. (13). These results may be obtained by considering the explicit expression, Eq. (6.2a), of a solution of the phase equation in terms of a solution of the corresponding radial Schrödinger equation, and from the easily ascertainable behavior near the origin of the solutions of the Schrödinger equation. (Notice that this is simply the procedure used in Chapter 13.) Taking a general solution

$$u(r) = u_R(r) + Au_I(r), \qquad (14)$$

where $u_R(r)$ is the solution that vanishes at the origin while $u_I(r)$ is the solution that diverges there, we find for the corresponding phase function the expansion equation (12) in the physical case $A = 0$, and the expansion equation (13) in all the other cases $A \neq 0$. It should be emphasized that these conclusions hold only in the case of a singular potential that is repulsive near the origin. In the case of an attractive singular potential, with this procedure we would indeed find a real solution of the phase equation, but it would be a function that did not tend to any definite value as r vanished. In conclusion, we see that the results obtained directly from the phase equation are confirmed.

Finally we note that as implied by Eq. (9), all solutions of the phase equation (5) and of the boundary condition equation (6) also satisfy the condition

$$\delta'(0) = -k. \qquad (15)$$

This is consistent with the result obtained in Chapter 13, Eqs. (13.26b) and (13.26c), because the present case, with potentials that are more singular in the origin than the centrifugal term, should be compared with those results in the $l \to \infty$ limit.

Our clarification of the behavior of the phase function near the origin—obviously the critical region in the case of singular potentials—beside confirming the validity of the phase approach in the case of singular potentials, is also very instructive because it displays in which fashion the phase shift is accumulated. We may now assert that most of the results obtained in the preceding chapters remain valid, except for the modifications due to the different behavior of the phase function near the origin. For instance, all the variational and extremum principles are still valid; of course, the fact that one has to do with a singular potential must be kept in mind while manufacturing the trial functions to be used. The criterion for their construction is always their maximal similarity with the optimal ones, whose relations with the phase function remain those previously stated, and whose behavior in the origin is therefore correspondingly modified. There are, however, certain results and certain approximations that depend for their validity on the assumed regularity of the potential—in particular, the vanishing of the phase shift as the energy diverges (see Eq. (2.14) and Appendix III) and the validity of the Born and improved Born approximations, at least in certain cases. Using the known behavior of the phase function near the origin, it is now possible not only to understand the reasons of the breakdown of these results, but also to find the new results or approximations to be substituted in their place.

We consider first of all the asymptotic behavior of the phase shift as the momentum k diverges. It is easily seen that it is related to the behavior of the phase function near the origin—a fact that might have been anticipated on the basis of the analogous result in the regular case (see Appendix III), or, equivalently, on the physical grounds that high-energy scattering is a probe of the inner structure of the potential (see the explicit examples of Chapter 5). In fact, substituting the expansion of the phase function near the origin, Eq. (12), in the exact expression for the phase shift,

$$\delta = -k^{-1} \int_0^\infty dr \, V(r) \sin^2[kr + \delta(r)], \qquad (16)$$

and evaluating the result in the limit of large k, we immediately see that the two leading terms in the expansion equation (12) provide the dominant term of the large k behavior of the phase shift:

$$\delta \xrightarrow[k\to\infty]{} -k^{-1} \int_0^\infty dr \, V(r) \sin^2\{k[V(r)]^{-1/2}\}. \qquad (17)$$

It is also easy to extract from this integral the dominant term in the large k limit, and we thus secure

$$\delta \xrightarrow[k\to\infty]{} -A(kr_0)^{1-(2/m)}, \qquad (18)$$

with

$$A = \left[\frac{(\pi/m)}{\sin(\pi/m)}\right]\left[\frac{2^{1-(2/m)}}{(2-(2/m))!}\right]. \qquad (19)$$

Here r_0 and m are related to the behavior of the potential near the origin through Eq. (1a).

It is also easy to evaluate explicitly the subsequent term in the high-energy expansion of the phase shift [19]; we limit ourselves to recording its order relative to the dominant term, writing

$$\delta = -A(kr_0)^{1-(2/m)}\{1 + O[(kr_0)^{-2/m}]\} \qquad \text{for} \quad m \geqslant 4, \qquad (20\text{a})$$

$$\delta = -A(kr_0)^{1-(2/m)}\{1 + O[(kr_0)^{(2/m)-1}]\} \qquad \text{for} \quad 2 < m \leqslant 4. \qquad (20\text{b})$$

It should be emphasized that, while this result is restricted to potentials that behave in the origin as an inverse power of r, Eq. (1a), the fact that the r.h.s. of Eq. (17) yields the dominant term in the high-energy behavior of the phase shift holds for any singular potential. In particular, if the potential is only logarithmically more divergent than the centrifugal term, then the phase shift diverges only logarithmically with k (in fact, as the square root of $\ln k$), while if the potential is exponentially singular, then the phase shift diverges only logarithmically less than linearly. (See Appendix III.) It should be noted that, while for singular potentials the magnitude of the phase shift increases asymptotically with energy, it can never grow faster than linearly in k. This is consistent with the limitation implied by Wigner's theorem [29].

We proceed now to derive an approximate formula for the phase shift in the case of singular potentials. We recall that the substitution in the exact expression for the phase shift, Eq. (16), of the zeroth-order approximation for the phase function $\delta(r) = 0$ would yield the Born approximation for the phase shift; this diverges, however, for the class of potentials that we are considering (at least if $m \geqslant 3$; otherwise the divergences occur only in subsequent terms of the Born series). Clearly we need a better approximation for the phase function. Because the potential is very large close to the origin, it is from this region that the major contribution to the phase shift originates (at least if the potential is sufficiently "weak" away from the origin, so that Born-type approximations have a chance to apply); therefore, it is in this region that the phase function must be approximated more carefully. But we have already ascertained the behavior of the phase function near the origin, Eq. (12). We might then try to substitute in the r.h.s. of Eq. (16) the first two terms of this expansion, Eq. (12). But in this way, while accurately approximating the behavior of the phase function near the origin, we would approximate it very badly at large r (where the phase function should become asymptotically constant rather than diverge). When the energy is large, this is acceptable; in fact, we have just obtained in this manner the high-energy behavior of the scattering phase shift. But to obtain an approximate expression for the phase shift valid at all energies, it is necessary to manufacture an approximate expression for $\delta(r)$ which, while correctly reproducing the first two terms of Eq. (12) at small r, also yields a reasonable result at large r. One such expression, which reduces to the zeroth-order result $\delta(r) = 0$ at large r, is

$$-kr + kr\{r[V(r)]^{1/2} + 1\}^{-1}. \tag{21}$$

This expression, while relatively simple, has the additional feature of yielding a result, correct up to a constant factor, for the third term in the expansion equation (12). Inserting this expression in Eq. (16) we obtain the following approximate expression for the scattering phase shift:

$$\delta_{app} = -k^{-1} \int_0^\infty dr\, V(r) \sin^2\{kr(1 + r[V(r)]^{1/2})^{-1}\}. \tag{22}$$

This expression may be considered a modified Born approximation; the presence of the term $(1 + r[V(r)]^{1/2})^{-1}$ in the argument of the sine function marks the difference from the Born formula. Note that the nonanalyticity in the strength of the interaction appears as a built-in feature of this approximation, and that this expression is real only for nowhere attractive potentials. (The modifications for the case of a singular potential that, although repulsive near the origin, is attractive in some region, are mentioned below.)

As implied by its derivation, this approximation should be more accurate for potentials that diverge strongly at the origin ($m \gg 2$) (so that the neglect of the subsequent terms in the expansion equation

(12) is more justifiable) and that are not too strong away from the repulsive core, where the integrand reduces to that of the Born case. It is nonetheless amusing to apply it to the centrifugal potential $V(r) = l(l + 1)r^{-2}$, in which case it yields

$$\delta_{\text{app}} = -[l(l + 1)/(1 + [l(l + 1)]^{1/2})]\pi/2.$$

The exact result is, of course, $\delta = -l\pi/2$; it is easily seen that $0 < \delta - \delta_{\text{app}} < \pi/4$. The Born approximation (which is convergent in this case) yields $\delta_{\text{B}} = -l(l + 1)\pi/2$, and for all positive values of l provides a less accurate approximation (in fact a very bad one for large l). We also note that in the limiting case of a hard sphere, $V(r) = \infty$ for $r < R$, $V(r) = 0$ for $r > R$, Eq. (22) yields the correct result $\delta = -kR$. For a check of the approximation in less extreme cases, we refer to Ref. [19], where a detailed numerical discussion is given for the potential $V(r) = gr^{-m}\exp(-\mu r)$ for various choices of the parameters g, m, and μ and various choices of the energy. It is thereby explicitly verified that the approximation becomes exact at high energy, and that it remains reasonably accurate at all energies.

The generalization of these results to all partial waves is easy [19]. In place of Eq. (22), we find

$$\delta_{l,\text{app}} = -k^{-1}\int_0^\infty dr\, V(r)\hat{D}_l^2(kr)\,\sin^2\{\hat{S}_l(kr)(1 + k^{-1}\hat{S}_l(kr)\hat{D}_l^2(kr)[V(r)]^{1/2})^{-1}\}.$$

$$(23)$$

As before, this may be viewed as a modified Born approximation. Again it yields the correct phase shifts $\delta_l = -\hat{S}_l(kR)$ for a hard sphere of radius R. It is easily shown that this approximation becomes exact in the limit of large k, and it yields the high-energy behavior of the phase shifts

$$\delta_l \xrightarrow[k\to\infty]{} -A(kr_0)^{1-(2/m)}, \qquad m > 2. \qquad (24a)$$

This is the same expression, Eq. (18), that we found for the S wave, and A is also defined in the same way, Eq. (19). We may therefore assert that the dominant term in the asymptotic behavior at high energy of all partial wave phase shifts δ_l is the same. This result is not surprising once it is recognized that the high-energy behavior of the phase shift is determined by the potential in the inner region because the centrifugal term is now dominated, in that region, by the (singular) potential. It should be emphasized, however, that this conclusion refers to the asymptotic behavior in k of the phase shift corresponding to a fixed finite value of l, but it does not imply anything about the behavior of the phase shift as both k and l diverge. Thus it would be incorrect to draw from Eq. (24a) any conclusion concerning the angular dependence of the full scattering amplitude in the high-energy limit because the partial wave sum that defines the full scattering amplitude extends to infinity.

In the low-energy limit the approximate expression (23) yields the correct behavior of the phase shift (we assume here that the potential vanishes at infinity sufficiently fast; see Chapter 11)

$$\delta_{l,\text{app}} \xrightarrow[k\to 0]{} a_{l,\text{app}} k^{2l+1}[1 + O(k^2)], \tag{24b}$$

with the following expression for the quantities $a_{l,\text{app}}$:

$$a_{l,\text{app}} = -[(2l - 1)!!]^{-2} \int_0^\infty dr\, r^{2l+2} V(r)(2l + 1 + r[V(r)]^{1/2})^{-2}. \tag{25}$$

In particular, for $l = 0$, we thus obtain an approximate expression a_{app} for the scattering length, namely,

$$a_{\text{app}} = - \int_0^\infty dr\, r^2 V(r)(1 + r[V(r)]^{1/2})^{-1}. \tag{26}$$

A comparison of these approximate expressions with the exact values is given in Ref. [19] for the class of potentials $gr^{-m}\theta(R - r)$, for which both the exact quantities a_l and their approximations $a_{l,\text{app}}$ may be computed in closed form. Again the approximations are found to be satisfactory. In particular, it is found that a_{app} coincides with a for the potential $V(r) = r_0^{-2}(r_0/r)^4\theta(R - r)$, irrespective of the values of r_0 and R. Of course, $a_{l,\text{app}}$ coincides with the exact value

$$a_l = -[(2l - 1)!!(2l + 1)!!]^{-1}R^{2l+1}$$

in the case of a hard sphere of radius R. It is also verified that for these potentials, the approximate expression (25) also yields the correct asymptotic result in the limit of large l,

$$a_{l,\text{app}} = a_l[1 + O(1/l)]. \tag{27}$$

We thus see that even in the limit of large l and small k the present approximation yields the correct behavior. This success may be

understood by remembering the relationship of the present approximation to the Born approximation, which is known to yield correctly
—for regular potentials—the dominant term in the asymptotic
behavior of the phase shift as l diverges. In fact, when the angular
momentum is large and the energy small, it is the outer part of the
potential that plays the major role in determining the phase shift;
and in the treatment of the outer region, the present approximation
does not differ from the Born approximation.

In the long-range case $R = \infty$, i. e., for the simple potential

$$V(r) = r_0^{-2}(r_0/r)^m, \tag{28}$$

both the exact and the approximate expressions for the scattering
length are rather simple:

$$a = -r_0(\pi p/\sin \pi p)(p^p/p!)^2, \tag{29}$$

$$a_{\text{app}} = -r_0(\pi p/\sin \pi p)(1 - 2p)/\cos \pi p, \tag{30}$$

with

$$p = (m - 2)^{-1}.$$

(For dimensional reasons these functions must be equal to r_0 times
a function of m only.) They are plotted in Fig. 1. (We have set

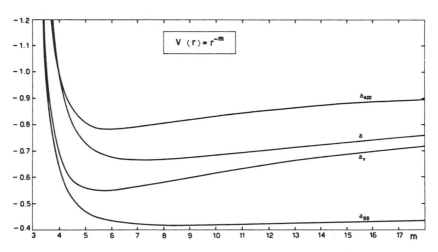

FIG. 1.   Scattering length for the potential $V(r) = r^{-m}$.

$r_0 = 1$ for convenience.) In this figure we have also included the improved Born and variational expressions a_{BB} and a_V (Eqs. (12.2) and (12.3)), which may also be evaluated in closed form in this case:

$$a_{BB} = -\tfrac{1}{2}r_0(\pi p/\sin \pi p)(2p)^p/p!, \tag{31}$$

$$a_V = a_{BB} \max_{w}[(2 - w)w^p], \tag{32a}$$

$$= -r_0(\pi p/\sin \pi p)(2p)^{2p}/[(p+1)^{p+1}p!]. \tag{32b}$$

To obtain Eq. (32b) we have used the value

$$w_M = 2p/(p+1) = 2/(m-1). \tag{33}$$

It should be noted that in the limit of large m (small p), both the approximation a_{app} introduced in this chapter and the variational approximation a_V approach the exact result, although the variational approximation approaches it better. This is apparent from Fig. 1 and also from the asymptotic expressions

$$a = -r_0\{1 - 2p(-\ln p - 0.577) + O[(p \ln p)^2]\}, \tag{34a}$$

$$a_V = -r_0\{1 - 2p(-\ln p - 0.481) + O[(p \ln p)^2]\}, \tag{34b}$$

$$a_{app} = -r_0\{1 - 2p + O(p^2)\}. \tag{34c}$$

The limiting value $a = -r_0$ is, of course, simply the scattering length produced by an infinitely repulsive sphere of radius r_0. In this limit the improved Born approximation tends to one half of the exact result:

$$a_B = -\tfrac{1}{2}r_0\{1 + O(p \ln p)\}. \tag{34d}$$

The explanation of this fact is identical to that given in Chapter 10, where the same result obtains for the behavior of the improved Born approximation as the strength of the potential diverges.

Up to now we have restricted our consideration to nowhere attractive potentials. If one deals with a potential that is attractive in some region, the approximate expressions (22) and (23) are inapplicable because they are not real. It will be obvious in every case, however, how they should be modified. The simpler solution is to suppress the potential in the argument of the sine function whenever it becomes negative. Otherwise, by using techniques such as those of Chapter 13, one can always reduce the problem to one in which only the repulsive part of the potential appears explicitly. One can then treat the rest of the potential exactly (or use some other approximation) and obtain an approximate expression for the phase shift due to the repulsive part of the interaction in terms of the "amplitude" and "phase" of the radial wave function apposite to the problem without repulsive contribution. The explicit form of this expression may be read by analogy from Eq. (23).

Concluding finally our discussion of the approximate formula for the phase shifts produced by singular potentials, Eq. (23), we emphasize that its main advantage is its validity over the whole energy range; it yields correctly up to a multiplicative constant the low-energy behavior and becomes exact as the energy diverges with fixed l. Moreover, it presumably yields the correct value also when l becomes very large for fixed energy.

We end this chapter by emphasizing that the phase approach has been very successful in coping with the problem of singular potential scattering. This may be understood since this approach concentrates directly on the physically most relevant quantity—the phase shift—rather than on the wave function. As we have seen, the accumulation of the phase shift never diverges; at most it grows linearly with r, which corresponds to a complete shift of the wave function, as is the case for an infinitely repulsive potential. On the other hand, the wave function in the case of a singular potential vanishes at the origin in a manner whose details, while physically irrelevant, are in fact the origin of the mathematical difficulties met in the study of this problem. However, although the phase approach is very convenient for the study of the phase shifts produced by singular potentials, it is by no means a good method for their numerical evaluation: the phase equation is very unstable with respect to computational errors because, in the r.h.s., we have an almost complete cancellation between two large quantities. Thus any attempt to obtain the scattering phase shift produced by a strongly singular potential through numerical integration of the phase equation from the origin onward would be very foolish. This is particularly so because in this case the radial Schrödinger equation integrated from the origin is very stable against computational errors (they introduce small components of the irregular solution, but these disappear very quickly owing to the rapid decrease of the irregular solution and the rapid increase of the regular one).

16

Further generalization
of the phase method

This chapter presents a further generalization of the phase method. The main difference from the treatment of Chapter 13 is that we take as our starting point a system of two coupled first-order differential equations, rather than a single second-order differential equation. The general results are then specialized to the potential scattering of Schrödinger particles, thereby rederiving the phase equations previously given and also some new ones. In the following chapter the general results are applied to the scattering of Dirac particles, thereby obtaining phase equations for the determination of the scattering phase shifts in that case. We follow rather closely the treatment of Refs. [15] and [17].

We take as our starting point the system of equations

$$y_1'(x) = A(x)y_1(x) - [1 - B(x)]y_2(x), \qquad (1a)$$

$$y_2'(x) = [1 - C(x)]y_1(x) - A(x)y_2(x). \qquad (1b)$$

As is well known [17], this is essentially the most general system of two coupled first-order differential equations. Both the Schrödinger and the Dirac radial equations may be cast into this form.

We recall that these equations imply that the "Wronskian"

$$Q = y_1(x)z_2(x) - y_2(x)z_1(x) \qquad (2)$$

is a constant, provided (y_1, y_2) and (z_1, z_2) are two solutions of the system (1).

The functions $A(x)$, $B(x)$, $C(x)$ are assumed to behave near the

113

origin so that a unique "regular" solution to Eqs. (1) is identified up to a multiplicative constant by the conditions

$$y_1(0) = 0, \qquad y_2(0) = \text{finite or zero}. \qquad (3)$$

Moreover, the functions $A(x)$, $B(x)$, and $C(x)$ are assumed to vanish sufficiently fast as x tends to infinity, so that all the solutions, with appropriate normalization, have the asymptotic behavior

$$y_1(x) \xrightarrow[x \to \infty]{} \sin(x + \Delta), \qquad (4a)$$

$$y_2(x) \xrightarrow[x \to \infty]{} -\cos(x + \Delta), \qquad (4b)$$

where Δ is a constant phase shift characteristic of each solution. Our purpose is to evaluate Δ for the regular solution.

The method is based on the comparison of the solutions of the system (1) with those of an appropriate comparison system, whose solutions are assumed to be known:

$$\bar{y}_1'(x) = \bar{A}(x)\bar{y}_1(x) - [1 - \bar{B}(x)]\bar{y}_2(x), \qquad (5a)$$

$$\bar{y}_2'(x) = [1 - \bar{C}(x)]\bar{y}_1(x) - \bar{A}(x)\bar{y}_2(x). \qquad (5b)$$

The functions $\bar{A}(x)$, $\bar{B}(x)$, $\bar{C}(x)$ are restricted by the same conditions as $A(x)$, $B(x)$, and $C(x)$; there is thus a "regular" solution $(\bar{y}_1(x), \bar{y}_2(x))$ with an asymptotic behavior similar to that in Eqs. (4), and with a phase shift that we denote by $\bar{\Delta}_R$. We also introduce a second "irregular" solution $(\bar{z}_1(x), \bar{z}_2(x))$, characterized by the asymptotic behavior of Eqs. (4) with phase shift $\bar{\Delta}_I (\neq \bar{\Delta}_R)$. The constant quantity $\bar{Q} = \bar{y}_1(x)\bar{z}_2(x) - \bar{y}_2(x)\bar{z}_1(x)$ is then easily evaluated, and we find

$$\bar{Q} = \sin(\bar{\Delta}_I - \bar{\Delta}_R). \qquad (6)$$

It should be emphasized that the conditions given identify uniquely the comparison solutions $(\bar{y}_1(x), \bar{y}_2(x))$ and $(\bar{z}_1(x), \bar{z}_2(x))$ and the phase shift $\bar{\Delta}_R$; the "regular" solution is identified up to a normalization constant by the condition (3), and the normalization constant is fixed by the asymptotic relation (4a), which also specifies $\bar{\Delta}_R$; the "irregular" solution is completely identified by the asymptotic condition, once $\bar{\Delta}_I$ is given. Needless to say, all phase shifts are defined up to a mod (π) ambiguity. They are defined absolutely by the phase equations given below. We do not discuss this point any further, since it has been dealt with previously.

We now introduce two auxiliary functions $c(x)$, $s(x)$, which relate the regular solution of the original problem, $(y_1(x), y_2(x))$, to the solutions of the comparison system,

$$y_1(x) = c(x)\bar{y}_1(x) + s(x)\bar{z}_1(x), \tag{7a}$$

$$y_2(x) = c(x)\bar{y}_2(x) + s(x)\bar{z}_2(x). \tag{7b}$$

These equations may be solved for $c(x)$ and $s(x)$:

$$c(x) = \bar{Q}^{-1}[y_1(x)\bar{z}_2(x) - y_2(x)\bar{z}_1(x)], \tag{8a}$$

$$s(x) = \bar{Q}^{-1}[y_1(x)\bar{y}_2(x) - y_2(x)\bar{y}_1(x)]. \tag{8b}$$

If we now compare Eqs. (7) with the asymptotic equations (4) and the corresponding relations for the barred quantities, we infer

$$\tan(\varDelta - \bar{\varDelta}_R) = t(\infty) \sin(\bar{\varDelta}_I - \bar{\varDelta}_R)/[1 + t(\infty) \cos(\bar{\varDelta}_I - \bar{\varDelta}_R)], \tag{9}$$

having introduced the "tangent function" $t(x)$:

$$t(x) = s(x)/c(x). \tag{10}$$

We have assumed that $t(\infty)$ exists, which is implied by the previous assumptions. In the special case $\bar{\varDelta}_I = \bar{\varDelta}_R + \pi/2$, $\bar{Q} = 1$ and the result, Eq. (9), simplifies to

$$\tan(\varDelta - \bar{\varDelta}_R) = t(\infty). \tag{11}$$

In terms of the "phase function" $\delta(x)$, defined by

$$\tan \delta(x) = t(x) = s(x)/c(x), \tag{12}$$

Eq. (11) becomes simply

$$\varDelta = \bar{\varDelta}_R + \delta(\infty). \tag{13}$$

We see, even in the general case, that to obtain $\varDelta$ it is sufficient to know $t(\infty)$ or, equivalently, $\delta(\infty)$. It is now a matter of trivial algebra to derive the differential equation satisfied by $t(x)$ [17]. We find

$$t'(x) = -\bar{Q}^{-1}\{[C(x) - \bar{C}(x)][\bar{y}_1(x) + t(x)\bar{z}_1(x)]^2$$
$$+ [B(x) - \bar{B}(x)][\bar{y}_2(x) + t(x)\bar{z}_2(x)]^2$$
$$+ 2[A(x) - \bar{A}(x)][\bar{y}_1(x) + t(x)\bar{z}_1(x)][\bar{y}_2(x) + t(x)\bar{z}_2(x)]\}. \tag{14}$$

This Riccati equation is easily recognized to be a more general version of the similar equations previously obtained. As usual, its solution has poles whenever the phase function $\delta(x)$, Eq. (12), passes through an odd multiple of $\pi/2$. The phase function itself remains, of course, always bounded. It satisfies the differential equation

$$
\begin{aligned}
\delta'(x) = & -\bar{Q}^{-1}\{[C(x) - \bar{C}(x)][\bar{y}_1(x) \cos \delta(x) + \bar{z}_1(x) \sin \delta(x)]^2 \\
& + [B(x) - \bar{B}(x)][\bar{y}_2(x) \cos \delta(x) + \bar{z}_2(x) \sin \delta(x)]^2 \\
& + 2[A(x) - \bar{A}(x)][\bar{y}_1(x) \cos \delta(x) + \bar{z}_1(x) \sin \delta(x)] \\
& \times [\bar{y}_2(x) \cos \delta(x) + \bar{z}_2(x) \sin \delta(x)]\}.
\end{aligned} \tag{15}
$$

In conclusion, we see that the phase shift Δ may be obtained by integrating this phase equation or the tangent equation (14) from the origin to infinity, and then using Eq. (9) or, in the special case $\Delta_I = \Delta_R + \pi/2$, Eq. (11) or (13). The starting values $t(0)$ or $\delta(0)$ are fixed by Eqs. (8), (10), and (12); they depend on the choice of the comparison system and on the behavior of the quantities $A(x)$, $B(x)$, and $C(x)$ near the origin, as will be discussed in each case. (We note, however, that in most cases, they vanish.)

For completeness we consider an "amplitude function" $\alpha(x)$, analogous to that discussed in Chapter 6:

$$
\alpha^2(x) = c^2(x) + s^2(x), \tag{16a}
$$

$$
c(x) = \alpha(x) \cos \delta(x), \qquad s(x) = \alpha(x) \sin \delta(x). \tag{16b}
$$

The expressions (7) become now

$$
y_1(x) = \alpha(x)[\bar{y}_1(x) \cos \delta(x) + \bar{z}_1(x) \sin \delta(x)], \tag{17a}
$$

$$
y_2(x) = \alpha(x)[\bar{y}_2(x) \cos \delta(x) + \bar{z}_2(x) \sin \delta(x)]. \tag{17b}
$$

It is easily shown [17] that once the phase function $\delta(x)$ is known, the amplitude function may be obtained with one quadrature:

$$
\begin{aligned}
\alpha(x) = \exp \Big[\bar{Q}^{-1} \int^x dx' \{\cos 2\delta \, [(C - \bar{C})\bar{y}_1 \bar{z}_1 \\
+ (B - \bar{B})\bar{y}_2 \bar{z}_2 + (A - \bar{A})(\bar{y}_1 \bar{z}_2 + \bar{y}_2 \bar{z}_1)] \\
+ \tfrac{1}{2} \sin 2\delta \, [(C - \bar{C})(\bar{y}_1{}^2 - \bar{z}_1{}^2) \\
+ (B - \bar{B})(\bar{y}_2{}^2 - \bar{z}_2{}^2) + 2(A - \bar{A})(\bar{z}_1 \bar{z}_2 - \bar{y}_1 \bar{y}_2)]\} \Big].
\end{aligned} \tag{18}
$$

As is apparent from the phase equation (15), there are comparison systems that yield rather simple equations. A particular example is that furnished by $\bar{A}(x) = \bar{B}(x) = \bar{C}(x) = 0$, which implies $\bar{\Delta}_R = 0$ and

$$\bar{y}_1(x) = \sin x, \qquad \bar{y}_2(x) = -\cos x. \tag{19a}$$

Choosing in addition $\bar{\Delta}_I = \pi/2$, which implies

$$\bar{z}_1(x) = \cos x, \qquad \bar{z}_2(x) = \sin x, \tag{19b}$$

we reduce the phase equation to the simple form

$$\delta'(x) = -C(x)\sin^2[x + \delta(x)] - B(x)\cos^2[x + \delta(x)] + A(x)\sin 2[x + \delta(x)]. \tag{20}$$

In this case we have simply $\Delta = \delta(\infty)$. The starting value $\delta(0)$ depends on the behaviors of $A(x)$, $B(x)$, and $C(x)$ near the origin; if each of them, when multiplied by x, vanishes at the origin, then $\delta(0) = 0$. Other cases are discussed below.

For this comparison system the amplitude function also takes a simple form:

$$\alpha(x) = \exp\left[\int^x dx'\{\tfrac{1}{2}(C - B)\sin 2(x' + \delta) - A\cos 2(x' + \delta)\}\right]. \tag{21}$$

We now apply these results to the case of the radial Schrödinger equation. First of all we note that the system (1) yields for $y_1(x)$ the second-order differential equation

$$y''(x) + B'(x)[1 - B(x)]^{-1}y'(x)$$
$$+ \{[1 - B(x)][1 - C(x)] - A^2(x) - A'(x) - A(x)B'(x)[1-B(x)]^{-1}\}y(x) = 0. \tag{22}$$

This could be reduced to an equation of Schrödinger type by the substitution $w(x) = [1 - B(x)]^{-1/2}y(x)$, but it turns out that the only choice leading to simple results is $B(x) = 0$, in which case Eq. (22) becomes simply

$$y''(x) + [1 - C(x) - A^2(x) - A'(x)]y(x) = 0. \tag{23}$$

This is to be compared with the radial Schrödinger equation (2.6), which, with the substitutions $x = kr$, $y(x) = u_l(r)$, $v(x) = k^{-2}V(r)$, becomes

$$y''(x) + [1 - v(x) - l(l + 1)x^{-2}]y(x) = 0. \tag{24}$$

There are three simple ways in which Eq. (23) may be identified with Eq. (24). They are

$$A(x) = (l + 1)/x, \qquad C(x) = v(x), \tag{25a}$$

$$A(x) = -l/x, \qquad C(x) = v(x), \tag{25b}$$

$$A(x) = 0, \qquad C(x) = v(x) + l(l + 1)x^{-2}. \tag{25c}$$

With the simple choice of the comparison functions (19), we obtain the phase equations

$$\alpha_l'(r) = -k^{-1}V(r)\sin^2[kr + \alpha_l(r)] + \left[\frac{l+1}{r}\right]\sin 2[kr + \alpha_l(r)],$$

$$\alpha_l(0) = \tan^{-1}\left\{\frac{2(l+1)k}{\lim_{r\to 0}[rV(r)]}\right\}, \qquad \delta_l = \alpha_l(\infty) + \frac{l\pi}{2}; \tag{26a}$$

$$\beta_l'(r) = -k^{-1}V(r)\sin^2[kr + \beta_l(r)] - \left(\frac{l}{r}\right)\sin 2[kr + \beta_l(r)],$$

$$\beta_l(0) = 0, \qquad \delta_l = \beta_l(\infty) + \frac{l\pi}{2}; \tag{26b}$$

$$\gamma_l'(r) = -k^{-1}[V(r) + l(l + 1)r^{-2}]\sin^2[kr + \gamma_l(r)],$$

$$\gamma_l(0) = 0, \qquad \gamma_l'(0) = -\frac{kl}{(l+1)}, \qquad \delta_l = \gamma_l(\infty) + \frac{l\pi}{2}. \tag{26c}$$

We have written these equations using the original variable r and the potential $V(r)$, and we have indicated in each case the boundary condition in the origin and the relationship between the asymptotic value of each phase function and the scattering phase shift δ_l. Note that the phase function $\gamma_l(r)$ is identical with that introduced in Chapter 13 (see Eq. (13.24)); the value of $\gamma_l'(0)$ has to be specified because of the singularity of the centrifugal potential, as was discussed in detail in Chapter 13. Assuming the potential $V(r)$ to be less singular than r^{-2} in the origin, the other two equations do not require the specification of the derivative in the origin. However, the value of $\alpha_l(0)$ depends on the behavior of the potential in the origin, as indicated in Eq. (26a); if $rV(r)$ vanishes in the origin, $\alpha_l(0) = \pi/2$; if $rV(r)$ diverges in the origin, $\alpha_l(0) = 0$.

The explicit relations connecting $\alpha_l(r)$ and $\beta_l(r)$ with the phase function $\gamma_l(r)$ discussed in Chapter 13 may be obtained easily. They are

$$\tan[\alpha_l(r) - \gamma_l(r)] = - [(l + 1)/(kr)]$$
$$\times \{1 + [\cot(kr + \gamma_l(r)) - (l + 1)/(kr)] \cot(kr + \gamma_l(r))\}^{-1},$$
$$(27)$$

and, for $\beta_l(r)$, a similar equation with $-l/(kr)$ in place of $(l + 1)/(kr)$. The somewhat strange appearance in Eqs. (26a) and (26b) of a "centrifugal" coefficient that behaves like r^{-1} rather than r^{-2} is connected with the fact that the whole term is oscillatory rather than positive-definite as in Eq. (26c). It is this oscillation that produces the asymptotic convergence of the phase functions $\alpha_l(r)$ and $\beta_l(r)$. In fact, the detailed behavior of these functions relative to $\gamma_l(r)$ may be read from Eq. (27). The rather slow convergence of $\alpha_l(r)$ and $\beta_l(r)$, or for that matter $\gamma_l(r)$, need not be a disadvantage from the computational point of view, as has already been noted in Chapter 13. The integration need be carried only beyond the range of the potential $V(r)$; from there one fits on to known functions, as indicated in Chapter 13 and, more generally, in Ref. [17]. Which one of these three phase functions is more convenient from a practical point of view depends on the specific problem. Note that for $l = 0$, $\beta_0(r)$ and $\gamma_0(r)$ are identical, while the equation for $\alpha_0(r)$ still contains a "centrifugal" term. (Needless to say, the functions $\alpha_l(r)$ discussed here have nothing to do with those introduced in Chapter 11, nor with the "amplitude" function introduced above and in Chapter 6.)

There are other convenient choices for the functions $A(r)$, $B(r)$, and $C(r)$, in which the centrifugal term of the Schrödinger equation is absorbed into the comparison system. It turns out that the only simple phase equations secured in this manner are those obtained in Chapter 3 and extensively discussed in the preceding chapters. We also mention the possibility of including in the comparison system a part of the potential whose effect is known. For a more detailed analysis of this possibility, we refer to Chapter 13, where it was discussed in the framework of a formulation of the phase method slightly less general than that given in this chapter.

17

Scattering of Dirac particles

In this chapter we apply the phase method to the potential scattering of a Dirac particle [5, 15, 17].

We begin by recalling briefly the results of the theory of scattering of a Dirac particle. For a more detailed treatment, see Ref. [25] and the literature quoted there. We assume the potential to be spherically symmetric and to transform as the fourth component of a relativistic vector—namely, we take as our starting point the Dirac equation

$$[-i\alpha\nabla + \beta m + V(r) - E]\chi(\mathbf{r}) = 0. \tag{1}$$

Here α and β are the usual Dirac anticommuting matrices, and $\psi(\mathbf{r})$ is a four-component spinor. In this chapter we use a unit system such that $\hbar = c = 1$. After separation of the spin-angular part, we obtain from this equation the radial Dirac equation

$$y_1'(r) = (n/r)y_1(r) - [k - \chi V(r)]y_2(r), \tag{2a}$$

$$y_2'(r) = [k - \chi^{-1}V(r)]y_1(r) - (n/r)y_2(r). \tag{2b}$$

This is a system of two coupled differential equations of first order. Here k is the linear momentum,

$$k = (E^2 - m^2)^{1/2}, \tag{3}$$

and the quantity χ is defined by

$$\chi = [(E - m)/(E + m)]^{1/2}. \tag{4}$$

Thus in the nonrelativistic limit $\chi = k/(2m)$ ($= k$ in the unit system adopted in the other chapters), while in the extreme relativistic limit (or, equivalently, in the zero-mass case), $\chi = 1$. The quantum number n is connected with the total angular momentum j and the "orbital" angular momentum l by the relation

$$j = |n| - \tfrac{1}{2} = l + \tfrac{1}{2}n/|n|. \tag{5}$$

The scattering phase shifts δ_{jl} are defined by the following asymptotic behavior of the "regular" solution:

$$y_1(r) \xrightarrow[r\to\infty]{} \text{const} \times \sin(kr - l\pi/2 + \delta_{jl}), \tag{6a}$$

$$y_2(r) \xrightarrow[r\to\infty]{} -\text{const} \times \cos(kr - l\pi/2 + \delta_{jl}), \tag{6b}$$

the regular solution being that solution for which $y_1(0) = 0$. Note that for each value of the total angular momentum j there are two phase shifts, corresponding to the two possible values $l - j \pm \tfrac{1}{2}$ of the "orbital" angular momentum. In the extreme relativistic limit, i. e., $\chi - 1$, these are identical. In the nonrelativistic limit $\chi \approx k/2m \ll 1$, it is the two phase shifts with equal l that are identical. Both of these well-known statements are proved below.

For completeness we also give the expressions for the full scattering amplitudes. We have for the non-spin-flip amplitude,

$$f(\theta) = (2ik)^{-1} \sum_{l=0}^{\infty} \{(l+1)[\exp(2i\delta_{l+\frac{1}{2},l}) - 1] + l[\exp(2i\delta_{l-\frac{1}{2},l}) - 1]\}P_l(\cos\theta), \tag{7a}$$

and for the spin-flip amplitude,

$$g(\theta) = (2ik)^{-1} \sum_{l=1}^{\infty} \{\exp(2i\delta_{l+\frac{1}{2},l}) - \exp(2i\delta_{l-\frac{1}{2},l})\}P_l^1(\cos\theta). \tag{7b}$$

Here θ is the scattering angle, $P_l(z)$ is a Legendre polynomial, and

$$P_l^1(z) = (1 - z^2)^{1/2}P_l'(z). \tag{8}$$

The differential cross section for an unpolarized beam is

$$\frac{d\sigma(\theta)}{d\Omega} = |f(\theta)|^2 + |g(\theta)|^2. \tag{9}$$

In the nonrelativistic limit $g(\theta)$ vanishes and Eq. (7a) becomes identical with Eq. (2.11).

The system of two coupled differential equations (2) can be reduced by straightforward differentiation into a single radial "Schrödinger" equation for

$$u_{l\pm}(r) = [E + m - V(r)]^{-1/2}y_1(r), \tag{10}$$

namely,

$$u_{l\pm}''(r) + [k^2 - l(l+1)r^{-2} - 2mV_D(\pm, l, k; r)]u_{l\pm}(r) = 0. \tag{11}$$

The effective Dirac potential $V_D(\pm, l, k; r)$ is defined by

$$2mV_D(\pm, l, k; r) = 2EV(r) - V^2(r)$$
$$+ [\tfrac{1}{2} \pm (l + \tfrac{1}{2})]r^{-1}a(r) - \tfrac{1}{2}a'(r) - \tfrac{1}{4}a^2(r), \tag{12}$$

where

$$a(r) = V'(r)[E + m - V(r)]^{-1}. \tag{13}$$

Note that the effective potential depends on the spin, the angular momentum, and the energy, and is a complicated function of the original potential. The scattering phase shifts are defined in the usual way from the asymptotic behavior of that solution $u_{l\pm}(r)$ of Eq. (11) which vanishes in the origin:

$$u_{l\pm}(r) \xrightarrow[r\to\infty]{} \text{const} \times \sin(kr - l\pi/2 + \delta_{l\pm\frac{1}{2},l}). \tag{14}$$

In this manner a Dirac problem can be reduced to an equivalent Schrödinger problem.

There are, however, two caveats to be remembered. First of all, we must assume that the potential $V(r)$ is continuous. If the potential is not continuous, then a continuous $u_{l\pm}(r)$ corresponds to a discontinuous $y_1(r)$, and vice versa. Thus, in such a case, the solution of the Dirac problem—and, in particular, the scattering phase shift—is not the same as that computed for an equivalent Schrödinger scattering problem. Of course the physical requirement to be maintained in order to obtain the scattering phase shifts in the Dirac case is that the Dirac wave functions be continuous.

The second point is that the Dirac problem has an unambiguous physical meaning only if the behavior of the potential in the origin satisfies the condition

$$\lim_{r\to 0} r|V(r)| < 1. \tag{15}$$

In fact, it is easily seen that unless this condition is satisfied, the condition that the upper component $y_1(r)$ of the Dirac wave function vanish in the origin is not sufficient to identify the solution of the radial equation; in this respect the situation is quite analogous to that met in the Schrödinger case with an attractive singular potential (see Chapter 15). It should be emphasized that this difficulty is not restricted to the reformulation of the Dirac case as an equivalent Schrödinger problem, as was the case for the point raised in the preceding paragraph. The present difficulty is really inherent in the Dirac problem. Thus, in the following, we shall always restrict our attention to potentials that do not violate the condition (15). Needless to say, we also assume the potential to vanish sufficiently fast at infinity.

In conclusion, we have seen that the problem of computing the scattering phase shifts for a particle obeying the Dirac equation in the presence of a central potential $V(r)$ may be reduced to an equivalent Schrödinger problem with a complicated effective potential $V_D(r)$, Eq. (12). Thus one way of extending the phase approach to the Dirac case proceeds through the reformulation in terms of the equivalent Schrödinger problem and the application to this problem of the methods extensively illustrated in the preceding chapters. We do not write explicitly any of the resulting equations; nor do we insist on the many additional results (variational principles for the phase shift, approximate expressions, etc.) that are also immediately applicable. We emphasize two disadvantages of this way of applying the phase approach to the Dirac equation. In the first place, it should be noted that the phase function thus obtained does not have a physical meaning as scattering phase shift of the problem with truncated potential; only the asymptotic value of the phase function has a physical meaning, being directly related to the scattering phase shift. This is connected with the first of the two caveats mentioned above. In the second place, the dependence of the effective potential on the original potential, Eq. (12), is so complicated as to becloud all physical significance.

Both of these disadvantages, however, are bypassed if we apply directly the procedure of the preceding chapter to the radial Dirac equation (2). There is an obvious choice of A, B, and C in Eqs. (16.1) in order to identify those equations with Eqs. (2):

$$A(r) = n/r, \qquad B(r) = \chi V(r), \qquad C(r) = \chi^{-1} V(r). \qquad (16)$$

Of course we also change the dependent variable from $x = kr$ to r.

Various choices of comparison system may now be made. We consider first a choice that absorbs the centrifugal term:

$$\bar{A}(r) = n/r, \qquad \bar{B}(r) = \bar{C}(r) = 0. \qquad (17)$$

With this choice and an appropriate selection for the asymptotic phases of the comparison solutions, we introduce phase functions $\delta_{l\pm\frac{1}{2},l}(r)$ that satisfy the phase equations

$$\delta'_{l\pm\frac{1}{2},l}(r) = - V(r)\{\chi^{-1}[\hat{j}_l(kr)\cos\delta_{l\pm\frac{1}{2},l}(r) + \hat{n}_l(kr)\sin\delta_{l\pm\frac{1}{2},l}(r)]^2$$

$$+ \chi[\hat{j}_{l\pm1}(kr)\cos\delta_{l\pm\frac{1}{2},l}(r) + \hat{n}_{l\pm1}(kr)\sin\delta_{l\pm\frac{1}{2},l}(r)]^2\} \qquad (18a)$$

$$= - V(r)\{\chi^{-1}\hat{D}_l{}^2(kr)\sin^2[\hat{\delta}_l(kr) + \delta_{l\pm\frac{1}{2},l}(r)]$$

$$+ \chi\hat{D}_{l\pm1}^2(kr)\sin^2[\hat{\delta}_{l\pm1}(kr) + \delta_{l\pm\frac{1}{2},l}(r)]\}, \qquad (18b)$$

with boundary conditions

$$\delta_{l\pm\frac{1}{2},l}(0) = 0. \qquad (19a)$$

If the potential is such that V_{-1}, defined by $V_{-1} = \lim_{r\to0}[rV(r)]$, does not vanish in the origin, Eq. (19a) is not sufficient to identify the phase function and must be supplemented by the more specific condition

$$\delta_{j,l}(r) \xrightarrow[r\to0]{} \{[(j+\tfrac{1}{2})^2 - V_{-1}^2]^{1/2} - (j+\tfrac{1}{2})\}\, V_{-1}^{-1}[(2j)!!]^{-2}\chi^{2(l-j)}(kr)^{2j+1}. \qquad (19b)$$

(The other solutions have a minus sign in front of the square root.) Note that a sufficient and necessary condition for the reality of this expression for all physical values of j is the validity of Eq. (15). The scattering phase shifts are then given directly by the asymptotic values of these phase functions:

$$\delta_{jl} = \delta_{jl}(\infty). \qquad (20)$$

The analogy of the phase equation (18) to that for the Schrödinger case is evident. Note that now the phase functions $\delta_{jl}(r)$ yield the phase shifts due to the potential truncated at r. Thus the comments made in Chapter 4 are also valid in this case. Moreover, the difference between this phase equation and that valid in the Schrödinger case, Eq. (3.14), is also very illuminating for the physical understanding of the problem. It displays the effect of the spin, which causes a coupling between orbital angular momenta differing by one unit. The mixing parameter is χ^2, which displays the relativistic nature of this effect. In the nonrelativistic limit, χ may be neglected with respect to χ^{-1}, and the equation for the Schrödinger case is recovered; the fact that in this limit the phase shifts—or, for that matter, the phase functions—depend only on l and not on j is thereby also proved. Similarly, in the extreme-relativistic or zero-mass limit, $\chi = 1$, it is apparent from the structure of the phase equations that the phase functions depend only on j and not on l.

In the limit of very high energy, namely for $\chi \approx 1$ and $k\bar{r} \gg j$, where $\bar{r}$ is some measure of the range of the potential, substituting for the Riccati–Bessel functions their asymptotic expressions we obtain simply

$$\delta'_{jl}(r) = -V(r). \tag{21}$$

Thus we may conclude that all phase shifts tend to the same value as k diverges:

$$\lim_{k\to\infty} \delta_{jl} = -\int_0^\infty dr\, V(r). \tag{22}$$

This result was previously discovered by Parzen [35]. It should be emphasized that this result holds in the limit of large k for fixed j. Incidentally, this result lifts the mod (π) ambiguity inherent in the original definition of the phase shift; it is the analog of Eq. (2.14) valid in the Schrödinger case.

(Needless to say, the result (22) applies only provided V_{-1} vanishes, i. e., only if the integral in the r.h.s. of Eq. (22) converges. This is also implied by its derivation because if V_{-1} does not vanish, we cannot neglect the contribution from the region where kr is small, even in the limit of large k. On the other hand, Eq. (22) might still be considered valid even for $V_{-1} \neq 0$, in the sense that it implies in this case that the scattering phase shifts diverge as k diverges.)

On the basis of the phase equation (18) it is easy to extend to the Dirac case all of the results that we have derived and discussed in the preceding chapters for the Schrödinger case—in particular, variational and approximate expressions for the phase shifts, expressions for the whole wave function in terms of the phase function, etc. The interested reader may derive them using the analogy with the Schrödinger case, and he may check his results with those published [15].

Before proceeding to discuss other types of phase equations, we mention in passing that the incompatibility of singular potentials with the Dirac equation may be read directly from the phase equation (18). In fact, as was discussed in detail in Chapter 15, the validity of the Schrödinger phase equation is ensured, in the case of singular potentials, by the fast vanishing of the factor that multiplies the potential in the r.h.s.; this fast vanishing is brought about by an appropriate behavior of the phase function. But in the Dirac case, because we have two separate contributions (which may be interpreted as corresponding to the "orbital" angular momenta $j + \frac{1}{2}$ and $j - \frac{1}{2}$), such a cancellation cannot occur.

To derive other types of phase equations, similar to those obtained in the preceding chapter for the Schrödinger case, we again apply the procedure of the preceding chapter to the Dirac radial equation (2), but we take as a comparison solution the functions (16.19). We obtain in this manner the following equations for the phase functions $\mu_{j\pm}(r)$,

$$\mu'_{j\pm}(r) = -V(r)\{\chi^{-1} \sin^2[kr + \mu_{j\pm}(r)] + \chi \cos^2[kr + \mu_{j\pm}(r)]\}$$
$$\pm [(j + \tfrac{1}{2})/r] \sin 2[kr + \mu_{j\pm}(r)], \tag{23}$$

with the following boundary conditions:

$$\mu_{j\pm}(0) = \tan^{-1}\{\pm \chi[(A^2 - 1)^{1/2} + A]^{\pm 1}\}, \tag{24}$$

where

$$A = (j + \tfrac{1}{2})/\lim_{r \to 0}[rV(r)] \equiv (j + \tfrac{1}{2})/V_{-1}. \tag{25}$$

Note that $|A| > 1$, as implied by Eq. (15). We emphasize that Eq. (24) also remains valid for potentials for which V_{-1} vanishes, in which case it yields simply

$$\mu_{j+}(0) = \pi/2, \qquad \mu_{j-}(0) = 0. \tag{26}$$

The relation of these phase functions to the scattering phase shifts is given by

$$\delta_{j,j\mp\frac{1}{2}} = \mu_{j\pm}(\infty) + (j \mp \tfrac{1}{2})\pi/2. \tag{27}$$

In the nonrelativistic limit $\chi \approx k/(2m) \ll 1$, we easily see that

$$\mu_{j+}(r) = \alpha_l(r), \qquad l = j - \tfrac{1}{2}, \tag{28a}$$
$$\mu_{j-}(r) = \beta_l(r), \qquad l = j + \tfrac{1}{2}, \tag{28b}$$

where $\alpha_l(r)$ and $\beta_l(r)$ are the functions introduced in the preceding chapter. This demonstrates again, in the nonrelativistic limit, the identification of the two Dirac phase shifts corresponding to the same l with the same Schrödinger phase shift.

To discuss the extreme relativistic limit (or the zero-mass case), it is convenient to perform a trivial modification, introducing the phase functions $\nu_{j\pm}(r)$ through

$$\nu_{j+}(r) = \mu_{j+}(r) + \pi/2, \qquad \nu_{j-}(r) = \mu_{j-}(r). \tag{29}$$

The phase equations then become

$$\nu'_{j\pm}(r) = - V(r)\{\chi^{\pm 1}\sin^2[kr + \nu_{j\pm}(r)] $$
$$+ \chi^{\mp 1}\cos^2[kr + \nu_{j\pm}(r)]\} - [(j + \tfrac{1}{2})/r]\sin 2[kr + \nu_{j\pm}(r)], \tag{30}$$

and the boundary conditions

$$\nu_{j\pm}(0) = \tan^{-1}\{-\chi^{\mp 1}[(A^2 - 1)^{1/2} + A]^{-1}\}, \tag{31}$$

with A defined by Eq. (25). In the case of a potential such that V_{-1} vanishes, the boundary conditions become simply

$$\nu_{j\pm}(0) = 0. \tag{32}$$

The relationship between the asymptotic value of the phase functions $\nu_{j\pm}(r)$ and the scattering phase shifts is

$$\delta_{j,j\mp\frac{1}{2}} = \nu_{j\pm}(\infty) + (j + \tfrac{1}{2})\pi/2. \tag{33}$$

In the extreme relativistic limit $\chi \approx 1$, the two phase functions $\nu_{j\pm}(r)$ clearly become identical and satisfy the remarkably simple equation

$$\nu'_j(r) = -V(r) - [(j + \tfrac{1}{2})/r]\sin 2[kr + \nu_j(r)]. \tag{34}$$

The identification, in this limit, of the two phase shifts corresponding to the same value of j is thus demonstrated. In this case the amplitude function of Chapter 16 also becomes quite simple:

$$\alpha(r) = \exp\left\{(j + \tfrac{1}{2})\int^r ds \cos 2[ks + \nu_j(s)]/s\right\}. \tag{35}$$

The potential occurs here only implicitly, in $\nu_j(s)$.

We note that if j takes the unphysical value $j = -\frac{1}{2}$, Eq. (34) becomes exactly solvable:

$$v_{-\frac{1}{2}}(r) = -\int_0^r ds\, V(s). \tag{36}$$

(In this case the Dirac radial equation itself can also be easily solved.) We thus have an analytic continuation in j of the phase shifts such that

$$\delta_{-\frac{1}{2}} = -\int_0^\infty dr\, V(r). \tag{37}$$

This result is independent of k and coincides with the high-energy limit of all phase shifts, as previously mentioned. This result suggests the introduction of yet another phase function $\omega_j(r) = v_j(r) - v_{-\frac{1}{2}}(r)$, which satisfies the equation

$$\omega_j'(r) = -[(j + \tfrac{1}{2})/r]\sin 2[kr + \omega_j(r) + v_{-\frac{1}{2}}(r)]. \tag{38}$$

This intriguing equation contains no explicit reference to the potential; it could also have been obtained directly from the formalism of Chapter 16, with the choice $\bar{A}(r) = 0$, $\bar{B}(r) = \bar{C}(r) = V(r)$.

To justify this somewhat long discussion of the zero-mass case, we recall that this case is of present interest in the theoretical analysis required for the interpretation of high-energy electron scattering experiments designed to probe the inner structure of nuclei, because for all practical purposes the electron mass may be neglected at the energies involved. It should be emphasized that the extreme relativistic or zero-mass approximation is not the same thing as the high-energy approximation $k\bar{r} \gg 1$, $\bar{r}$ being some measure of the interaction range. There may be cases when either one of these approximations is valid, while the other is not. Only if both approximations are valid will the equality of all phase shifts predicted by Parzen's theorem, Eq. (22), occur—but even then, only for those values of j such that $k\bar{r} \gg j$.

Finally we observe that just as in the Schrödinger case, it is possible to write many other types of phase equations by choosing other comparison systems. For instance, it is possible to include some part of the potential; a case in point is the example just mentioned of the scattering of electrons by nuclei, in which case a point Coulomb potential might be absorbed in the comparison system. Then only the difference between the potential due to the actual charge distribution in the nucleus and the point Coulomb potential would be exposed in the phase equation, and the relativistic Coulomb functions would appear in place of the Riccati–Bessel or circular functions.

18

Scattering on nonlocal potentials
and on complex potentials

In this chapter we indicate briefly the possibility of extending the phase approach to the case of scattering on nonlocal potentials. We recall that nonlocal potentials play a role in several physical problems, for instance, in the investigation of nuclear matter. We also mention the extension of the phase method to the case of complex potentials, a case which is also of interest in several phenomenological applications (optical model, etc.).

We begin with the study of nonlocal potentials. The stationary Schrödinger equation is assumed to be of the form

$$[\nabla^2 + k^2]\psi(\mathbf{r}) = \int d\mathbf{s}\, V(\mathbf{r}, \mathbf{s})\psi(\mathbf{s}).$$ (1)

The assumption that the potential is spherically symmetric corresponds to the requirement that $V(\mathbf{r}, \mathbf{s})$ depend only on r, s and the angle θ between $\mathbf{r}$ and $\mathbf{s}$. We then obtain in the usual way the radial wave equation

$$u_l''(r) + [k^2 - l(l+1)r^{-2}]u_l(r) = \int_0^\infty ds\, V_l(r, s)u_l(s),$$ (2)

where

$$V_l(r, s) = 2\pi rs \int_{-1}^1 d(\cos\theta)\, P_l(\cos\theta)V(\mathbf{r}, \mathbf{s}).$$ (3)

From now on we consider for simplicity the S wave only, and we drop its subscript zero. The generalization to all partial waves is trivial [18].

129

We assume the usual conditions on the behavior of the potential, asymptotically and at the origin. They imply the existence of a "regular" solution of Eq. (2), characterized by the boundary condition

$$u(0) = 0, \tag{4}$$

and defining the scattering phase shift δ through its asymptotic behavior

$$u(r) \xrightarrow[r\to\infty]{} \text{const} \times \sin(kr + \delta). \tag{5}$$

We now introduce, just as in Chapter 6, an amplitude function $\alpha(r)$ and a phase function $\delta(r)$, setting

$$u(r) = \alpha(r) \sin[kr + \delta(r)], \tag{6a}$$

$$u'(r) = k\alpha(r) \cos[kr + \delta(r)]. \tag{6b}$$

Differentiating the first of these equations and comparing with the second, we find

$$\alpha'(r) = -\alpha(r)\delta'(r) \cot[kr + \delta(r)], \tag{7}$$

which may be formally integrated to yield

$$\alpha(r) = \exp\left\{ - \int^r ds\ \delta'(s) \cot[ks + \delta(s)] \right\}. \tag{8}$$

We thus see that just as in the local case, once the phase function is known, the amplitude function may be obtained with one quadrature. Note that the lower limit of the integration in Eq. (8) is irrelevant; it corresponds to a constant normalization factor in the wave function. As for the integrand, we show below that it is not singular because the poles of $\cot[ks + \delta(s)]$ are cancelled by zeros of $\delta'(s)$.

We then differentiate Eq. (6b), and, using Eqs. (2) and (7), we secure

$$\delta'(r) = -k^{-1} \sin[kr + \delta(r)] \int_0^\infty ds\ V(r, s)u(s)/\alpha(r). \tag{9}$$

From this equation, using Eqs. (6a) and (8), we finally obtain

$$\delta'(r) = - k^{-1} \sin[kr + \delta(r)] \int_0^\infty ds\ V(r, s) \sin[ks + \delta(s)]$$
$$\times \exp\left\{ \int_s^r dt\ \delta'(t) \cot[kt + \delta(t)] \right\}. \tag{10}$$

This integrodifferential equation, together with the boundary condition

$$\delta(0) = 0, \tag{11}$$

determines the phase function, and therefore also the scattering phase shift δ,

$$\delta = \delta(\infty). \tag{12}$$

It is the analog of the phase equation (3.15), to which it reduces in the case of a local potential $V(r, s) = V(r)\delta(r - s)$. We also note that an equation for $\alpha(r)$ that resembles closely the analogous equation of the local case, Eq. (6.9), is

$$\alpha'(r) = k^{-1} \cos[kr + \delta(r)] \int_0^\infty ds\, V(r, s) \sin[ks + \delta(s)]\alpha(s). \tag{13}$$

For the phase function it is also possible to derive an equation that resembles more closely the phase equation of the local case, Eq. (3.15), and that does not contain the derivative $\delta'(s)$ in the r.h.s. In fact, using the formal identity

$$\exp\left\{ \int_s^r dt\, \delta'(t) \cot[kt + \delta(t)] \right\} \sin[ks + \delta(s)]$$

$$= \exp\left\{ -k \int_s^r dt\, \cot[kt + \delta(t)] \right\} \sin[kr + \delta(r)], \tag{14}$$

we may bring Eq. (10) into the form

$$\delta'(r) = -k^{-1} \sin^2[kr + \delta(r)] \int_0^\infty ds\, V(r, s) \exp\left\{ -k \int_s^r dt\, \cot[kt + \delta(t)] \right\}. \tag{15}$$

This equation, however, has only a formal meaning because the integrand in the exponential term is singular. To interpret it, one should always refer back to the formal identity (14). It is also easily seen that

$$\exp\left[-k \int_s^r dt\, \cot[kt + \delta(t)] \right] = u(s)/u(r), \tag{16}$$

where $u(r)$ is the radial wave function. Thus Eq. (15) may also be interpreted as identifying the phase function produced by the nonlocal potential $V(r, s)$ with that produced by the local potential

$$V(r) = \int_0^\infty ds\, V(r, s)u(s)/u(r), \tag{17}$$

a result that may be read directly from the radial equation (2).

It should be emphasized that the phase function $\delta(r)$ does not have a simple physical meaning for all values of r, as it did in the local case. This is due to the nonlocality of the potential, which implies that the accumulation of the phase depends on the wave function for all values of r. We note that the phase equation (10) has a very complicated mathematical structure. It should, however, be solvable by the method of successive approximations, irrespective of the strength of the potential; in fact, this might turn out to be the most convenient manner in this case for computing numerically the scattering phase shift.

We end this discussion by mentioning the result obtained in the special case of a separable potential

$$V(r, s) = f(r)g(s). \tag{18}$$

(Actually in physical applications $g(r)$ equals $f(r)$, but we may consider the more general case.) In this case we find for the phase function

$$\delta(r) = -\tan^{-1}\left\{\frac{\int_0^r ds\, f(s)\sin ks}{A + \int_0^r ds\, f(s)\cos ks}\right\}, \tag{19}$$

with

$$A = \left[k - \int_0^\infty dr\, g(r) \int_0^r ds\, f(s)\sin k(r - s)\right]\left[\int_0^\infty dr\, g(r)\sin kr\right]^{-1}. \tag{20}$$

As previously noted, this is the same phase function that would be produced by the local energy-dependent potential

$$V(r) = f(r)\int_0^\infty ds\, g(s)\, u(s)/u(r), \tag{21}$$

with the radial wave function given by

$$u(r) = A \sin kr + \int_0^r ds\, f(s)\sin k(r - s). \tag{22}$$

Let us finally consider the scattering on complex potentials, simply to indicate how the phase method can be applied in this case. We recall that complex potentials are often used as phenomenological representations of inelastic interactions. The imaginary part of the potential (which must be negative; see below) accounts for the disappearance of the particles removed from the scattering beam through some process other than elastic scattering. As a consequence, the S matrix is not unitary; in fact, the modulus of S_l represents the ratio of the number of scattered particles (with angular momentum l) to that of incident particles (with angular momentum l: angular momentum is a constant of the motion), and it is therefore less than unity if there is absorption. A typical example of a situation that is reasonably described by the model of nonrelativistic scattering on a complex potential is the scattering of antiprotons by nuclei for kinetic energies up to a few hundreds of million electron volts. The absorption associated with the imaginary part of the potential corresponds to the annihilation process.

The elementary theory of scattering, as reviewed in Chapter 2, remains valid even if the potential is complex. The only difference is that the phase shifts δ_l are not real, but have a positive imaginary part. In addition to the elastic scattering amplitude, Eq. (2.11), we now have an absorption cross section

$$\sigma_a = \pi k^{-2} \sum_{l=0}^{\infty} (2l+1)(1-\eta_l^2), \tag{23}$$

where

$$\eta_l = |S_l| = \exp(-2\,\mathrm{Im}\,\delta_l). \tag{24}$$

Also in the phase method no departure is required from the development of Chapter 3; the only difference is that now the potential $V(r)$ is complex:

$$V(r) = V_R(r) + iV_I(r), \qquad V_I(r) \leqslant 0. \tag{25}$$

Thus, for instance, we still have for the S-matrix function the equation (3.19b),

$$S_l'(r) = -(2ik)^{-1}V(r)[\hat{h}_l^{(2)}(kr) - S_l(r)\hat{h}_l^{(1)}(kr)]^2, \tag{26}$$

with boundary condition

$$S_l(0) = 1, \tag{27}$$

and the scattering matrix is still determined by the asymptotic condition

$$S_l = S_l(\infty). \tag{28}$$

However, the complexity of the potential makes it impossible to obtain from this equation a single equation for one real function; we still have, of course, the phase equation (3.14), but now the phase function $\delta_l(r)$ is complex. It is more convenient to parametrize the S-matrix function, setting

$$S_l(r) = \eta_l(r) \exp[2i\epsilon_l(r)], \tag{29}$$

with $\eta_l(r)$ and $\epsilon_l(r)$ real. We then find for these two functions the following system of coupled nonlinear equations:

$$\begin{aligned}
\epsilon_l'(r) = &- [4k\eta_l(r)]^{-1}\hat{D}_l^2(kr) \\
&\times \{V_R(r)[[1 + \eta_l(r)]^2 \sin^2[\hat{\delta}_l(kr) + \epsilon_l(r)] \\
&- [1 - \eta_l(r)]^2 \cos^2[\hat{\delta}_l(kr) + \epsilon_l(r)]] \\
&- V_I(r)[1 - \eta_l^2(r)] \sin 2[\hat{\delta}_l(kr) + \epsilon_l(r)]\}, \tag{30}
\end{aligned}$$

$$\begin{aligned}
\eta_l'(r) = &\ (2k)^{-1}\hat{D}_l^2(kr) \\
&\times \{V_I(r)[[1 + \eta_l(r)]^2 \sin^2[\hat{\delta}_l(kr) + \epsilon_l(r)] \\
&- [1 - \eta_l(r)]^2 \cos^2[\hat{\delta}(kr) + \epsilon_l(r)]] \\
&+ V_R(r)[1 - \eta_l^2(r)] \sin 2[\hat{\delta}_l(kr) + \epsilon_l(r)]\}, \tag{31}
\end{aligned}$$

with boundary conditions

$$\epsilon_l(0) = 0, \tag{32}$$

$$\eta_l(0) = 1. \tag{33}$$

It is, of course, easily seen that if $V_I(r) = 0$, then $\eta_l(r) = 1$, and Eq. (30) reduces to the usual phase equation. More generally, we infer from Eq. (31) the condition

$$-1 \leqslant \eta_l(r) \leqslant 1, \tag{34}$$

because for $\eta_l(r) = 1$ we have

$$\eta_l'(r) = 2k^{-1}V_I(r)\hat{j}_l^2(kr) \leqslant 0, \tag{35}$$

while for $\eta_l(r) = -1$ we have

$$\eta_l'(r) = -2k^{-1}V_I(r)\hat{n}_l^2(kr) \geqslant 0. \tag{36}$$

Note that this proves that the modulus of $S_l(r)$ cannot exceed one; this is a consequence of our assumption that $V(r)$ is absorptive, i. e., $V_I(r)$ is negative. We also note that from each solution $\eta_l(r)$, $\epsilon_l(r)$ we may obtain a second solution of the differential equation through the substitution

$$\eta_l(r) \to -\eta_l(r), \qquad \epsilon_l(r) \to \epsilon_l(r) + \pi/2. \tag{37}$$

These two solutions correspond, through Eq. (29), to the same S matrix. Finally, we emphasize that Eq. (30) is apparently singular for $\eta_l(r) = 0$; but, of course, it implies that if $\eta_l(\bar{r}) = 0$ at a certain distance $\bar{r}$, we also have

$$V_R(\bar{r}) \cos 2[\delta_l(k\bar{r}) + \epsilon_l(\bar{r})] + V_I(\bar{r}) \sin 2[\delta_l(k\bar{r}) + \epsilon_l(\bar{r})] = 0, \tag{38}$$

so that $\epsilon_I'(\bar{r})$ is finite.

19

The multichannel case

In this chapter we indicate how the phase approach can be applied to multichannel potential scattering problems. We content ourselves with outlining the procedure, our main purpose being to show how the phase approach can also be made to work in this case. For a more general and more detailed treatment we refer the reader to the literature [5, 20–23]. Here we follow the treatment of Degasperis [20], with some modifications.

We begin with a brief introduction on the formalism of multichannel potential scattering. We take as our starting point the matrix radial Schrödinger equation

$$\mathbf{\Psi}''(r) + \mathbf{M}[2E - r^2\mathbf{L}\mathbf{M}^{-1} - 2\mathbf{V}(r)]\mathbf{\Psi}(r) = 0. \tag{1}$$

Here and in the following we denote matrices by upper-case boldface characters, and the vectors on which these matrices operate by lower-case boldface characters. In this equation $\mathbf{M}$ is the diagonal mass matrix (in this chapter we use units such that $\hbar = 1$, but we indicate the masses explicitly); $\mathbf{L}$ is the diagonal angular momentum matrix with elements $l_j(l_j + 1)\delta_{ij}$; $\mathbf{V}(r)$ is the potential matrix (we assume that its matrix elements satisfy the usual restrictions of scattering theory, namely, that they diverge less than r^{-2} in the origin and that they vanish asymptotically faster than r^{-1}); and E is the total energy. We introduce channel momenta setting

$$k_j{}^2 = 2m_jE. \tag{2}$$

We have assumed that all the channels have the same threshold. The case with different thresholds (and, in particular, with open and closed channels) has been discussed by Zemach [21].

The solution $\Psi(r)$ is a (real) matrix whose columns are linearly independent regular solutions of Eq. (1), and it satisfies the boundary condition

$$\Psi(0) = 0. \tag{3}$$

The $\mathbf{S}$ matrix is defined through its asymptotic behavior. In fact, by introducing the two matrices $\mathbf{F}$ and $\mathbf{F}^*$ through

$$\Psi(r) \xrightarrow[r\to\infty]{} i[-\hat{\mathbf{H}}_a^{(1)}(r)\mathbf{F} + \hat{\mathbf{H}}_a^{(2)}(r)\mathbf{F}^*], \tag{4}$$

where the matrices $\hat{\mathbf{H}}_a^{(1,2)}(r)$ are diagonal and have matrix elements $(m_j/k_j)^{1/2} \exp[\pm i(k_j r - l_j \pi/2)]$, we find

$$\mathbf{S} = \mathbf{F}\mathbf{F}^{*-1}. \tag{5}$$

It is easily seen that the arbitrariness in the definition of $\mathbf{F}$ and $\mathbf{F}^*$ through Eq. (4) cancels in the ratio (5). The $\mathbf{S}$ matrix is complex; it is connected in the usual way with the differential cross section for the various processes. It is also convenient to consider the reactance or tangent matrix $\mathbf{T}$, defined by

$$\mathbf{T} = i(\mathbf{I} - \mathbf{S})(\mathbf{I} + \mathbf{S})^{-1}, \tag{6}$$

where $\mathbf{I}$ is the unit matrix. If, as we assume for simplicity, the potential matrix not only is hermitian but also is real (as is required by time-reversal invariance), then the $\mathbf{S}$ matrix is unitary and symmetric and the $\mathbf{T}$ matrix is real and symmetric. Because knowledge of the $\mathbf{T}$ matrix implies knowledge of the $\mathbf{S}$ matrix,

$$\mathbf{S} = (\mathbf{I} - i\mathbf{T})^{-1}(\mathbf{I} + i\mathbf{T}), \tag{7}$$

we may conclude that the number of independent parameters entering the scattering matrix is $n(n + 1)/2$, where n is the number of channels.

It is now convenient to introduce diagonal matrices made up of the Riccati–Bessel functions:

$\hat{\mathbf{J}}(r)$ with matrix elements $\delta_{ij}(m_j/k_j)^{1/2}\hat{j}_{l_j}(k_j r),$

$\hat{\mathbf{N}}(r)$ with matrix elements $\delta_{ij}(m_j/k_j)^{1/2}\hat{n}_{l_j}(k_j r),$ (8)

$\hat{\mathbf{H}}^{(1,2)}(r)$ with matrix elements $\delta_{ij}(m_j/k_j)^{1/2}\hat{h}_{l_j}^{(1,2)}(k_j r).$

These relations imply, through Eq. (I.6), that

$$\hat{\mathbf{J}}(r)\hat{\mathbf{N}}'(r) - \hat{\mathbf{J}}'(r)\hat{\mathbf{N}}(r) = \mathbf{M}, \tag{9}$$

and, through Eqs. (I.23, I.24), that

$$\hat{\mathbf{H}}^{(1,2)}(r) = -\hat{\mathbf{N}}(r) \pm i\hat{\mathbf{J}}(r), \tag{10}$$

$$\hat{\mathbf{J}}(r) = (2i)^{-1}[\hat{\mathbf{H}}^{(1)}(r) - \hat{\mathbf{H}}^{(2)}(r)], \tag{11a}$$

$$\hat{\mathbf{N}}(r) = -\tfrac{1}{2}[\hat{\mathbf{H}}^{(1)}(r) + \hat{\mathbf{H}}^{(2)}(r)]. \tag{11b}$$

We also note that the matrices $\hat{\mathbf{H}}_a^{(1,2)}(r)$ of Eq. (4) are simply the asymptotic values of the matrices $\hat{\mathbf{H}}^{(1,2)}(r)$, as implied by their definitions and Eqs. (I.23) and (I.21).

Using these matrices, we now write an integral equation for the matrix $\mathbf{\Psi}(r)$:

$$\mathbf{\Psi}(r) = \hat{\mathbf{J}}(r) - 2\int_0^r ds[\hat{\mathbf{J}}(r)\hat{\mathbf{N}}(s) - \hat{\mathbf{J}}(s)\hat{\mathbf{N}}(r)]\mathbf{V}(s)\mathbf{\Psi}(s). \tag{11}$$

It is easily seen that the matrix $\mathbf{\Psi}(r)$ defined by this integral equation satisfies the differential equation (1) and the boundary condition (3). The same integral equation may also be written in the form

$$\mathbf{\Psi}(r) = i[-\hat{\mathbf{H}}^{(1)}(r)\mathbf{F}(r) + \hat{\mathbf{H}}^{(2)}(r)\mathbf{F}^*(r)], \tag{12}$$

where $\mathbf{F}(r)$, $\mathbf{F}^*(r)$ are defined by

$$\mathbf{F}(r) = \frac{1}{2}\left[\mathbf{I} + 2\int_0^r ds\,\hat{\mathbf{H}}^{(2)}(s)\mathbf{V}(s)\mathbf{\Psi}(s)\right], \tag{13a}$$

$$\mathbf{F}^*(r) = \frac{1}{2}\left[\mathbf{I} + 2\int_0^r ds\,\hat{\mathbf{H}}^{(1)}(s)\mathbf{V}(s)\mathbf{\Psi}(s)\right]. \tag{13b}$$

A comparison of Eqs. (12), (4), and (5) suggests introducing the matrix

$$\mathbf{S}(r) = \mathbf{F}(r)\mathbf{F}^{*-1}(r), \tag{14}$$

whose asymptotic value directly yields the scattering matrix

$$\mathbf{S} = \mathbf{S}(\infty). \tag{15}$$

On the other hand, from Eqs. (13) it follows that

$$\mathbf{S}(0) = \mathbf{I}. \tag{16}$$

It is now easy to derive the differential equation satisfied by $\mathbf{S}(r)$. In fact, differentiating Eq. (14), we obtain

$$\mathbf{S}'(r) = \mathbf{F}'(r)\mathbf{F}^{*-1}(r) - \mathbf{F}(r)\mathbf{F}^{*-1}(r)\mathbf{F}^{*\prime}(r)\mathbf{F}^{*-1}(r). \tag{17}$$

But differentiating Eqs. (13) and using Eq. (12), we obtain

$$\mathbf{F}'(r) = -i\hat{\mathbf{H}}^{(2)}(r)\mathbf{V}(r)[\hat{\mathbf{H}}^{(1)}(r)\mathbf{F}(r) - \hat{\mathbf{H}}^{(2)}(r)\mathbf{F}^{*}(r)], \tag{18a}$$

$$\mathbf{F}^{*\prime}(r) = -i\hat{\mathbf{H}}^{(1)}(r)\mathbf{V}(r)[\hat{\mathbf{H}}^{(1)}(r)\mathbf{F}(r) - \hat{\mathbf{H}}^{(2)}(r)\mathbf{F}^{*}(r)]. \tag{18b}$$

Inserting these relations in (17), we secure

$$\mathbf{S}'(r) = i[\mathbf{S}(r)\hat{\mathbf{H}}^{(1)}(r) - \hat{\mathbf{H}}^{(2)}(r)]\mathbf{V}(r)[\hat{\mathbf{H}}^{(1)}(r)\mathbf{S}(r) - \hat{\mathbf{H}}^{(2)}(r)]. \tag{19}$$

This is the desired equation. Together with the boundary condition (16), it determines the matrix $\mathbf{S}(r)$, whose asymptotic value directly yields the scattering matrix, Eq. (15). This equation is the analog of Eq. (3.19b) of the one-channel case. It should be noted that the function $\mathbf{S}(r)$ is, for all r, the scattering matrix that would be produced by the potential if it were truncated at r.

It is also convenient to introduce the matrix $\mathbf{T}(r)$, related to $\mathbf{S}(r)$ through

$$\mathbf{T}(r) = i[\mathbf{I} - \mathbf{S}(r)][\mathbf{I} + \mathbf{S}(r)]^{-1}, \tag{20a}$$

$$\mathbf{S}(r) = [\mathbf{I} - i\mathbf{T}(r)]^{-1}[\mathbf{I} + i\mathbf{T}(r)]. \tag{20b}$$

With a little algebra we find

$$\mathbf{T}'(r) = -2[\hat{\mathbf{J}}(r) - \mathbf{T}(r)\hat{\mathbf{N}}(r)]\mathbf{V}(r)[\hat{\mathbf{J}}(r) - \hat{\mathbf{N}}(r)\mathbf{T}(r)] \tag{21}$$

and the boundary conditions become

$$\mathbf{T}(0) = 0, \tag{22}$$

$$\mathbf{T}(\infty) = \mathbf{T}, \tag{23}$$

where $\mathbf{T}$ is the reactance matrix. Obviously, Eq. (21) is the analog of Eq. (3.10) of the one-channel case. The advantage of the function $\mathbf{T}(r)$ over $\mathbf{S}(r)$ is that it is real; however, it is not bounded, in contrast to $\mathbf{S}(r)$.

To cure this last difficulty and to gain more insight into the problem it is convenient to introduce the "eigenphase shifts" and the "mixing parameters." There are several ways to do this. While we consider only one possibility here, we emphasize that these various possibilities have different advantages and disadvantages. In a specific problem this additional freedom might prove quite helpful. For a discussion of this point the reader is referred to the work of Cox and Perlmutter [22, 23]. For simplicity, in the following we consider a problem with equal masses and angular momenta in all channels; in this case the matrices $\hat{J}(r)$, $\hat{N}(r)$, etc., Eqs. (8), become multiples of the unit matrix. Moreover, we limit our attention to a two-channel problem.

We now introduce the two eigenvectors $v_j(r)$ of the matrix $T(r)$, and we call $t^{(j)}(r)$ the corresponding eigenvalues:

$$T(r)v_j(r) = t^{(j)}(r)v_j(r), \qquad j = 1, 2. \tag{24}$$

We also introduce the parameter $\epsilon(r)$ with the condition that the matrix

$$U(r) = \begin{pmatrix} \cos \epsilon(r) & \sin \epsilon(r) \\ -\sin \epsilon(r) & \cos \epsilon(r) \end{pmatrix} \tag{25}$$

diagonalizes the matrix T:

$$U(r)TU^{-1}(r) = \begin{pmatrix} t^{(1)}(r) & 0 \\ 0 & t^{(2)}(r) \end{pmatrix}. \tag{26}$$

Note that this implies for the eigenvectors the expressions

$$v_1(r) = \begin{pmatrix} \cos \epsilon(r) \\ \sin \epsilon(r) \end{pmatrix}, \qquad v_2(r) = \begin{pmatrix} -\sin \epsilon(r) \\ \cos \epsilon(r) \end{pmatrix}. \tag{27}$$

Incidentally, we also note that if we set

$$t^{(j)}(r) = \tan \delta^{(j)}(r), \qquad j = 1, 2, \tag{28}$$

we find that the matrix $S(r)$ has eigenvalues $\exp[2i\delta^{(j)}(r)]$; it is, of course, diagonalized by the same matrix $U(r)$, Eq. (25), which diagonalizes $T(r)$, and it has the same eigenvectors.

Clearly we can characterize the matrix $T(r)$, or, for that matter, $S(r)$, by the three real parameters $\delta^{(1)}(r)$, $\delta^{(2)}(r)$ [or $t^{(1)}(r)$, $t^{(2)}(r)$], and $\epsilon(r)$. We term the $\delta^{(j)}(r)$'s "eigenphase functions," and $\epsilon(r)$ "mixing parameter function." Their asymptotic values, which determine the values of the reactance and scattering matrices, are usually referred to in the literature as "eigenphase shifts" and "mixing parameter."

It is now a matter of algebra to write down the equations satisfied by these functions. They are

$$\delta^{(1)\prime}(r) = -\frac{2m}{k}\left[\cos^2\epsilon(r)V_{11}(r) + \sin^2\epsilon(r)V_{22}(r) + \sin 2\epsilon(r)V_{12}(r)\right]$$

$$\times\left[\cos\delta^{(1)}(r)\hat{j}_l(kr) - \sin\delta^{(1)}(r)\hat{n}_l(kr)\right]^2, \qquad (29a)$$

$$\delta^{(2)\prime}(r) = -\frac{2m}{k}\left[\sin^2\epsilon(r)V_{11}(r) + \cos^2\epsilon(r)V_{22}(r) - \sin 2\epsilon(r)V_{12}(r)\right]$$

$$\times\left[\cos\delta^{(2)}(r)\hat{j}_l(kr) - \sin\delta^{(2)}(r)\hat{n}_l(kr)\right]^2, \qquad (29b)$$

$$\epsilon'(r)\sin[\delta^{(1)}(r) - \delta^{(2)}(r)]$$

$$= -\frac{2m}{k}\left[\tfrac{1}{2}\sin 2\epsilon(r)(V_{11}(r) - V_{22}(r)) - \cos 2\epsilon(r)V_{12}(r)\right]$$

$$\times\left[\cos\delta^{(1)}(r)\hat{j}_l(kr) - \sin\delta^{(1)}(r)\hat{n}_l(kr)\right]$$

$$\times\left[\cos\delta^{(2)}(r)\hat{j}_l(kr) - \sin\delta^{(2)}(r)\hat{n}_l(kr)\right]. \qquad (30)$$

As for the boundary conditions, those for the $\delta^{(j)}(r)$'s follow immediately from Eqs. (22), (24), and (28):

$$\delta^{(j)}(0) = 0, \qquad j = 1, 2. \qquad (31)$$

The boundary condition for $\epsilon(r)$ depends instead on the details of the behavior of the potential near the origin. Assuming a behavior

$$V_{ij}(r)\underset{r\to 0}{\longrightarrow}C_{ij}r^{-m_{ij}}, \qquad m_{ij} < 2, \qquad (32)$$

one finds [20]

$$\tfrac{1}{2}\tan 2\epsilon(r)\underset{r\to 0}{\longrightarrow}(2l + 3 - m_{12})^{-1}V_{12}(r)$$

$$\times\left[(2l + 3 - m_{11})^{-1}V_{11}(r) - (2l + 3 - m_{22})^{-1}V_{22}(r)\right]^{-1}. \qquad (33)$$

Incidentally, with a different type of parametrization, this difficulty is eliminated [22, 23].

The phase equations (29) have a direct physical meaning; they display the effective potentials acting in each eigenchannel. It is easily seen that the potentials acting in the eigenphase equations (29) are simply the mean values of the potential matrix in the eigenstates $\mathbf{v}_j(r)$; while the potential acting in the equation for $\epsilon(r)$, Eq. (30), is the nondiagonal matrix element of the potential matrix taken between the two eigenstates $\mathbf{v}_j(r)$. Of course, these potentials depend on the mixing parameter function $\epsilon(r)$, which in turn depends on the eigenphase functions, as implied by Eq. (30). It may be easily shown that the necessary and sufficient condition for the mixing parameter to be a constant is that the potential matrix be diagonalizable by a constant matrix. In such a case we find

$$\tfrac{1}{2} \tan 2\epsilon(r) = V_{12}(r)[V_{11}(r) - V_{22}(r)]^{-1} = \text{const.} \qquad (34)$$

Note the consistency of this result with Eqs. (30) and (33). In general the system (29) and (30) represents a very complex nonlinear problem. However, the direct role played by all the quantities of physical relevance, being vividly exposed in the phase equations, should help in understanding the problem and prove useful in deriving approximate or qualitative results.

We note that in general, if $\delta^{(1)}(r)$, $\delta^{(2)}(r)$, and $\epsilon(r)$ are solutions of Eqs. (29) and (30), then $\delta^{(2)}(r)$, $\delta^{(1)}(r)$, and $\epsilon(r) + \pi/2$ are also solutions. (The latter solutions also satisfy the correct boundary conditions.) This corresponds simply to the exchange of the two channel labels.

Finally, we emphasize that just as in the one-channel problem, it is possible to set up a more general formulation of the phase method, using as a comparison system more general (or more simple) functions than the Riccati–Bessel functions, and in this manner absorbing in the comparison system one portion of the interaction, or exhibiting also the centrifugal part.

20

Bound states. Discussion of the pole equation and of the behavior of the pole functions for q > 0

In this chapter we indicate how to apply the phase approach in order to study bound states. For simplicity of presentation we discuss only the case of S waves (dropping the subscript zero on all relevant quantities); the extension to all partial waves is given at the end of the chapter.

To study the problem of bound states we set

$$k = iq, \qquad q > 0. \tag{1}$$

Recalling the relationships between the radial wave function $u(r)$ and the function $S(r)$, Eqs. (6.16), which now read

$$u(q, r) = (i/2)\alpha(q, r)[S^{-1/2}(q, r)e^{qr} - S^{1/2}(q, r)e^{-qr}], \tag{2a}$$

$$u'(q, r) = q(i/2)\alpha(q, r)[S^{-1/2}(q, r)e^{qr} + S^{1/2}(q, r)e^{-qr}], \tag{2b}$$

we immediately assert that the bound state condition is

$$S^{-1}(q, \infty) = 0. \tag{3}$$

Here and in the following we also indicate explicitly the dependence on the variable q.

This bound state condition, Eq. (3), obviously expresses the well-known correspondence between bound states and poles of the S matrix, analytically continued in k to the positive imaginary axis. However, to obtain Eq. (3), we must assume that except for certain special values of q corresponding to bound states, the limit $S(q, \infty)$

exists (and also $\alpha(q, \infty)$); similarly, the correspondence between poles of the S matrix and bound states obtains only if an analytic continuation of the S matrix away from the physical region (positive real k) exists. The connection between these two points is discussed below. Concerning the second point, we recall that the S matrix is certainly meromorphic in k inside the Bargmann strip of the k plane defined by the condition

$$|\operatorname{Im} k| < \mu/2, \tag{4}$$

with μ determined by the asymptotic behavior of the potential through

$$\mu = \max[\mu'], \tag{5}$$

where

$$\lim_{r\to\infty} e^{\mu'r}V(r) = 0. \tag{6}$$

Thus if the potential vanishes faster than exponentially (or, *a fortiori*, if it vanishes identically beyond a given range r_∞), the S matrix is meromorphic in k in the whole k plane; on the other hand, if the potential vanishes more slowly than exponentially, say, as an inverse power of r, then the Bargmann strip shrinks to naught. (Incidentally, this remark is also relevant to the introductory discussion of Chapter 11.)

We now consider the equation satisfied by the function $S(q, r)$; it is obtained directly from Eq. (3.19b), through Eq. (1). We obtain

$$S'(q, r) = (2q)^{-1}V(r)[e^{qr} - S(q, r)e^{-qr}]^2, \tag{7}$$

with boundary condition

$$S(q, 0) = 1. \tag{8}$$

Note that the function $S(q, r)$ is now real.

It is easy to read directly from this equation the condition on the potential that is sufficient to guarantee that the function $S(q, r)$ has a well-defined limit as r diverges (except for certain special values of q; see below). The condition is

$$\lim_{r\to\infty} e^{2qr}V(r) = 0. \tag{9}$$

This condition coincides with the requirement that we stay within the Bargmann strip of the complex k plane. In fact, it would be easy to *derive* the existence of the Bargmann strip of meromorphy from the present remark and the well-known property of meromorphy of the solution of a Riccati equation. But this discussion is outside the scope of the present monograph, as was emphasized in Chapter 1.

One way to eliminate the difficulty inherent in the asymptotic divergence of $S(q, r)$ for values of q that lie outside the Bargmann strip is through the assumption that the potential $V(r)$ vanishes identically beyond the distance r_∞. Then the Bargmann strip invades the whole plane, and there is no convergence problem because

$$S(q, \infty) = S(q, r_\infty). \tag{10}$$

On the other hand, it is obvious (see also below) that given any potential $V(r)$ (which vanishes at infinity faster than r^{-1}, as is always assumed in this book), it is always possible to choose a distance r_∞ sufficiently large that, for all practical purposes, $V(r)$ and $V(r)\theta(r_\infty - r)$ are equivalent; and, in particular, the values of the energies of their bound states are very close. In fact, as will be explained, the results obtained remain valid without further ado even for potentials that vanish less than exponentially at infinity.

In conclusion, we assert that the bound state condition is Eq. (3), which for cut-off potentials may be written

$$S^{-1}(q_i, r_\infty) = 0. \tag{11}$$

Here we have introduced explicitly an index i, to label different solutions of this eigenvalue equation. To each solution there corresponds a bound state, with binding energy $-q_i{}^2$.

It is now natural to focus attention on the poles of $S(q, r)$, and to study their behavior in detail. Thus we introduce the functions $q_i(r)$ through the implicit equation

$$S^{-1}[q_i(r), r] = 0 \tag{12}$$

and investigate their behavior as functions of r.

First of all, we note that if the potential is nowhere attractive, Eq. (12) has no solution in the bound state region $q > 0$. In fact, in this case, from the differential equation (7) and the boundary condition (8) we immediately obtain

$$1 \leqslant S(q, r) \leqslant e^{2qr}. \tag{13}$$

(Proof: $S'(q, r)$ is nonnegative in this case, so $S(q, r)$ cannot become smaller than its initial value, which is unity, unless it diverges; on the other hand, it cannot overtake e^{2qr} because at the point of overtaking, its derivative should be positive, while Eq. (7) implies that it would vanish.)

If the potential is attractive in some region, Eq. (12) may admit one or several solutions. We now discuss these solutions, namely, the functions $q_i(r)$ defined implicitly through Eq. (12). This discussion is based on the equation they satisfy:

$$\frac{dq_i(r)}{dr} = -V(r)\{1 + 2q_i(r)P[q_i(r), r]\}^{-1}, \tag{14}$$

where the quantity $P(q, r)$ is defined by

$$P(q, r) = [u(q, r)]^{-2} \int_0^r ds\, u^2(q, s). \tag{15}$$

It is very important to note that this quantity is positive for real q (except at $r = 0$, where for finite q it vanishes as $r/3$). This equation is derived in Appendix IV, where it is also written in other forms that may prove more convenient for numerical computations. In the following we refer to it as "the pole equation," and we term the quantities $q_i(r)$ "pole functions." Note that in the definition of $P(q, r)$, the function $u(q, r)$ is the radial wave function, i. e., the solution of the radial Schrödinger equation that vanishes in the origin, evaluated for a fixed value q. (Incidentally, $P[q_i(r), r]$ is very simply related to the residue of $S(q, r)$ at the pole $q = q_i(r)$.)

The pole equation (14) is not sufficient to identify the functions $q_i(r)$; we also need boundary conditions. It is convenient to choose these conditions of the form

$$q_i(b_i) = 0, \tag{16}$$

namely, to assign the distances b_i at which the functions $q_i(r)$ vanish. As is proved in Appendix IV, these distances b_i are simply the zeros of the derivative of the radial wave function, evaluated for $q = 0$:

$$u'(0, b_i) = 0. \tag{17}$$

Needless to say, all the b_i's are different. We label them in increasing order:

$$b_{i+1} > b_i. \tag{18}$$

Let us discuss the pole equation (14). It is strongly nonlinear; however, as we now show, it has a very direct physical meaning, and it is easy to extract by inspection from its structure a lot of information on the pole functions $q_i(r)$. We consider first the simpler case of a nowhere repulsive potential, $V(r) \leqslant 0$. Then the r.h.s. of Eq. (14) is positive and finite (for positive q), so that starting from the distances b_i, defined through Eq. (16), the functions $q_i(r)$ are monotonically increasing. Their asymptotic value

$$q_i = q_i(\infty) \tag{19}$$

yields the energy $E_i = -q_i^2$ of the ith bound state. Note that $q_i(\infty)$ is certainly finite because the potential $V(r)$ is assumed to vanish at infinity; it is easily seen that it is sufficient that it vanishes faster than r^{-1}. (For a more detailed discussion of the asymptotic convergence of $q_i(r)$, see Chapter 21.) In this case we may also assert immediately that the number of bound states is identical to the number of solutions of Eq. (17). (This remark is connected with Levinson's theorem; see Chapter 22.) We also see that the index i labels the bound states in increasing order:

$$E_{i+1} > E_i . \tag{20}$$

This follows from Eq. (18) and from the fact that two functions $q_i(r)$ cannot cross in the region where $q > 0$ because they are solutions of the same first-order differential equation, and this equation is nonsingular in that region.

In analogy to the phase functions, the pole functions $q_i(r)$ are also susceptible of a direct physical interpretation for all values of r, as is implied by their original definition through Eq. (12), or simply by the differential equation that they satisfy: If $b_n < \bar{r} < b_{n+1}$, the potential $V(r)\theta(\bar{r} - r)$, i. e., the original potential truncated at $\bar{r}$, has n bound states, with binding energies $-q_i^2(\bar{r})$, $i = 1, 2,..., n$. This also implies a direct physical interpretation for the pole equation (14): It describes the increase in binding energy that obtains by taking progressively more potential into account; every time r goes through one of the b_i's, we have one more pole function that starts from the value zero, to account for the fact that the potential can now accommodate one more bound state.

It is also quite instructive and conducive to physical insight to investigate the pole equation and the pole functions in the $q < 0$ region. This discussion in relegated to Appendix IV.

In this case of a nowhere repulsive potential we may turn the pole equation around, namely, we may consider q as the independent variable and r as the dependent variable, writing

$$\frac{dr_i(q)}{dq} = -\{1 + 2qP[q, r_i(q)]\}/V[r_i(q)], \qquad (21)$$

with $P(q, r)$ always defined by Eq. (15). For every value of the independent variable q we may now have several solutions $r_i(q)$ corresponding to the boundary conditions

$$r_i(0) = b_i, \qquad (22)$$

with the b_i's defined through Eq. (17). Now the physical significance of the functions $r_i(q)$ is the following: The potential $V(r)\theta[r_i(q) - r]$ has i bound states, the lower one with binding energy $-q^2$. For a numerical computation, one would assume that the potential vanishes identically for $r > r_\infty$ and would integrate Eq. (21) until, one after the other, the successive r_i's reach the value r_∞. The corresponding values of q yield the energies of the bound states. It is obvious that the resulting values of q are practically independent of the value assigned to r_∞, provided it is in the asymptotic region where $V(r)$ is very small; as is implied by Eq. (21) (or, equivalently, by Eq. (14)), even a large change in r in this region corresponds to a very small change in q. What was in any case obvious on physical grounds is thus confirmed, namely, that the bound states of $V(r)$ and $V(r)\theta(r_\infty - r)$ have very similar binding energies, provided r_∞ is so large that $V(r)$ for $r > r_\infty$ is negligibly small. This point is clarified further in the following chapter.

We proceed now to discuss the general case of a potential that may also change sign. We restrict our analysis here to the region $q > 0$; this is sufficient for the discussion of bound states. A more general treatment is given in Appendix IV.

For $q \geqslant 0$ the denominator in the r.h.s. of the pole equation (14) never vanishes; therefore the equation is nonsingular, and, moreover, the derivative dq/dr has the opposite sign to the potential. We emphasize that this also happens at the initial values $r = b_i$, $q_i = 0$, where in fact we have

$$\left.\frac{dq_i(r)}{dr}\right|_{r=b_i} = -V(b_i). \qquad (23)$$

We now introduce a distinction among the quantities b_i : We call $b_i^{(+)}$ those occurring where the potential is negative or, equivalently, where $q_i(r)$ crosses the $q = 0$ line from below to above, and $b_i^{(-)}$ those where $q_i(r)$ decreases across the $q = 0$ line. If we now recall that two distinct functions $q_i(r)$ can never cross one another, and that they can neither go to nor come from infinity, we conclude that the behavior of the functions $q_i(r)$ must be of the type shown in Fig. 1. (This is a schematic representation; for realistic examples corresponding to actual potentials, see the following chapter.) The physical interpretation of the situation illustrated in this figure is quite obvious: In the region where the potential is attractive, by taking progressively more potential into account we increase the magnitude of the binding energies of bound states, and we may also add one extra bound state (this happens whenever $r = b_i^{(+)}$); in the region where the potential is repulsive, by taking progressively more potential into account we decrease the magnitude of the bound state energies, and we may even decrease it so much that it goes through the value zero, thus implying that the bound state is not present any more (this happens whenever $r = b_i^{(-)}$). Of course, the physical interpretation of the $q_i(r)$'s as the square roots of the magnitudes of the binding energies of the bound states possessed by the potential truncated at r remains valid. In the particular example of Fig. 1 we see, for instance, that the potential truncated at $\bar{r}$ has three bound states if $b_3^{(+)} < \bar{r} < b_1^{(-)}$, two if $b_1^{(-)} < \bar{r} < b_4^{(+)}$, four if $b_5^{(+)} < \bar{r} < b_2^{(-)}$, three again if $b_2^{(-)} < \bar{r}$, etc.; and we might read the corresponding energies directly from the graphs. Incidentally, we note that as is

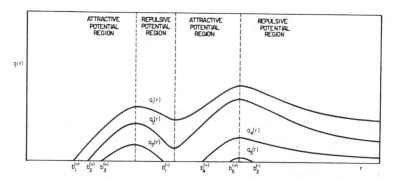

FIG. 1. Schematic representation of the behavior of the pole functions $q_i(r)$ in the $q > 0$ region.

suggested by the example of Fig. 1, it is possible to link certain graphs through the $q < 0$ region—for instance, that ending at $b_1^{(-)}$ with that beginning at $b_4^{(+)}$. This point is discussed in Appendix IV. It should be emphasized that every $b^{(-)}$ follows a $b^{(+)}$, or, more physically, that at most one bound state may be dissolved, as the effect of more repulsive potential is progressively taken into account (and even that, only provided the bound state is not too strictly bound). This is proved in the following chapter. Thus, if one is interested only in the bound states due to the whole potential $V(r)$, and not in those associated with its truncated versions, it is only required to consider the graphs starting at the unpaired $b^{(+)}$'s because only these graphs yield asymptotically positive values for q and therefore correspond to bound states. This also implies that the number N of (S-wave) states bound by the potential $V(r)$ is given by the rule

$$N = n^{(+)} - n^{(-)}. \tag{24}$$

Here $n^{(+)}$ is the number of $b^{(+)}$'s, i. e., the number of solutions of Eq. (17) occurring in regions where $V(r) < 0$, and $n^{(-)}$ is the number of $b^{(-)}$'s, i. e., the number of solutions of Eq. (17) occurring in regions where $V(r) > 0$. (If it happens that a solution of Eq. (17) occurs where $V(r) = 0$, the discrimination between "plus" and "minus" solutions depends on the sign of the potential after the zero.) This remark implies Levinson's theorem, as is shown in Chapter 22. Expressions for N that are more convenient for numerical computations and for approximate evaluations are given below and in Appendix IV; they are exploited in Chapter 23 to obtain bounds on the number of bound states in a given potential.

In conclusion, we have seen that the pole equation (14) describes the changes in the bound state energies that result as the effect of more and more potential is taken into account, from the origin outward. The pole functions $q_i(r)$ yield the energies of the bound states possessed by the potential, when it is amputated of its part extending beyond r. The boundary conditions that they satisfy, Eqs. (16) and (17), provide the distances at which the truncated potentials have zero-energy bound states; they account for the possibility that a new bound state sets in as more portions of attractive potential are progressively taken into account, or, conversely, that a bound state is dissolved as more portions of repulsive potential are progressively taken into account. The pole equation might be used for numerical computations of the bound state energies; alternatively, a direct search for the poles of $S(q, r)$ may be undertaken. A discussion of the procedure to evaluate the energies of bound states is given in the following chapter, where examples of numerical computations are also presented.

Finally, we mention the generalization to all partial waves. Below, we drop the subscript l whenever this is possible without ambiguity.

One trivial way to extend our results to all partial waves is by treating explicitly the centrifugal potential, namely, by performing everywhere the substitution

$$V(r) \Rightarrow V(r) + l(l+1)r^{-2}. \tag{25}$$

Of course, the resulting potential may be repulsive in some region, even if the original potential $V(r)$ is attractive everywhere; in particular, the resulting potential is generally repulsive at large distances. Moreover, it converges asymptotically only as r^{-2}. However, as discussed above, this presents no problem of principle. Neither does the r^{-2} singularity at the origin entail any difficulty; in fact, as far as the discussion of this chapter is concerned, the potential might have any singularity in the origin, provided the singular core is repulsive so that the wave function is unambiguously defined by the condition that it vanishes in the origin (see Chapter 15).

One disadvantage of this approach is, however, that we lose the simple physical significance of the functions we are dealing with for all but their asymptotic values, in analogy to the situation discussed in Chapter 13. The connection of the interpolating functions for all values of r with physical properties of the potential truncated at r is, instead, maintained if a formulation is adopted in which the centrifugal term is absorbed in the comparison system. Such a formulation results if one concentrates on the poles of the S-matrix function defined through the (real) equation

$$S_l'(q, r) = -(2q)^{-1}V(r)[\hat{h}_l^{(2)}(iqr) - S_l(q, r)\hat{h}_l^{(1)}(iqr)]^2, \tag{26}$$

with boundary condition

$$S_l(q, 0) = 1. \tag{27}$$

The equation ruling the change with r of these poles is then again of the form

$$\frac{dq_i(r)}{dr} = -V(r)/D_l(r), \tag{28}$$

with the denominator D_l defined by

$$D_l(q, r) = U_l(qr) + 2qu_l^{-2}(q, r) \int_0^r ds\, u^2(q, s). \tag{29}$$

Here $u_l(q, r)$ is again the radial wave function; thus these equations resemble closely those of the S-wave case, Eqs. (14) and (15). The only difference is due to the presence of the (real) function $U_l(q, r)$, defined by

$$U_l(x) = 2[\hat{h}_l^{(1)}(ix)]^{-2} \int_x^\infty dy [\hat{h}_l^{(1)}(iy)]^2, \tag{30}$$

which reduces to unity for $l = 0$. Equivalent definitions and other properties of these functions are given in Appendix I. It should be emphasized that for positive x, these functions are positive; it is this property that allows the extention to arbitrary l, almost without modifications, of all the considerations developed above for the S-wave case. (However, in contrast to the S-wave case, they vanish linearly with their argument (see Eq. (I.30)), and therefore imply the vanishing of $D_l(0, r)$). These functions tend to unity as x diverges, so that the asymptotic condition on the potential that is sufficient to guarantee that $q_i(\infty)$ exist is also the same as in the S-wave case, namely, $\lim_{r \to \infty} rV(r) = 0$.

The boundary conditions that it is convenient to impose on the pole functions $q_i(r)$ are again of the form

$$q_i(b_i) = 0; \tag{31}$$

namely, they consist in assigning the positions b_i at which the different pole functions $q_i(r)$ vanish. These are determined by the zero-energy radial wave function and by its derivative through the condition

$$b_i u_l'(0, b_i) = -l u_l(0, b_i). \tag{32}$$

Of course, the number of solutions of this equation and their values depend on l in addition to the potential. They also may be determined by the equation

$$\mu_l(b_i) = (2n + 1)\pi/2, \qquad n = 0, +1, +2,..., \tag{33}$$

where $\mu_l(r)$ is defined by the differential equation

$$\mu_l'(r) = -(2l + 1)^{-1}RV(r)[(r/R)^{l+1} \cos \mu_l(r) + (r/R)^{-l} \sin \mu_l(r)]^2, \tag{34}$$

with boundary condition

$$\mu_l(0) = 0. \tag{35}$$

Here R is an arbitrary constant. The function $\mu_l(r)$ is related to the S-matrix function through

$$\tan \mu_l(r) = \frac{i}{2}(2l + 1)!!(2l - 1)!! \lim_{q \to 0}\{[S_l(q, r) - 1](iRq)^{-(2l+1)}\}. \tag{36}$$

This definition, together with Eq. (26), implies the equations written above.

The same function $\mu_l(r)$ was also introduced in Chapter 11. It is connected with the function $\varphi(0, r)$ used in the S-wave case in Appendix IV by the simple relation

$$\tan \varphi(0, r) = \tan \mu_0(r) + r/R. \tag{37}$$

As we have noted before, all the considerations made in the S-wave case carry over to the case of general l without change. The graphs of the functions $q_i(r)$ have the same physical significance and display the same pattern (except that, in contrast to the S-wave case, they start with an infinite tangent due to the vanishing of $D_l(0, b)$). And, in particular, we may still draw a distinction between the distances $b^{(+)}$'s and $b^{(-)}$'s (see above), and assert that the number N_l of bound states with angular momentum l is given by the difference between the number of $b^{(+)}$'s and the number of $b^{(-)}$'s. An equivalent, but more convenient, definition, is inferred from Eq. (33). It asserts that we have N_l bound states if

$$(2N_l - 1)\pi/2 < \mu_l(\infty) < (2N_l + 1)\pi/2. \tag{38}$$

The equivalence of this statement to the previous one is completely trivial for everywhere attractive potentials, in which case we have no $b^{(-)}$'s, and $\mu_l(r)$ is an increasing function of r. But it is true quite generally because at every $b^{(+)}$ (and only at a $b^{(+)}$) μ_l *increases* through an odd multiple of $\pi/2$, while at every $b^{(-)}$ (and only at a $b^{(-)}$) it *decreases* through an odd multiple of $\pi/2$. Note that we have not committed ourselves as to what happens if $\mu_l(\infty)$ *equals* an odd multiple of $\pi/2$; this case is discussed in Chapter 22, where the present results are used to prove Levinson's theorem.

21

Behavior of pole functions and computation of binding energies. Examples

In the preceding chapter we introduced the pole functions and discussed their physical meaning when $q > 0$. The situation in the $q < 0$ region is treated in Appendix IV. In this chapter the actual behavior of the pole functions, both in the $q > 0$ and in the $q < 0$ regions, is discussed on the basis of specific examples, which are investigated by analytic means and also numerically. For simplicity the consideration is always restricted to the S-wave case; examples for higher waves may be found in Ref. [36] (for Coulomb potentials). At the end of the chapter a numerically convenient procedure for computing binding energies is briefly outlined; its extension to all l values is also indicated.

We begin with a discussion of the behavior of the pole functions in the simple case of an attractive square well potential,

$$V(r) = -| V_0 | \theta(R - r). \tag{1}$$

In this case the pole equation (20.14) becomes, for $r < R$,

$$q_i'(r) = | V_0 | \left\{ 1 + r q_i(r)[\sin(r p_i(r))]^{-2} \left[1 - \frac{\sin(2r p_i(r))}{2r p_i(r)} \right] \right\}^{-1}, \tag{2}$$

where

$$p_i(r) = [| V_0 | - q_i{}^2(r)]^{1/2}. \tag{3}$$

Note that this equation remains real and unambiguous also for those values of q such that p becomes imaginary. The distances b_i are defined by the condition

$$b_i = (i + \tfrac{1}{2})\pi | V_0 |^{-1/2}, \qquad b_i < R. \tag{4}$$

Of course, the differential equation (2), with the boundary condition $q_i(b_i) = 0$, is solved by the implicit equation

$$\tan[rp_i(r)] = -p_i(r)/q_i(r), \tag{5}$$

which is the well-known implicit equation defining the energies of the bound states possessed by a square well potential of depth $|V_0|$ and range r. Using this equation one may easily recast the pole equation (2) in the simpler form

$$q_i'(r) = [|V_0| - q_i^2(r)]/[1 + rq_i(r)]. \tag{6}$$

This form applies only in the region $r \leqslant R$; for $r \geqslant R$ the pole functions are constant, $q_i(r) = q_i(R)$.

Let us discuss the pole functions, $q_i(r)$, solutions of these equations. First we consider the $q > 0$ region, and subsequently we analyze the situation in the $q < 0$ region.

In the $q > 0$ region, the pole functions increase monotonically but at a decreasing rate; this property is displayed clearly by Eq. (6), which implies that the derivative $q_i'(r)$ decreases with increasing r because the numerator in the r.h.s. decreases and the denominator increases. It is also clear that $q_i(r)$ can never overtake the value $|V_0|^{1/2}$, independently from the range of the potential—a fact whose physical meaning is obvious.

In the $q < 0$ region the situation is somewhat more complex. First of all we see from Eq. (6) that the negative hyperbola defined by the equation

$$1 + rq = 0 \tag{7}$$

cannot be crossed by a pole trajectory except at the point

$$q = -|V_0|^{1/2}, \qquad r = |V_0|^{-1/2}. \tag{8}$$

In other words, the condition $q = -1/r$, together with the pole condition (5), determines the values of r at which two poles meet, and the corresponding values of q (cf. the discussion in Appendix IV). It is easily verified that these values are given by the formula

$$r_n = [(1 + x_n^2)/|V_0|]^{1/2}, \qquad q = -1/r_n, \tag{9}$$

where the numbers x_n are the positive roots of the equation

$$x_n = \tan x_n. \tag{10}$$

As we have already remarked, the value $r_0 = |V_0|^{-1/2}$, $q = -|V_0|^{1/2}$, corresponding to $x_0 = 0$, is not the position of a double pole; in fact, while the first pole trajectory does go through it, the derivative of the pole function is not unbounded there, but it has the value $q_1'(r_0) = 3|V_0|$, as may be easily verified either from Eq. (6) or from Eq. (2).

The situation just described is displayed graphically in Fig. 1, where the numerically computed pole functions for an attractive

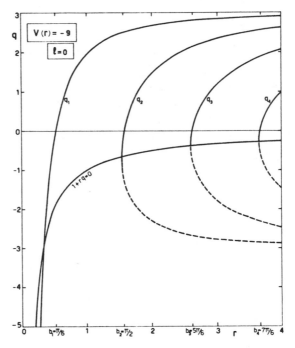

FIG. 1.   The S-wave pole functions $q_i(r)$ are plotted as a function of r up to $r = 4$ for the attractive square well potential $V(r) = -9$. The distances $b_i = (\pi/3)(i - \tfrac{1}{2})$ are the minimum ranges of square well potentials of the same depth possessing i bound states (of which the last is with vanishing binding energy). The hyperbola $1 + rq = 0$ is also plotted; all the double poles lie on this curve. The solid graphs give the locations of the bound state or virtual state poles ($D > 0$); the broken graphs give the positions of the antibound or antivirtual states ($D < 0$). The points at which these graphs meet are given by Eq. (9). The asymptotic behavior of the curve q_1 as r vanishes is given by Eq. (11). From this figure one may read immediately the binding energies of all S-wave bound states for any square well potential of depth 9 and range smaller than 4, as also the position of the poles corresponding to virtual, antibound, or antivirtual states.

square well potential with $|V_0| = 9$ are plotted for $r \leqslant 4$. This, incidentally, is just the same potential whose S-wave phase function is plotted for various values of k in Fig. 4.1. We draw attention to the role that the distances b_i play in the two cases: In one case they are the positions at which the S-wave phase function $\delta_0(r)$ becomes discontinuous in the zero-energy limit; in the other case they are the minimum distances at which a new S-wave bound state appears. This double meaning of the distances b_i is the essence of Levinson's theorem (see Chapter 22).

As is apparent from Fig. 1, and as may be immediately inferred from Eq. (6) and the preceding discussion, all of the trajectories of the "antivirtual" poles, i. e., those occurring at values of r and q such that the denominator D of the phase equation is negative (see Appendix IV), are confined in the region $- |V_0|^{1/2} < q < 0$. The region $q < - |V_0|^{1/2}$ is penetrated only by the first trajectory, along which D is always positive. The asymptotic behavior of this trajectory may be computed by expanding the pole equation (5), and we find, as r vanishes,

$$q_1(r) = - r^{-1}\Big\{ -\ln(r|V_0|^{1/2}) + \ln[-2\ln(r|V_0|^{1/2})]$$

$$+ O\left[\frac{\ln[-\ln(r|V_0|^{1/2})]}{\ln(r|V_0|^{1/2})}\right]\Big\}. \tag{11}$$

It is easily seen that this last result is of general validity provided the potential is regular and attractive near the origin; of course, in place of the constant V_0, the actual behavior of the potential near the origin must be inserted in Eq. (11), to obtain the behavior of the first pole trajectory near the origin. Note that the requirement that the potential be regular coincides with the condition that $r |V(r)|^{1/2}$ vanish as r vanishes (see Chapter 2); thus the behavior (11) is not radically modified, whichever is the behavior of the potential at the origin (provided it is attractive and regular). If, instead, the potential is repulsive near the origin, no real pole function is able to penetrate close to it. (It is easy also to see that these results apply to all even partial waves; for odd l, however, the first trajectory is missing. Just the opposite situation occurs for regular potentials which are repulsive near the origin; in this case the first trajectory, Eq. (11), is present only for odd l).

Finally we draw attention to the fact that while in Fig. 1 we have plotted the hyperbola defined by the equation $1 + rq = 0$, on which all the double poles must lie, this curve is not the one we obtain from the condition $D = 0$, Eq. (IV.54). As seen from Eq. (2), the curve defined by this condition in this case is characterized by the equation

$$rq = -\sin^2(rp)\left[1 - \frac{\sin(2rp)}{2rp}\right]^{-1}, \qquad (12)$$

where p is always given by q through Eq. (3). Of course, this curve goes through the same values of the double poles as the hyperbola; to get a complete picture of its behavior it is sufficient to remark that it touches the $q = 0$ axis at $r = n\pi \mid V_0 \mid^{-1/2}$, $n = 1, 2, 3,...$, while it crosses the hyperbola at the locations r_n of the double poles, Eq. (9), and at the distances $r = [(n + \frac{1}{2})^2\pi^2 - 1]^{1/2} \mid V_0 \mid^{-1/2}$, $n = 1, 2, 3,...$. But the more interesting result concerns the asymptotic behavior of this curve as r vanishes. From Eq. (12), we find

$$q = -r^{-1}\{-\ln(r\mid V_0 \mid^{1/2}) + \tfrac{3}{2}\ln[-2\ln(r\mid V_0 \mid^{1/2})]$$

$$+ O\left[\frac{\ln[-\ln(r\mid V_0 \mid^{1/2})]}{\ln(r\mid V_0 \mid^{1/2})}\right]. \qquad (13)$$

Again this formula applies to any regular attractive potential, once $V(r)$ is substituted in place of V_0. It should be emphasized that this curve has the property that it cannot be crossed by any pole trajectory, because by definition a pole trajectory may reach it only at a singular point. It is gratifying to verify that the nonsingular first trajectory does not in fact reach it, as is apparent from a comparison of the asymptotic behaviors (11) and (13).

In conclusion, from the study of the attractive "square well" potential we have learned quite generally that for a regular potential that is attractive near the origin, the first pole trajectory has the behavior (11) near the origin. Of course, this trajectory need not reach the $q > 0$ region; in fact, it certainly does not reach it if the potential is attractive everywhere but has no bound states. (In this case this trajectory would actually be ignored in our approach, which is based on the boundary condition $q_i(b_i) = 0$. This is just one example of singularity of the S matrix that is contained in the pole equation but is ignored by our choice of boundary conditions, which have been selected for the purpose of locating only those poles of the S-matrix function that are relevant for the study of bound states.

See the remarks at the end of Appendix IV.) The subsequent trajectories, instead, do not penetrate to arbitrarily small r, but at a certain distance hit the $D = 0$ curve; for smaller values of r they become complex, while for larger values of r they are accompanied by a companion pole, which corresponds to an "antivirtual" or "antibound" state and behaves accordingly (see Appendix IV). If the potential is repulsive near the origin, the first "unpaired" trajectory is missing. (The differences between these results and those for $l > 0$ have been mentioned above; for a brief summary, see the end of Appendix IV).

We have also established quite generally, for any regular potential attractive near the origin, the behavior of the $D = 0$ curve in proximity to the origin, Eq. (13); this behavior is compatible with that of the first pole trajectory, in the sense that this trajectory, at small r, remains always above the $D = 0$ curve. It should be emphasized that the $D = 0$ curve discussed is that characterized by Eq. (IV.54); in general, a different curve obtains if we set, instead of $1 + 2qP = 0$, $1 + 2q\bar{P} = 0$ (in the notation of Appendix IV), although of course the singular points, i. e., the locations of the double poles, lie on both curves. For instance, in the special case of the square well potential, in place of Eq. (12) we would obtain the condition

$$rq = -\sin^2(rp)\left[1 + \frac{\sin(2rp)}{2rp}\right]^{-1}\frac{1 + R^2p^2\cot^2(pr)}{1 + R^2q^2}, \qquad (14)$$

which of course reduces to Eq. (12) using the pole condition equation (5). Similarly, the pole equation could be written in the equivalent form

$$q_i'(r) = |V_0|\left\{1 + rq_i(r)[\sin(rp_i(r))]^{-2}\left[1 - \frac{\sin(2rp_i(r))}{2rp_i(r)}\right]\right.$$
$$\times \left.\frac{1 + R^2q_i^2(r)}{1 + R^2p_i^2(r)\cot^2(rp_i(r))}\right\}^{-1}, \qquad (15)$$

which is, in fact, what one would obtain from a straightforward application of Eq. (IV.24). Note that although the pole equation apparently depends on the arbitrary constant R, in fact, the pole functions are independent from it.

Finally, we have displayed the actual behavior of the pole functions for an attractive square well potential, and we have analyzed their behavior using a transformed form of the pole equation; these considerations are characteristic of the example considered, however.

We turn now to more realistic potentials, for which the behavior of the pole functions has been evaluated by numerical integration of the pole equation, starting from the boundary conditions $q_i(b_i) = 0$ (the b_i's were also evaluated numerically). Two independent programs have been used for the integration of the pole equation, in order to check the accuracy of the results: The first program was based on the form (IV.24) of the pole equation; the second program was based on the form (20.14). (In the former procedure we evaluate the function $\partial\varphi/\partial q$, integrating the differential equation for $\varphi(q, r)$, Eq. (IV.17), from the origin to r for two slightly different values of q; in the latter, we evaluate $u(q, r)$, integrating the radial Schrödinger equation from the origin, and we then evaluate the integral $\int_0^r ds u^2(q, s)$. It turns out, as anticipated, that the former procedure is definitely faster.) We have considered only the trajectories in the $q > 0$ region.

The potentials that we consider are the same used in the numerical examples of Chapters 5 and 10, namely, the attractive Yukawa potential

$$V(r) = -(10/r)e^{-r}, \tag{16}$$

and the superposition of this potential with a repulsive Yukawa potential of shorter range,

$$V(r) = (20/r)e^{-2r} - (10/r)e^{-r}. \tag{17}$$

The pole functions for these potentials are plotted in Fig. 2. These potentials possess two S-wave bound states and one S-wave bound state, respectively. A comparison with Figs. 5.1 and 5.9 is instructive; again we note the Levinson effect, namely, the coincidence of the distances at which the pole functions emerge in the $q > 0$ region with the distances at which the phase function becomes discontinuous in the zero-energy limit. It is also worth noting that the rise of the pole functions is rather fast (a characteristic that is even more pronounced for all the other partial waves, whose pole functions start upward with infinite tangent), and the leveling to the asymptoting values is fairly prompt. This last point is discussed below.

Let us now treat a simple potential that possesses both attractive and repulsive sectors, to analyze the actual behavior of the pole functions in this more complex case. Specifically we consider a piecewise constant potential:

$$\begin{aligned} V(r) &= V_1 &\text{for } r < R_1, \\ &= V_2 &\text{for } R_1 < r < R_2, \\ &= V_3 &\text{for } R_2 < r. \end{aligned} \tag{18}$$

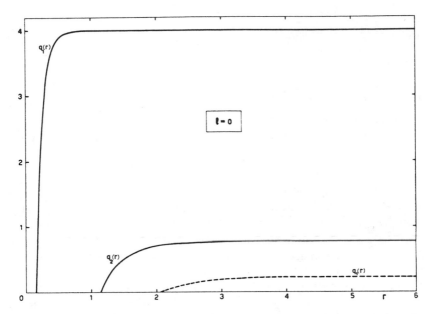

FIG. 2. The S-wave pole functions for the attractive Yukawa potential $V(r) = -(10/r)e^{-r}$ (solid line) and for the potential $V(r) = (20/r)e^{-2r} - (10/r)e^{-r}$ (broken line), in the $q > 0$ region.

The corresponding pole functions may be obtained by integrating the pole equation or, more directly, by inverting the implicit equations

$$r = -p_1^{-1} \tan^{-1}(p_1/q) \quad \text{for } r \leqslant R_1, \tag{19a}$$

$$r = R_1 - p_2^{-1} \tanh^{-1}\left[\frac{p_2(p_1 \cos p_1 R_1 + q \sin p_1 R_1)}{qp_1 \cos p_1 R_1 + p_2^2 \sin p_1 R_1}\right]$$
$$\text{for } R_1 < r < R_2, \tag{19b}$$

$$r = R_2 + p_3^{-1} \tan^{-1}\left[\frac{\begin{aligned}&p_3 p_2 \cosh \varphi_2(p_1 \cos \varphi_1 + q \sin \varphi_1)\\ &\quad + p_3 \sinh \varphi_2(p_2^2 \sin \varphi_1 + qp_1 \cos \varphi_1)\end{aligned}}{\begin{aligned}&p_2 \cosh \varphi_2(-qp_1 \cos \varphi_1 + p_3^2 \sin \varphi_1)\\ &\quad + \sinh \varphi_2(p_3^2 p_1 \cos \varphi_1 - pq_2^2 \sin \varphi_1)\end{aligned}}\right]$$
$$\text{for } R_2 < r, \tag{19c}$$

where

$$\varphi_1 = R_1 p_1, \tag{20}$$

$$\varphi_2 = (R_2 - R_1)p_2, \tag{21}$$

and

$$p_1 = (-V_1 - q^2)^{1/2}, \qquad (22a)$$
$$p_2 = (V_2 + q^2)^{1/2}, \qquad (22b)$$
$$p_3 = (-V_3 - q^2)^{1/2}. \qquad (22c)$$

We have written these equations in the form most convenient when $V_1 < 0$, $V_2 > 0$, $V_3 < 0$, which is the only case we shall consider; but it is easily seen that they remain valid in all cases.

The pole functions corresponding to the potential of Eq. (18), with

$$V_1 = -9, \qquad V_2 = +9, \qquad V_3 = -9, \qquad (23)$$

are plotted in Figs. 3–10 up to $r = 3$, for various choices of R_1 and R_2. All the pole functions that fall within the range of values of q included in each figure are plotted, even if they never reach the $q > 0$ region. From these graphs it is possible to read directly the energies, as well as the number, of (S-wave) bound states possessed by the potential $V(r)\theta(\bar{r} - r)$, for any $\bar{r} < 3$, $V(r)$ being given by Eq. (18), with the values of R_1, R_2 indicated in each figure. Moreover, it is possible to infer a general idea of the effect of the potential on the behavior of the pole functions, and also on their number. Observe, for instance, how new bound states appear as more attractive potential is taken into account. It is also worth noting that there are cases where a small change in the potential entails a qualitative modification of the pattern; however, this need not be associated with a marked change in the binding energies of the states bound by the whole potential (see, for instance, Figs. 6–8).

There are two qualitative points that deserve a detailed analysis: (1) the behavior of the pole functions in regions where the potential is repulsive, and, in particular, the possibility that they there cross the $q = 0$ line, thereby indicating that the repulsive potential dissolves

---

FIGS. 3–10.   The S-wave pole functions for the piecewise constant potential

$$V(r) = -9 \qquad \text{for} \quad r < R_1,$$
$$= +9 \qquad \text{for} \quad R_1 < r < R_2,$$
$$= -9 \qquad \text{for} \quad r > R_2,$$

are plotted up to $r = 3$ for various values of R_1 and R_2 (indicated in each figure by the broken vertical lines). All pole functions occurring in the range of q values included in each figure are plotted. The solid graphs provide the locations of the bound state ($q > 0$) or virtual state ($q < 0$) poles; the broken lines give the positions of the antibound or antivirtual states. The points at which these graphs meet are indicated with a cross. These pole functions have been computed from Eqs. (19). The shaded regions (forbidden to the graphs) are given by Eq. (24).

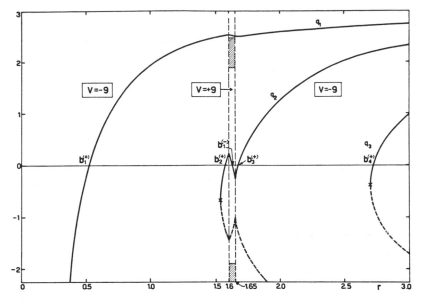

Fig. 3.

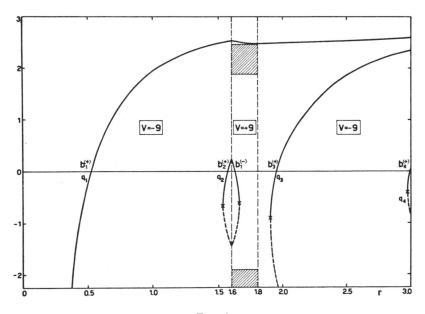

Fig. 4.

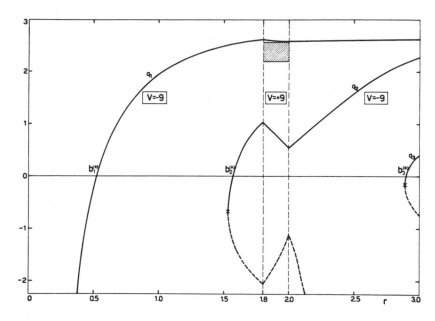

FIG. 5.

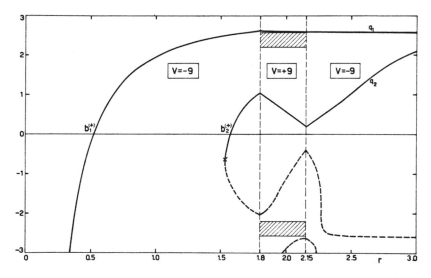

FIG. 6.

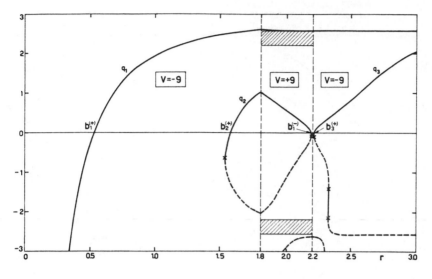

FIG. 7.

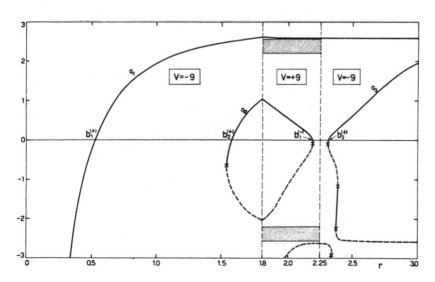

FIG. 8.

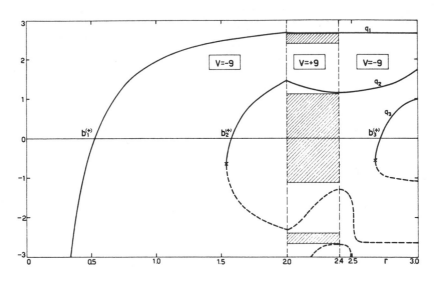

FIG. 9.

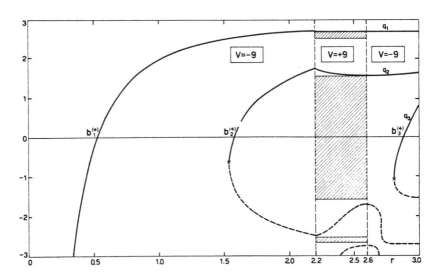

FIG. 10.

an otherwise bound state; and (2) the fact that the pole functions tend to become rapidly almost constant, the more so the larger (in modulus) are the corresponding energies (see, for instance, the uppermost trajectory in the examples considered). In fact, we shall find that on both these points it is possible to reach conclusions whose validity is not merely limited to the examples under scrutiny.

To discuss the first point, we refer back to the implicit equations (19), and we notice that Eq. (19b), which is valid in the repulsive region, implies (a) that in this region r is a one-valued function of q, and (b) that in this region there are some ranges of values of q that are "off limits" for the pole trajectories—namely, those causing the argument of the inverse hyperbolic tangent to be larger than unity in modulus. These forbidden regions are shaded in Figs. 3–10. It is easily seen that they are limited by the q's solutions of the two equations

$$p_1 \cos p_1 R_1 = \pm p_2 \sin p_1 R_1 . \tag{24}$$

Thus their location depends only on R_1, V_1, and V_2, and they occur symmetrically with respect to the $q = 0$ axis.

The existence of these forbidden regions, together with remark (a), above, accounts qualitatively for the behavior of the pole functions in the repulsive region. For instance, it implies that at most one graph can cross the $q = 0$ line in this region. Moreover, if the repulsive region is very extended, or if the potential there is very strong, at its end the pole functions will have been pushed quite close to the limiting values of q corresponding to the boundaries of the forbidden regions (see, for instance, Fig. 9). As a rule, in such a case they also stay almost constant in the subsequent sector. (For an explanation of this fact, see below.)

But the most remarkable result is that if the forbidden region includes the $q = 0$ line, as is the case in the examples of Figs. 9–10, then no matter how long the range of the repulsive region is, it is impossible to dissolve even one of the existing bound states. The condition for this to occur depends, as already noted, on the strength V_2 of the repulsive potential, besides the range and strength of the attractive potential in the inner region. It may happen that if the potential V_2 in the repulsive region is sufficiently increased, the shaded region forbidding the crossing of the $q = 0$ line disappears; this is illustrated by the example of Fig. 11, which refers to the case $V_2 = 150$, the values of the other parameters of the potential being identical to those of the case considered in Fig. 9. In fact we see in this case not only that the shaded region has disappeared but also that one pole function does indeed cross the $q = 0$ axis. On the other hand, it is easily seen that there are cases in which the values of V_1 and R_1 are such that, no matter how strong the potential in the repulsive region, it is impossible to dissolve any one of the existing bound states. In these cases, by increasing the repulsive potential it might still be possible to eliminate the shaded region protecting the $q = 0$ line; but this happens in such a fashion that no pole function can cross the $q = 0$ line. The situation is illustrated by the case represented in Fig. 12, which should be compared with that of Fig. 10. (Roughly speaking, the difference between the previous case and the present one is that, while the increase of the repulsive potential previously caused a dissolution of the shaded region, now a doubling has occurred.)

Summarizing, we may assert that there are cases when the addition of an outer repulsive region may cause the dissolution of one (but not more than one) otherwise bound state, but there are also cases when this is impossible.

It is easy to prove that this conclusion is of general validity, not merely limited to the special example discussed so far. Assume in fact that the potential $V(r)\theta(R - r)$ has n bound states; then the corresponding zero-energy wave function has n zeros for $r > 0$. (This well-known fact can be proved easily from the results of Chapter 20 and Appendix IV.) Of these zeros, at least $n - 1$ must occur for $r < R$, because for $r > R$ the zero-energy wave function is a straight line. But then the potential $V(r)$ must also have at least

---

FIGS. 11 AND 12. The S-wave pole functions for the piecewise constant potential

$$
\begin{aligned}
V(r) &= -9 && \text{for} \quad r < R_1, \\
&= +150 && \text{for} \quad R_1 < r < R_2, \\
&= -9 && \text{for} \quad r > R_2,
\end{aligned}
$$

are plotted up to $r = 3$ for various values of R_1 and R_2 (indicated in each figure by the broken vertical lines). All pole functions occurring in the range $-3 < q < 3$ are plotted. The solid graphs provide the locations of the bound state ($q > 0$) or virtual state ($q < 0$) poles; the broken lines give the positions of the antibound or antivirtual states. The points at which these graphs meet are indicated with a cross (at these points $D = 0$). These pole functions have been computed from Eqs. (19). The shaded regions correspond to those values of q for which the argument of the inverse hyperbolic tangent in Eq. (19b) is larger in modulus than unity. The points at which two graphs seem to cross each other are indicated with a circle; for the detailed behavior of the pole functions in these regions, see Fig. 13.

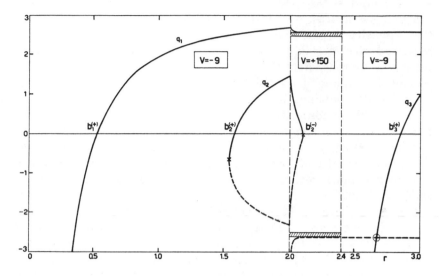

FIG. 11.

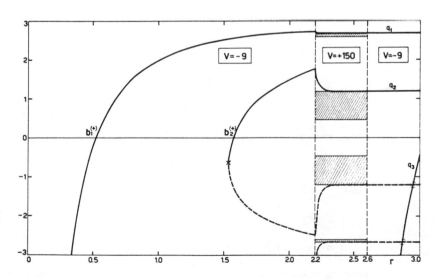

FIG. 12.

$n - 1$ bound states, because the corresponding zero-energy wave function has at least $n - 1$ zeros, since it is identical for $r < R$ to that apposite to the potential $V(r)\theta(R - r)$. Q.E.D. It may be remarked that beside proving that the number of bound states possessed by the potential $V(r)\theta(R - r)$ may be decreased at most by one by adding a repulsive contribution in the $r > R$ region, we have also obtained a sufficient condition to exclude even this possibility, the condition being that the n zeros of the zero-energy wave function corresponding to the n bound states possessed by the potential $V(r)\theta(R - r)$ all occur for $r < R$. It is easily verified that this condition is consistent with the examples considered above, in which case in the inner region the zero-energy wave function is simply $\sin[(-V_1)^{1/2}r]$.

Before considering the second point mentioned above, we insert two qualitative remarks. First of all, we draw attention to the rather complex behavior of the pole functions in the $q < 0$ region; see, for instance, Figs. 7–8. Then we recall that contrary to what might be inferred from Figs. 11 and 12, two trajectories cannot cross each other, as is implied by the discussion of Appendix IV; in fact, the

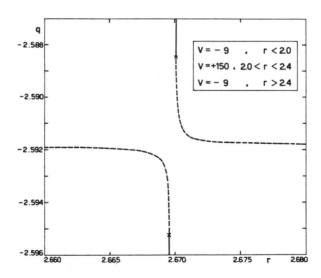

FIG. 13.   Blown-up detail of Fig. 11. The detailed behavior of the two "crossing" pole functions of Fig. 11 in the neighborhood of the "crossing point." The ordinate scale has been amplified, with respect to Fig. 11, by a factor of 700; the abscissa scale by a factor of 100.

crossing in Figs. 11 and 12 is only apparent, and a more detailed analysis reveals that it does not take place, as is shown in Fig. 13.

Finally, we come to the question of the asymptotic behavior of the pole functions as r increases. It should be emphasized that the leveling of the trajectories occurs in the present case, as in the first case considered in this chapter, even though the potential remains constant. Of course, in the case of a potential that decreases asymptotically and eventually vanishes, the leveling will be even more pronounced, as is implied by the structure of the pole equation. But even in that case the leveling occurs faster than might be inferred from a naive inspection of the pole equation. This point may be discussed quite generally, without reference to any specific example. Therefore we conclude here the analysis of the special case of a piecewise constant potential and turn to a general discussion of the asymptotic behavior of the pole functions.

The asymptotic behavior of the pole functions is easily obtained from the pole equation (20.14), and from the remark that the asymptotic behavior of the radial wave function appearing in the denominator as r diverges is

$$u(q, r) = \text{const} \times e^{-qr}, \tag{25}$$

because the value of q in the pole equation is just that appropriate for a bound state. (This argument, although essentially correct, is somewhat oversimplified; for the sake of simplicity we omit a more detailed discussion.) Thus from the pole equation (20.14) we obtain

$$q_i'(r) \xrightarrow[r \to \infty]{} \text{const} \times V(r)e^{-2q_i(\infty)r}. \tag{26}$$

This equation shows that there is an additional contribution, beside the asymptotic vanishing of the potential, to the asymptotic vanishing of $q_i'(r)$, or equivalently, to insure the asymptotic convergence of $q_i(r)$ to its limiting value $q_i(\infty)$. This phenomenon is important because it plays an important role in the computation of the binding energies (see below), and also because it has a simple physical interpretation. In fact, Eq. (26) may be interpreted as implying that at large values of r, the influence of the potential in determining the value of the ith bound state energy is suppressed by a factor of order $e^{-2rq_i(\infty)}$; one consequence is (at least in the simple case of monotonic potentials) that the larger the binding energy of a state, the less sensitive it is to the values of the potential at large distances.

But this simply corresponds to the fact that a particle more firmly bound by the potential is kept closer to the origin (more exactly, its probability of presence is more lumped near the origin), and therefore it feels the outer potential region less. In the present approach, this physical fact corresponds to the first pole trajectories being mainly built up in the inner potential region (we have in mind a monotonic potential possessing more than one bound state, such as the potential equation (16); see Fig. 2), and having practically leveled off in the outer potential region, and therefore being almost unaffected by the values of the potential at large distances (large, that is, relative to the scale length $[q_i(\infty)]^{-1}$, characteristic of each bound state; of course, the larger $q_i(\infty)$, the smaller the corresponding scale length— this remark being quite congruent with the preceding considerations because larger values of $q_i(\infty)$ correspond to larger binding energies and are characteristic of the first pole trajectories).

The fact we have just discussed may be interpreted as shedding some doubt on the convenience of the pole equation for the computation of bound states. It appears, in fact, that to integrate numerically the pole equation it should be possible to integrate the radial Schrödinger equation from the origin outward and in this manner obtain the asymptotic behavior of Eq. (26) at large r. (In this discussion we keep in mind the version (20.14) of the pole equation, but it is clear that the qualitative properties we are discussing also apply to other versions such as Eq. (IV.24).) It is well known, however, that this is practically impossible numerically because the numerical solution of the radial Schrödinger equation is inevitably infected by small portions of the other independent solution, which behaves as $e^{+2rq_i(\infty)}$ at infinity and therefore always dominates at sufficiently large r; or, equivalently, we may say that the asymptotic behavior $e^{+2rq_i(\infty)}$ is stable against computational errors, while the behavior $e^{-2rq_i(\infty)}$ is unstable. As a consequence, in any numerical integration of the pole equation the asymptotic behavior actually obtained for the derivative of the pole functions will be

$$q_i'(r) \xrightarrow[r\to\infty]{} -V(r) \xrightarrow[r\to\infty]{} 0, \qquad (27)$$

which is different from the correct one, Eq. (26). This fact may or may not seriously affect the accuracy of the numerical determination of $q_i(\infty)$ and consequently of the bound state energy, depending on the asymptotic rate of vanishing of the potential and on the energy of the bound state. In the light of the preceding discussion, it is also easy to convince oneself that if the pole function is mainly built up at distances small with respect to $[q_i(\infty)]^{-1}$ and is practically constant as soon as one gets out of this inner region, then the fact that in the numerical integration of the pole equation the asymptotic region is treated poorly has a negligible effect. This may be the case for potentials that vanish asymptotically faster than exponentially; if they vanish exponentially, we may hope for a good numerical result only if the asymptotic vanishing of the potential is definitely faster than $\exp[-2rq_i(\infty)]$. However, the strength of the potential and other details of its behavior are also important in assessing whether the numerical integration of the pole equation has a chance of producing a good result; and there are certainly many cases when the pole equation would be quite unreliable numerically. In any case, such a procedure is certainly not the most economical method, from the point of view of computing time, for the computation of bound state energies. The usefulness of the pole equation is rather of a theoretical nature: It consists mainly in the insight that it affords on the dependence of the energies of bound states on the potential (an insight that is complementary to that gained in the usual approach based on normalizable solutions of the radial Schrödinger equation), and in the results (see Chapters 22 and 23) that one can derive from it. Moreover, it is the pole equation that provides the theoretical foundation for the numerically more convenient procedure to compute the energies of bound states, to whose discussion we turn now.

The discussion could be based on any one of the various auxiliary functions introduced at the beginning of Appendix IV. For instance, the function $Y(q, r)$ is used in Ref. [13]. We prefer, however, to introduce yet another auxiliary function, setting

$$A(q, r) = R \tan \mu(q, r). \tag{28}$$

Here $A(q, r)$ is the function of Eq. (IV.1), i. e., the "scattering amplitude function" of Chapter 6, for $k = iq$; R is an arbitrary positive constant, which must be introduced for dimensional reasons, but obviously does not affect the final result; and the function $\mu(q, r)$ is unambiguously defined by this equation, together with the requirement (see below) that it vanishes in the origin and is a continuous function of r.

From Eq. (IV.3) satisfied by the function $A(q, r)$ we immediately obtain for $\mu(q, r)$ the equation

$$\mu'(q, r) = -RV(r) \left[\cos \mu(q, r) \frac{\sinh(qr)}{qR} + \sin \mu(q, r) e^{-qr} \right]^2, \qquad (29)$$

with boundary condition

$$\mu(q, 0) = 0. \qquad (30)$$

In the limit of vanishing q, this function coincides with the function $\mu_0(r)$ of Chapter 11.

(Incidentally, we note that generalization to arbitrary angular momenta of the following discussion is altogether trivial. It proceeds through the introduction of the continuous functions $\mu_l(q, r)$, defined by the differential equation

$$\mu_l'(q, r) = - RV(r) \left[\cos \mu_l(q, r) \frac{\hat{\jmath}_l(iqr)}{(iqR)^{l+1}} \right.$$

$$\left. + \sin \mu_l(q, r)(iqR)^l \hat{h}_l^{(1)}(iqr) \right]^2, \qquad (31)$$

with boundary condition

$$\mu_l(q, 0) = 0. \qquad (32)$$

In the $q = 0$ limit, these functions become the functions $\mu_l(r)$ of Chapter 11. No modification in the procedure described below for S waves is required to extend it to arbitrary l, other than the substitution of $\mu_l(q, r)$ in place of $\mu_0(q, r) \equiv \mu(q, r)$.)

Now the bound state energies are determined by the conditions

$$\mu(q_i, \infty) = (i - \tfrac{1}{2})\pi, \qquad i = 1, 2, 3, \dots . \qquad (33)$$

The best procedure to obtain them is the following. First select a distance r_∞ such that the potential is negligibly small beyond it, and substitute the condition

$$\mu(q_i, r_\infty) = (i - \tfrac{1}{2})\pi, \qquad i = 1, 2, 3, \dots, \qquad (34)$$

in place of the previous one, Eq. (33). There is, of course, a certain arbitrariness in the choice of r_∞, but the previous discussion implies that the two values of q_i obtained from two different r_∞'s differing by Δr_∞ differ from one another by a quantity

$$\Delta q_i = c \Delta r_\infty \cdot \exp(-2q_i r_\infty) V(r_\infty), \qquad (35)$$

thé constant c being independent from r_∞. We are therefore guaranteed that provided r_∞ is chosen sufficiently large, the error induced in q_i by the arbitrariness in the choice of r_∞ is negligible.

Equation (34) may now be solved numerically. The best procedure is first to compute $\mu(0, r_\infty)$ by numerical integration of Eq. (29); this determines directly the total number N of S-wave bound states, through the condition (see Chapter 23)

$$(N - \tfrac{1}{2})\pi < \mu(0, r_\infty) < (N + \tfrac{1}{2})\pi. \tag{36}$$

Then the N solutions q_i of Eq. (34) may be computed, for instance, by Newton's method, also keeping in mind that as a rule, $\mu(q, r_\infty)$ decreases as q increases. In general, to determine the q_i's with great precision it is sufficient to evaluate $\mu(q, r_\infty)$ for several—say, 10 or 20—values of q. Of course, each of these computations requires the numerical integration of the simple differential equation (29) from the origin to r_∞. (It is usually convenient to adopt a variable mesh in the integration, readjusting it at every integration step so as to maintain the increment of μ roughly constant.) It should be emphasized that a computation of this kind is not radically different from one based on the pole equation; in fact, they are rather similar. But in the pole equation one follows with continuity the change in $q_i(r)$ induced by the potential, and this requires much more computing time because, for each step in the evaluation of $q_i(r)$, we must integrate two first-order differential equations (see the pole equation (IV.24)), or one second-order equation (see Eq. (20.14)).

This concludes our outline of a convenient procedure for the numerical computation of bound states. We do not intend to enter into a more detailed discussion of it, which would carry us outside of the scope of this monograph.

22

Relation between the number of bound states and the value of the scattering phase shift at zero energy (Levinson's theorem)

In this chapter we prove Levinson's theorem [27], which provides an exact relationship between the number of bound states N_l with angular momentum l and the zero-energy value of the scattering phase shift δ_l. For an extension of this proof to include the case of energy-dependent potentials, see Ref. [37].

Before proceeding with the discussion, there is one important point to be clarified. The original definition of the phase shift, Eq. (2.9), suffers from a mod (π) ambiguity; thus an unambiguous formulation of Levinson's theorem refers to the difference between two values of the phase shift corresponding to two different energies, it being understood that the convention lifting the ambiguity is not modified as k is changed (or, equivalently, that the phase shift is a continuous function of k), so that the ambiguity is canceled in the difference. Thus Levinson's theorem is stated in the form

$$\pi N_l = \delta_l \mid_{k=0} - \delta_l \mid_{k=\infty} . \tag{1}$$

(There are exceptional cases which are taken into account by a more accurate formulation of Levinson's theorem, as is explained below. We disregard this possibility for the moment.) While we do not discuss now the conditions on the potential required for the validity of Eq. (1), we note immediately that this equation is certainly not valid in the case of singular potentials because, in such a case, the phase shift diverges as k diverges. On the other hand, for regular potentials the usual convention of settling the mod (π) ambiguity

176

ensures that the phase shift vanishes as k diverges. Then Eq. (1) becomes simply

$$N_l \pi = \delta_l \mid_{k=0} . \tag{2}$$

In the phase method, the phase shift δ_l is unambiguously defined as the asymptotic value of the phase function $\delta_l(r)$, which in turn is obtained from the phase equation (3.14) and the boundary condition equation (3.12). To be sure, the phase equation defines the phase shift only for $k \neq 0$; the value of the phase shift (or, for that matter, of the phase function) at $k = 0$ is defined by continuity from the values for $k \neq 0$. As we have seen, this definition corresponds to the usual convention inasmuch as it defines a phase shift which, for regular potentials, vanishes as k diverges (for details, see Appendix III).

In the following we adopt, of course, the definition of the phase shift through the phase equation, and we prove Levinson's theorem in the form (2). In view of the preceding remarks, this result is therefore, for regular potentials, equivalent to that expressed by Eq. (1). But, in fact, our proof of Eq. (2) is also valid for singular potentials. As has been discussed in detail in Chapter 15, the phase equation also defines unambiguously the scattering phase shift in this case, provided the more detailed boundary condition of Eq. (12) is imposed on the phase function near the origin. We therefore conclude that in this respect, the result we obtain is more general.

In the following we assume that the potential vanishes identically beyond a distance r_∞ . This assumption simplifies our discussion, but it is not essential for the validity of the theorem, as will be clear from its proof. At the end we discuss the conditions on the asymptotic behavior of the potential that are required for the validity of the theorem.

Let us now consider the value of the phase shift at zero energy, or, rather, for very small k. This problem has been treated in Chapter 11; we summarize here the main points of that discussion (with a slight change) and its conclusions. We set

$$\tan \delta_l(r) = (kR)^{2l+1}(2l + 1)!!(2l - 1)!! \tan\{\mu_l(r)[1 + O(k^2)]\}, \tag{3}$$

where R is an arbitrary positive constant. We then find for $\mu_l(r)$ the differential equation

$$\mu_l'(r) = - (2l + 1)^{-1}RV(r)[(r/R)^{l+1} \cos \mu_l(r) + (r/R)^{-l} \sin \mu_l(r)]^2, \tag{4}$$

with boundary condition

$$\mu_l(0) = 0. \tag{5}$$

We assume for the moment that the potential is regular, so that these equations suffice to specify the function $\mu_l(r)$; the case of singular potentials is considered below.

Obviously $\mu_l(r)$ is a continuous function of r; and the phase function $\delta_l(r)$, for $k \neq 0$, is also a continuous function of r. Thus Eq. (3) implies that for small k,

$$(2n - 1)\pi/2 < \delta_l(r) < (2n + 1)\pi/2 \qquad (6a)$$

if

$$(2n - 1)\pi/2 < \mu_l(r) < (2n + 1)\pi/2. \qquad (6b)$$

Here and in the following, n is an integer. This equation is valid for small k; its validity is implied by the convergence of the expansion of which Eq. (3) is the first term; the convergence of this expansion is in turn implied, even in the limit of large r, by our assumptions on the asymptotic vanishing of the potential. Let us also emphasize a difference between the present discussion and that of Chapter 11— namely, that while there we were directly expanding in powers of k^2 $\tan \delta_l(r)$ (see Eq. (11.1)), here we expand within the argument of a tangent (see Eq. (3)). This is more convenient for the present purpose because it provides a more straightforward justification for the validity of Eqs. (6); this is also implied by the approach of Chapter 11, however, once it is recognized that the coefficients of the higher powers of k in the expansion (11.1) are continuous functions of r wherever the first coefficient is continuous, i. e., wherever $\mu_l(r) \neq (2n + 1)\pi/2$.

We may now take the $k = 0$ limit; then from the continuity in k of $\delta_l(r)$ and from Eq. (3), we conclude

$$\delta_l(r)\,|_{k=0} = n\pi, \qquad (7)$$

with n defined by the condition (6b); of course, n depends on r.

We draw attention to the fact that we have excluded the equality sign in Eq. (6b). To include this case, let us consider the points at which $\mu_l(r)$ equals an odd integral multiple of $\pi/2$. Then from Eq. (3), we see that there is a difference between the $l = 0$ and the $l \geq 1$ cases. In the former case, $\mu_l(r) = (n + \frac{1}{2})\pi$ implies, in the $k = 0$ limit, $\delta_0(r) = (n + \frac{1}{2})\pi$, while in the latter, in the $k = 0$ limit, $\delta_l(r)$ is always an integral multiple of π, Eq. (7).

Thus for the scattering phase shift we conclude that

$$\delta_l \big|_{k=0} = n\pi \qquad\qquad \text{if} \quad (2n-1)\pi/2 < \mu_l(r_\infty) < (2n+1)\pi/2,$$

$$= n\pi \qquad\qquad \text{if} \quad \mu_l(r_\infty) = (2n+1)\pi/2, \quad l \geqslant 1, \qquad (8)$$

$$= (2n+1)\pi/2 \quad \text{if} \quad \mu_0(r_\infty) = (2n+1)\pi/2, \quad l = 0.$$

(Admittedly the present discussion of the case when $\mu_l(r_\infty) = (2n+1)\pi/2$ is not complete; for the sake of simplicity, we content ourselves with it, referring to the literature [28] for a more detailed proof of Levinson's theorem in this case.)

On the other hand, we have seen at the end of Chapter 20 that the number N_l of bound states with angular momentum l is specified by the condition

$$(2N_l - 1)\pi/2 < \mu_l(\infty) < (2N_l + 1)\pi/2. \qquad (9)$$

Because for the case we are now considering, $\mu_l(\infty) = \mu_l(r_\infty)$, we see that Eqs. (8) and (9) imply Levinson's result, Eq. (2). Q.E.D. We also notice that there is one exceptional circumstance when Levinson's theorem requires some extra care; this is the case when $\mu_l(r_\infty)$ equals an odd integral multiple of $\pi/2$. It is easily seen, through our discussion in Chapter 20, that this case corresponds to a situation in which the S matrix has a pole at $k = 0$. (Of course, the residue of this pole also vanishes, by unitarity.) This marginal situation corresponds, for $l \geqslant 1$, to the occurrence of a zero-energy bound state; for S waves, one should rather talk of a zero-energy resonance because the corresponding wave function is not normalizable while the zero-energy cross section diverges.

In conclusion, we state Levinson's theorem in its general form: *The zero-energy value of the phase shift δ_l (defined by continuity from the value of δ_l for small k, δ_l being the asymptotic value of the phase function $\delta_l(r)$) is π times the number N_l of bound states with angular momentum l, unless a zero-energy S-wave resonance occurs, in which case $\delta_0 \big|_{k=0} = (N_0 + \frac{1}{2})\pi$.*

We have assumed that the potential vanishes identically beyond r and that it is regular in the origin. Let us now discuss to what extent these conditions may be relaxed.

First of all we consider the regularity condition in the origin, and we show that it may be eliminated without invalidating the theorem. In fact, as was discussed in detail in Chapter 15, the phase equation is perfectly adequate to define the phase shift in this case, provided the more detailed condition (15.12) is imposed on the behavior of the phase function near the origin. (Of course, we consider only singular potentials that are repulsive near the origin, as has been emphasized in Chapter 15.) Therefore, all the previous results on the zero-energy value of the phase shift hold true, the function $\mu_l(r)$ being now the solution of Eq. (4) characterized by the condition that its behavior near the origin be

$$\mu_l(r) = -(r/R)^{2l+1}[1 - (2l + 1)/(r \sqrt{V(r)})]. \tag{10}$$

This condition may be derived using Eqs. (3) and (15.12) (for S-waves) or, more generally and directly, by investigating Eq. (4) in the neighborhood of the origin, after the fashion of Chapter 15.

So much for the zero-energy value of the scattering phase shift, in the case of singular potentials. As regards the number of bound states, again no change is required in the previous discussion, except for the fact mentioned immediately above concerning the proper definition of the function $\mu_l(r)$. Thus we are entitled to conclude that no limitation on the behavior of the potential in the origin, other than the requirement that it be repulsive if it is singular, is required for the validity of Levinson's theorem in the form given above.

Finally, we consider the limitation on the asymptotic behavior of the potential. First of all, there is no difficulty in extending the theorem to the case of a potential vanishing asymptotically exponentially or faster; in such a case, as emphasized in Chapter 11, the low-energy expansion (3) also remains valid in the limit of large r; neither does our discussion of bound states, as given in Chapter 20, run into any difficulty. As for the case of a potential that converges asymptotically as a power—say, as r^{-p}—it is not difficult to convince oneself that the theorem remains valid so long as there is no trouble with the asymptotic convergence of $\mu_l(r)$; as can be immediately seen from Eq. (4), this condition corresponds to the inequality

$$l < \tfrac{1}{2}(p - 3). \tag{11}$$

Thus in this case Levinson's theorem holds true for some partial waves, but not for all. A rigorous justification of these statements follows from a detailed treatment of the low-energy behavior of the scattering phase shifts for long-range potentials—a topic we have not discussed but which could be treated following the approach of Chapter 11. In fact, as we mentioned there, to carry out a complete analysis of this problem, Levy and Keller [10] have found it convenient just to use the phase method.

23

Bounds on the number and energies of bound states in a given potential. Necessary and sufficient conditions for the existence of bound states

In this chapter we indicate how the preceding results may be used to obtain information, in the form of upper and lower bounds, on the number of bound states and on their energies, in a given (central) potential. Our discussion reviews some of the results that have been obtained recently using this approach [38–41], and introduces some new results. We also present a derivation of the classical result of Bargmann [42, 43], which provides an upper limit to the number of bound states for each angular momentum in a given potential. Our aim, however, is to illustrate the kind of arguments to be used in this type of discussion, rather than to present a complete survey of all the results that may be obtained with these techniques.

For simplicity of presentation, whenever it is convenient we assume that the potential vanishes identically beyond the distance r_∞. But all the results we obtain remain valid for any potential vanishing asymptotically faster than r^{-1}. In fact, as has been repeatedly emphasized, once this condition is satisfied, which is sufficient to guarantee that a finite number of bound states exists, then, by choosing r_∞ sufficiently large we may be certain that all of our statements concerning physical quantities related to the truncated potential $V(r)\theta(r_\infty - r)$ approximate as closely as we like the corresponding statements referring to the potential $V(r)$.

We recall that the number n_l of bound states with angular momentum l is connected to the asymptotic value of the quantity $\mu_l(r)$, defined by the equations

$$\mu_l'(r) = -(2l + 1)^{-1}RV(r)[(r/R)^{l+1} \cos \mu_l(r) + (r/R)^{-l} \sin \mu_l(r)]^2, \quad (1)$$

$$\mu_l(0) = 0, \tag{2}$$

through the condition

$$(2n_l - 1)\pi/2 < \mu_l(r_\infty) < (2n_l + 1)\pi/2. \tag{3}$$

Here and in the following we disregard the marginal situation that obtains if $\mu_l(r_\infty)$ equals an odd integral multiple of $\pi/2$, whose physical meaning has been discussed in the preceding chapter.

We begin with a discussion of upper limits to n_l. First we derive Bargmann's result [42, 43], and then we give some additional results for the case of S waves [41].

In deriving upper bounds to n_l it is convenient to introduce the nowhere repulsive potential

$$\bar{V}(r) = V(r)\theta[-V(r)] = -| \bar{V}(r) |. \tag{4}$$

Obviously, any upper bound on the number of bound states associated with this potential holds *a fortiori* for the original potential $V(r)$. We also introduce the integrals

$$I_p = \int_0^\infty dr \, r^p | \bar{V}(r) |. \tag{5}$$

If some of these integrals diverge, the results that contain them become trivial.

The function $\mu_l(r)$ associated with the potential $\bar{V}(r)$ is a non-decreasing function. We now define the distances a_j and b_j, setting

$$\mu(a_j) = (j - 1)\pi, \qquad a_1 = 0, \tag{6a}$$

$$\mu(b_j) = (2j - 1)\pi/2, \tag{6b}$$

with j a positive integer. Obviously, these definitions imply the inequalities

$$a_j < b_j < a_{j+1} < b_{j+1}, \tag{7}$$

and the number n_l of bound states is the largest value of j for which Eq. (6b) has a solution. We now prove that

$$\int_{a_i}^{b_i} dr\, r|\,\bar{V}(r)\,| > 2l + 1. \tag{8}$$

This implies for the total number of bound states the upper limit, first derived by Bargmann [42],

$$n_l < (2l + 1)^{-1} \bar{I}_1 . \tag{9}$$

Incidentally, this result proves that any potential for which $\bar{I}_1$ is finite has a finite number of bound states for each angular momentum. (For a slightly stronger result, see Ref. [44].)

To prove Eq. (8), we perform the substitution

$$\tan \mu_l(r) = (r/R)^{2l+1} \tan \nu_l(r), \tag{10}$$

with the convention that $\nu_l(r)$ is a continuous function of r and that it vanishes in the origin. Then Eqs. (6) imply the conditions

$$\nu_l(a_j) = \mu_l(a_j) = (j - 1)\pi, \tag{11a}$$

$$\nu_l(b_j) = \mu_l(b_j) = (2j - 1)\pi/2. \tag{11b}$$

(We note, incidentally, that Eq. (10) also implies that $\nu_l(\infty) = n_l\pi$.) In the interval between a_j and b_j the function $\nu_l(r)$ has values such that $\sin 2\nu_l(r)$ is positive, and it satisfies the differential equation

$$\nu_l'(r) = -\frac{2l + 1}{2r} \sin 2\nu_l(r) + (2l + 1)^{-1}2r|\,\bar{V}(r)\,| \times \sin^2[\nu_l(r) + \pi/4]. \tag{12}$$

Therefore, we infer that

$$\tfrac{1}{2}\nu_l'(r)\sin^{-2}[\nu_l(r) + \pi/4] < (2l + 1)^{-1}r|\,\bar{V}(r)\,|, \tag{13}$$

and integrating both sides from a_j to b_j we obtain, using Eqs. (11), just Eq. (8). Q.E.D.

As remarked by Bargmann [42], condition (9) is "best possible in the sense that for a given l potentials may be constructed which have a prescribed number n_l of bound states for that angular momentum and for which I_1 approaches $(2l + 1)n_l$ arbitrarily closely." The potentials that saturate Bargmann's inequality have a rather peculiar shape: for a given n_l, they consist of n_l widely separated narrow and deep wells (these become Dirac distributions, in the limit of complete saturation).

Of course, the fact that Bargmann's inequality is "best possible" does not exclude the existence of different upper limits, which may or may not also be "best possible," but which do provide, in certain cases, more stringent limitations than does Bargmann's formula, Eq. (9). One simple example is obtained directly from Eq. (1), which implies

$$\mu_l'(r) < (2l+1)^{-1}R| \ \bar{V}(r) \ |[(r/R)^{2l+2} + (r/R)^{-2l}], \tag{14}$$

because the maximum value of $(P \cos x + Q \sin x)^2$ is $P^2 + Q^2$. Therefore, from Eq. (3) we conclude

$$n_l < \tfrac{1}{2} + \pi^{-1}(2l+1)^{-1}[R^{-(2l+1)}I_{2l+2} + R^{2l+1}I_{-2l}], \tag{15}$$

and, setting

$$R^{2(2l+1)} = I_{2l+2}/I_{-2l}, \tag{16}$$

we secure

$$n_l < \tfrac{1}{2} + (2l+1)^{-1}\frac{2}{\pi}[I_{2l+2}I_{-2l}]^{1/2}. \tag{17}$$

It should be emphasized that $I_{2l+2}I_{-2l}$ can not be smaller than I_1^2. Thus this limitation can never improve on Bargmann's inequality by more than a factor of $2/\pi$. Moreover, unless the potential vanishes sufficiently fast at the origin, I_{-2l} diverges. At any rate, for S waves and for a square well potential of range $\bar{r}$ and depth $|V_0|$, for instance, this equation yields $n_0 < \tfrac{1}{2} + 2/(\pi \sqrt{3})|V_0|\bar{r}^2$, while the Bargmann condition (9) yields $n_0 < \tfrac{1}{2}|V_0|\bar{r}^2$. Thus for values of $|V_0|\bar{r}^2$ larger than 3.8, this condition is more stringent than Bargmann's. However, for large values of $|V_0|\bar{r}^2$ both conditions yield rather poor upper bounds to n_0; in fact, the exact relationship is $n_0 < \tfrac{1}{2} + \pi^{-1}|V_0|^{1/2}\bar{r}_0$, and it implies that the number of bound states increases as the square root of the potential strength rather than linearly. This is a general property, valid for all potentials, as is proved below.

It is also possible to derive other bounds that are often more stringent than those given here, by shaking Eq. (1) a little before majorizing its r.h.s. The interested reader is referred to Ref. [41], where this is done in the S-wave case.

We now derive another upper bound for n_0 (and therefore also, *a fortiori*, for n_l); it is valid, however, only for attractive potentials that are monotonically increasing:

$$V(r) = -| V(r) |, \tag{18a}$$

$$V'(r) \geqslant 0. \tag{18b}$$

The proof is accomplished by introducing the new function $\psi(r)$ through

$$\tan \psi(r) = | V(r) |^{1/2}[r + R \tan \mu_0(r)],$$
$$\psi(0) = 0. \tag{19}$$

As before, we define $\psi(r)$ to be continuous, and we introduce the distances at which $\psi(r)$ equals an odd or an even integral multiple of $\pi/2$, setting

$$\psi(c_j) = (j - 1)\pi, \tag{20a}$$

$$\psi(b_j) = (2j - 1)\pi/2. \tag{20b}$$

The distances b_j are the same as those defined by Eq. (6a), and we again have the condition

$$c_j < b_j < c_{j+1} < b_{j+1}, \tag{21}$$

analogous to Eq. (7). (Recall that we are considering the case of an attractive potential, so that $\mu_0(r)$ increases monotonically.) We now prove that

$$\int_{c_j}^{b_j} dr| V(r) |^{1/2} > \pi/2. \tag{22}$$

From this we infer for the number n_0 of S-wave bound states the limitation

$$n_0 < (2/\pi) \int_0^{\infty} dr | V(r) |^{1/2}, \tag{23}$$

which is our result. It is remarkable that the quantity $\int_0^{\infty} dr | V(r)|^{1/2}$ is, in a sense, the simplest dimensionless quantity that one may construct with the potential (and of course, with the dimensional constants $\hbar$ and m, which are included in our system of units).

It remains to prove Eq. (22). This follows immediately from the inequality, valid for $c_j < r < b_j$,

$$\psi'(r) < |\, V(r)\,|^{1/2}, \tag{24}$$

which in turn is implied by the differential equation satisfied by $\psi(r)$,

$$\psi'(r) = |\, V(r)\,|^{1/2} - \frac{1}{4}\left[\frac{V'(r)}{|\, V(r)\,|}\right] \sin 2\psi(r), \tag{25}$$

because in this interval $\sin 2\psi(r)$ is positive. We emphasize that to deduce Eq. (24) from Eq. (25), we also require Eq. (18b); in fact, it is easily seen that if this condition is not satisfied, the result (23) may be violated.

The inequality (23) implies that the number of bound states for any given angular momentum increases at most as the square root of the potential strength (coupling constant). This last remark holds for any potential, not only for those satisfying the monotonicity condition (18b), because it is always possible to manufacture a monotonic potential that is everywhere more attractive than a given potential. (We exclude potentials that are unbounded at points other than $r = 0$.)

Setting $n = 1$ in Eq. (23), we obtain the necessary condition for the existence of bound states (for monotonic potentials) [40]

$$\int_0^\infty dr[-V(r)]^{1/2} > \pi/2. \tag{26}$$

This condition is saturated by a square well potential; thus we may assert that this condition is best possible in Bargmann's sense.

We proceed now to establish a lower limit to the number n_l of bound states. To obtain it, we introduce the function $\varphi_l(r)$, setting

$$(2l + 1) \tan \varphi_l(r) = (r/R)^{2l+1} + \tan \mu_l(r). \tag{27}$$

(Note that the function $\varphi_0(r)$ coincides with $\varphi(0, r)$ of Appendix IV.) As usual, we define $\varphi_l(r)$ to be continuous and to vanish in the origin; this, together with Eq. (27), implies that $\varphi_l(r)$ coincides with $\mu_l(r)$ whenever this equals an odd integral multiple of $\pi/2$. Therefore, Eq. (3) remains valid if we substitute $\varphi_l(r_\infty)$ in place of $\mu_l(r_\infty)$, and it implies

$$-\tfrac{1}{2} + \varphi_l(r_\infty)/\pi < n_l < \tfrac{1}{2} + \varphi_l(r_\infty)/\pi, \tag{28}$$

or, equivalently,

$$n_l = \{\{\tfrac{1}{2} + \varphi_l(r_\infty)/\pi\}\}, \tag{29}$$

where the symbol $\{\{\ \}\}$ indicates the integral part of the quantity within the braces.

We now minorize the quantity $\varphi_l(r_\infty)$. First, we write the differential equation satisfied by $\varphi_l(r)$:

$$\varphi_l'(r) = R^{-1}(r/R)^{2l} \cos^2 \varphi_l(r) - RV(r)(r/R)^{-2l} \sin^2 \varphi_l(r), \tag{30}$$

with boundary condition

$$\varphi_l(0) = 0. \tag{31}$$

But from Eq. (30) we immediately infer

$$\varphi_l'(r) \geqslant \min[R^{-1}(r/R)^{2l}, -RV(r)(r/R)^{-2l}], \tag{32}$$

because the minimum value of $P \cos^2 x + Q \sin^2 x$ is the smaller number between P and Q. The symbol $\min(x, y)$ is defined by

$$\begin{aligned} \min(x, y) &= x \quad \text{if} \quad x \leqslant y, \\ &= y \quad \text{if} \quad y \leqslant x. \end{aligned} \tag{33}$$

Thus, from Eqs. (31) and (32) we conclude that

$$\varphi_l(r_\infty) \geqslant \int_0^{r_\infty} dr \, \min[R^{-1}(r/R)^{2l}, -RV(r)(r/R)^{-2l}]. \tag{34}$$

But by assumption $V(r)$ vanishes identically beyond r_∞; therefore there is no change in extending the integration to ∞. In conclusion, from this equation and Eq. (29), we secure

$$n_l \geqslant \left\{\left\{\frac{1}{2} + \pi^{-1} \int_0^\infty dr \, \min[R^{-1}(r/R)^{2l}, -RV(r)(r/R)^{-2l}]\right\}\right\}. \tag{35}$$

This is the required lower bound to n_l. It should be emphasized that the choice of the positive constant R is arbitrary. We also note that the result in the present form does not depend on the fact that the potential vanishes identically beyond a range r_∞, although it was convenient to use this assumption in the derivation.

CONDITIONS ON BOUND STATES

For instance, for an exponential potential $V(r) = - |V_0| \exp(-r/r_0)$, we get from Eq. (35) for S waves

$$n_0 \geqslant \left\{\left\{\frac{1}{2} + \frac{2r_0|V_0|^{1/2}}{(\pi \sqrt{e})}\right\}\right\}, \tag{36}$$

having made for R the optimal choice $R = [e/|V_0|]^{1/2}$. From this inequality we find that the minimum values of the parameter $r_0^2|V_0|$ that are sufficient to secure, respectively, one and two bound states are 1.67 and 15. The exact minimum values are 1.44 and 6.1, respectively. The values of the same parameter that are necessary to secure n_0 bound states, as determined by Bargmann's inequality, are just n_0.

Condition (35) is best possible in Bargmann's sense. In fact, it is easily seen that the potentials

$$V_l(r) = -R^{-2}(r/R)^{4l}\theta(r_0 - r) \tag{37}$$

saturate it; i. e., it is possible to adjust r_0 so that $V_l(r)$ possesses n_l bound states of angular momentum l and is such that, when substituted in the r.h.s. of Eq. (35), it yields a value for the quantity within the braces that is arbitrarily close to n_l. For S waves the saturating potential is a square well. It is remarkable that this potential has just the opposite shape to the potential that saturates Bargmann's inequality; here the potential is spread out evenly over its whole range; there it is all concentrated around one, or a few, points.

The lower limit (35) implies that the number of bound states increases at least as the square root of the strength of the potential. This is immediately seen by choosing the arbitrary constant R in Eq. (35) proportional to g raised to the power $[2(2l + 1)]^{-1}$, where the coupling constant g is some measure of the strength of the potential. Together with the result obtained above, this result implies that n_l does indeed grow proportionally to the square root of g.

Finally we remark that by setting $n_l = 1$ in any one of the previous inequalities, Eqs. (9), (17), (23), or (35), we obtain conditions on the potential necessary (in the first three cases) and sufficient (in the last case) for the existence of at least one bound state (with angular momentum l; in the second and third cases, $l = 0$). Other sufficient conditions to the same effect may be derived using analogous methods; we record some of them here, but refer for their proof to the original papers [38, 39]. They state that a sufficient condition for the existence of at least one bound state with angular momentum L (and therefore also at least one for every $l \leqslant L$) is given by either one of the inequalities

$$-\int_0^R dr\, rV(r)(r/R)^{2L+1} - \int_R^\infty dr\, rV(r)(r/R)^{-(2L+1)} > 2L + 1, \quad (38)$$

$$-\int_0^\infty dr\, RV(r)[(r/R)^{2L} - (r/R)^{-2L}R^2V(r)]^{-1} > 1. \quad (39)$$

Both results hold only for nowhere repulsive potentials; in both inequalities R is an arbitrary positive constant. Both equations are best possible in Bargmann's sense. The first one is saturated by the same type of potentials that saturate Bargmann's inequality; the resemblance of this equation to Bargmann's formula is worth noticing. The second inequality is saturated by potentials of the form

$$V_L(r) = - R^{-2}\,(r/R)^{4L}$$
$$\times \{\exp[(r/R)^{2L+1}/(2L + 1)] - 1\}^{-1}. \quad (40)$$

For S waves, the saturating potential is of the Hulthén type.

We now derive another sufficient condition for a nowhere repulsive potential to possess bound states. For simplicity we restrict our consideration to the S-wave case; the generalization to all partial waves is trivial, and we merely indicate it at the end. We start from the equation for the scattering length function (see Chapter 11):

$$a'(r) = |\,V(r)\,|[r + a(r)]^2, \quad (41)$$

$$a(0) = 0. \quad (42)$$

We have explicitly indicated that the potential is negative semidefinite. We now perform a change of dependent variable, setting

$$a(r) = Ry(r)/[1 - y(r)], \quad (43)$$

where R is a positive constant. We then find for $y(r)$ the differential equation

$$y'(r) = R^{-1}|\,V(r)\,|[r + (R - r)y(r)]^2, \quad (44)$$

with boundary condition

$$y(0) = 0. \quad (45)$$

Obviously, $y(r)$ is a nondecreasing function of r, and a sufficient condition for the existence of at least one bound state is that

$$y(\infty) > 1, \tag{46}$$

because this condition implies, through Eq. (43), that $a(r)$ has at least one pole in the interval $0 < r < \infty$. On the other hand, if we apply to Eq. (44) the procedure employed in Appendix II to derive Eq. (II.35), we secure

$$y(\infty) \geqslant \max_t \{(RI_1 - I_2)(R^2I_0 - 2RI_1 + I_2)^{-1}t$$
$$\times [\exp\{4R^{-1}(RI_1 - I_2)(1 - t)\} - 1]\}, \tag{47}$$

where the integrals I_p are defined by Eq. (5). In this equation the constant R is still arbitrary. Setting

$$t = \tfrac{1}{2}(R^2I_0 - 2RI_1 + I_2)(RI_1 - I_2)^{-1}s, \tag{48}$$

it is easily seen that the optimal choice of this constant is

$$R = \{[(2 + s)/s](I_2/I_0)\}^{1/2}. \tag{49}$$

With this choice we conclude that

$$y(\infty) \geqslant \tfrac{1}{2}M[I_1, (I_0I_2)^{1/2}/I_1], \tag{50}$$

where the universal function $M(x, z)$ is defined by

$$M(x, z) = \max_{s \geqslant 0}\{s[\exp(4x\{1 + s - z[s(2 + s)]^{1/2}\}) - 1]\}. \tag{51}$$

Therefore we may assert in conclusion that a sufficient condition for the existence of at least one S-wave bound state is that

$$M[I_1, (I_0I_2)^{1/2}/I_1] \geqslant 2. \tag{52}$$

It is easy to see that the analogous condition sufficient to secure the existence of at least one bound state with angular momentum L (and therefore also at least one for each $l \leqslant L$) is

$$M[(2L + 1)^{-1}I_1, (I_{-2L}I_{2L+2})^{1/2}/I_1] \geqslant 2. \tag{53}$$

The condition (53) is more conveniently expressed in the form

$$I_1 \geqslant (2L + 1)B[(I_{-2L}I_{2L+2})^{1/2}/I_1], \tag{54}$$

where the universal function B is defined by

$$B(z) = \tfrac{1}{4} \min_{0 < s < s_1} \left[\{1 + s - z[s(2 + s)]^{1/2}\}^{-1} \ln \left(1 + \frac{2}{s}\right) \right] \qquad (55\text{a})$$

with

$$s_1 = z(z^2 - 1)^{-1/2} - 1. \qquad (55\text{b})$$

The function $B(z)$ is plotted in Fig. 1 (solid line) and it is tabulated in Table I. The limiting value

$$\lim_{z \to 1+} B(z) = 1 \qquad (56)$$

and the asymptotic behavior

$$B(z) \xrightarrow[z \to \infty]{} \tfrac{1}{2}[\ln z + \ln \ln z + 1] \qquad (57)$$

are easily evaluated. As previously noted, the argument of B in Eq. (54) is never smaller than one.

The condition (54) provides, for a nowhere repulsive potential, a simple lower bound for the strength of the potential (as measured by the value of $\bar{I}_1$) sufficient to guarantee the existence of at least

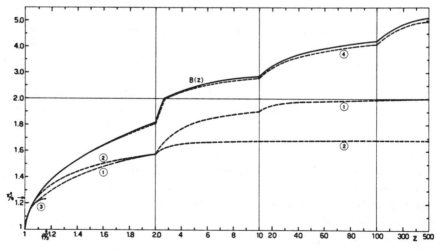

FIG. 1. The solid line is a graph of the universal function $B(z)$, Eqs. (55). The four broken-line graphs are explained in the text. Note that in this figure there is one change of scale in the ordinates and three changes in the abscissas.

TABLE I

THE UNIVERSAL FUNCTION $B(z)$ [a]

z	$B(z)$	z	$B(z)$	z	$B(z)$
1.01	1.083	2.4	1.956	30	3.527
1.02	1.118	2.6	2.012	40	3.691
1.03	1.145	2.8	2.062	50	3.821
1.04	1.168	3	2.110	60	3.927
1.05	1.188	4	2.300	70	4.017
1.06	1.206	5	2.443	80	4.088
1.07	1.223	6	2.557	90	4.155
1.08	1.238	7	2.653	100	4.215
1.09	1.253	8	2.736	200	4.610
1.1	1.267	9	2.808	300	4.841
1.2	1.379	10	2.872	400	5.005
1.3	1.465	11	2.929	500	5.117
1.4	1.535	12	2.982	600	5.218
1.5	1.597	13	3.030	700	5.304
1.6	1.651	14	3.075	800	5.378
1.7	1.700	15	3.117	900	5.443
1.8	1.745	16	3.156	1000	5.501
1.9	1.786	17	3.190	2000	5.885
2.0	1.825	18	3.224	3000	6.103
2.1	1.861	19	3.256	4000	6.269
2.2	1.894	20	3.286	5000	6.381

[a] Defined by Eqs. (55). An asymptotic estimate, which is already reliable for the last values given in the table, is provided by Eq. (57). The data of this table are plotted in Fig. 1.

one bound state. The lower bound depends on the shape of the potential, but not on its strength, and on the (maximum) angular momentum for which a bound state is guaranteed to be present. It requires only the evaluation of two moments of the potential, besides $\bar{I}_1$. Of course if one of the needed moments turns out to be divergent, the corresponding conclusions become trivial, as implied by Eq. (57). Thus we expect this approach to be more useful for S waves, because for higher partial waves the integral $\bar{I}_{-2l}$ is more likely to diverge, unless of course the potential vanishes very fast at the origin.

To afford an estimate of the usefulness of the condition (54) in the S-wave case we have plotted in Fig. 1 (broken lines) the exact minimum values of $\bar{I}_1$ which are just sufficient to secure one S-wave bound state, for four potentials which depend only on two parameters (so that, for each shape, the minimum value of $\bar{I}_1$ depends only on the shape parameter $z = (\bar{I}_0\bar{I}_2)^{1/2}/\bar{I}_1)$. These potentials are

$$V_1(r) = -\tfrac{1}{2}I_1[R_1^{-1}\,\delta(r - R_1) + R_2^{-1}\,\delta(r - R_2)],$$

$$z = \tfrac{1}{2}(R_1 + R_2)(R_1R_2)^{-1/2}, \tag{58a}$$

$$V_2(r) = -(n + 1)!\,\mu^2 I_1(\mu r)^n e^{-\mu r},$$

$$n > -1, \quad z = [(n + 2)/(n + 1)]^{1/2}, \tag{58b}$$

$$V_3(r) = -2(R_2{}^2 - R_1{}^2)^{-1}I_1\theta(R_2 - r)\,\theta(r - R_1),$$

$$R_2 \geqslant R_1, \quad z = \{\tfrac{4}{3}[1 - R_1R_2(R_1 + R_2)^{-2}]\}^{1/2}, \tag{58c}$$

$$V_4(r) = -[\ln(R_2/R_1)]^{-1}I_1 r^{-2}\theta(R_2 - r)\,\theta(r - R_1),$$

$$R_2 \geqslant R_1, \quad z = \frac{(R_2 - R_1)(R_2R_1)^{-1/2}}{\ln(R_2/R_1)}. \tag{58d}$$

The subscript on each potential corresponds to the label on the graph in Fig. 1. For $z = 1$ all these potentials reduce to the deltalike potential $V(r) = -\bar{I}_1\delta(r - R)$. In case 3 the range of the shape parameter z is restricted to the interval between 1 and $(4/3)^{1/2}$; for $z = (4/3)^{1/2}$ the potential becomes the ordinary square well $V(r) = -2\bar{I}_1 R^{-2}\theta(R - r)$. In the $z \to \infty$ limit, $V_1(r)$ becomes essentially the single deltalike potential $V(r) = -\tfrac{1}{2}\bar{I}_1 R^{-1}\delta(R - r)$, because the second delta function tends to the origin, where it is killed by the vanishing of the radial wave function; $V_2(r)$ becomes the Yukawa potential $V(r) = -\bar{I}_1\mu r^{-1}e^{-\mu r}$; and $V_4(r)$ becomes the singular potential $V(r) = -|g|\,r^{-2}\theta(R - r)$. Thus the asymptotic value 1.680 of the second broken curve is just the minimum value of $\bar{I}_1$ sufficient to secure one bound state for a Yukawa potential. As for the last broken curve, it is very close but of course always smaller than $B(z)$. (A straightforward calculation yields for the leading terms of its asymptotic behavior the expression $\tfrac{1}{2}[\ln z + \ln \ln z + \ln 2]$.) The minimum values of $\bar{I}_1$ plotted in Fig. 1 are given by a simple explicit formula in the first case and by implicit transcendental equations in the last two cases; in the second case a numerical integration is required. It may be inferred from these results that, in general, the bound on $\bar{I}_1$ is more stringent the smaller the shape parameter z is; and in fact for $z = 1$, which corresponds to a deltalike potential, the condition (54) becomes the exact condition $\bar{I}_1 > 2l + 1$. Incidentally, that the exact minimum value of $\bar{I}_1$ for which an attractive deltalike potential possesses one bound state with angular momentum l is just $2l + 1$ may be inferred directly from the simultaneous validity of Eqs. (9) and either (38) or (54) and (56).

We have discussed methods to derive limitations on the number of bound states, or conditions on the potential to secure the existence of bound states. In general, by an analogous treatment of the equations which refer to the $q > 0$ case and which reduce, for $q = 0$, to those used here (e. g., for the function $\varphi_0(r)$, see Appendix IV; for $\mu_l(r)$, Chapter 21), it is possible to establish limits for the binding energies of bound states. As a rule, the same procedure that yields an upper (or lower) bound for the number of bound states produces a lower (or upper) bound for the (negative) energies of bound states. Similarly, the procedure that yields a necessary (or sufficient) condition for the existence of at least one bound state with given angular momentum produces a lower (or upper) bound for the (negative) energy of the lowest-lying bound state with the same angular momentum. The restrictions that one obtains in this manner are usually in the form of implicit inequalities, and are therefore not very convenient.

We prefer to discuss lower limits for the bound state energies that are obtained, applying directly the approach of Chapter 20. For simplicity, we restrict our discussion to the S-wave case; of course, the results hold *a fortiori* for all partial waves. Also, we consider only potentials that are nowhere repulsive.

We recall that the energies E_i of (S-wave) bound states are determined by the asymptotic values of the pole functions $q_i(r)$:

$$E_i = -q_i^2(\infty). \tag{59}$$

In the following, we establish upper bounds for $q_i(\infty)$; they yield, through Eq. (59), lower limits for the binding energies.

As is implied by the analysis given in Chapter 20, the quantities $q_i(\infty)$ may be expressed by the formula

$$q_i(\infty) = -\int_{b_i}^{\infty} dr\, V(r)\{1 + 2q_i(r)P[q_i(r), r]\}^{-1}, \tag{60}$$

the distances b_i being defined by the condition

$$\mu_0(b_i) = (2i - 1)\pi/2. \tag{61}$$

As for the functions $q_i(r)$ and $P(q, r)$ in Eq. (60), they are defined in Chapter 20; all we need to know here is that they are nonnegative.

A bound that follows trivially from Eq. (60), and the positive semidefiniteness of $q_i(r)P[q_i(r), r]$, is the statement

$$q_i(\infty) < \int_{B_i}^{\infty} dr \mid V(r) \mid, \tag{62}$$

with

$$B_i \leqslant b_i . \tag{63}$$

We are also using the fact that the potential is nowhere repulsive. Of course, Eq. (62) also implies the condition

$$q_i(\infty) < \int_{0}^{\infty} dr \mid V(r) \mid, \tag{64}$$

but this estimate is much too crude. In fact, it has been proved by Schwinger [43] that this inequality holds true even if we divide the r.h.s. by 2.

More stringent bounds are obtained by inserting a value larger than zero in Eq. (62), in place of B_i. Of course, to maintain the validity of the bound of Eq. (62), it is required that the inequality (63) be respected. Thus the problem of establishing an upper bound for $q_i(\infty)$ is transformed into that of establishing a lower bound for b_i. But it is immediately recognized that this problem is completely analogous to that of establishing upper bounds for the number of bound states (at least in the present case of nowhere repulsive potentials). Thus we may take over the results of the previous discussions and conclude that any one of the following implicit definitions of B_i satisfies the inequality (63):

$$\int_{0}^{B_i} dr \, r \mid V(r) \mid = i, \tag{65a}$$

$$\left[\int_{0}^{B_i} dr \, r^2 \mid V(r) \mid \int_{0}^{B_i} dr \mid V(r) \mid \right]^{1/2} = (2i - 1)(\pi/4), \tag{65b}$$

$$\int_{0}^{B_i} dr \mid V(r) \mid^{1/2} = i\pi/2. \tag{65c}$$

The first two equations correspond to Eqs. (9) and (17), respectively; the third one, to Eq. (23), and the B_i that it defines provides a lower bound to b_i only provided the potential is monotonic (nondecreasing). Of course, for the same value of i these three equations yield generally three different values of B_i; the largest value, when inserted in Eq. (62), produces the most stringent upper bound for $q_i(\infty)$.

Each one of the three equations (65) yields a well-defined value for B_i, corresponding to each value of i up to N. N may vary from one equation to the other; it provides an upper limit to n_0, as discussed above. Of course, if $N - n_0 = p \geqslant 1$, the last p B_i's, corresponding to $i > n_0$, are of no interest, since the corresponding bound states do not exist.

These bounds may be compared with those obtained by Schwinger [43], which for S waves read

$$q_i(\infty) < k_i , \tag{66}$$

with k_i defined implicitly by the condition

$$\int_0^\infty dr(1 - e^{-2k_i r})|\ V(r)\ | = 2ik_i . \tag{67}$$

The disadvantage of Schwinger's bounds is that in order to use them one has to solve the implicit equation (67). The bounds derived here are, instead, given by the explicit relation (62). It, however, contains the quantity B_i, which must be evaluated from the implicit equations (65). The fact that we have various possibilities among which to choose may prove advantageous. As regards a comparison of the accuracies of these bounds and those obtained by Schwinger, we note that the present bounds are often more stringent for relatively weak potentials, but become less stringent than Schwinger's for strong potentials. In fact, it is easily seen by a comparison of Eqs. (62) and (67) that in the asymptotic limit of very strong potentials the Schwinger bound is more stringent by a factor of $(2i)^{-1}$ because, in this limit, $B_i \to 0$ and $k_i \to \infty$. (Note, however, that we are considering the limit of strong potential for fixed i; but as the strength of the potential increases, the number of bound states also increases. Thus this comparison applies to the deeper bound states, but not to the shallower ones.)

Finally, we reiterate that our aim in this chapter has been to display the techniques to be used to extract easily from the shape and strength of the potential some information concerning its bound states, rather than to give a complete survey of the results of this type that may be obtained with these techniques.

Appendix I

Riccati-Bessel, Riccati-Hankel, and other functions

The Riccati–Bessel and Riccati–Hankel functions are spherical Bessel and Hankel functions multiplied by their argument. It is convenient to use them in place of the spherical Bessel and Hankel functions because they satisfy the radial Schrödinger equation in the absence of potential and have a simple asymptotic behavior. In this appendix we collect a number of formulas that relate to them. For these functions we use the same symbol traditionally used for the corresponding spherical Bessel functions with the addition of a circumflex. We use the symbol $\hat{z}_l(x)$ to indicate a generic Riccati–Bessel or Riccati–Hankel function. At the end we define and give some properties of the functions $U_l(x)$, which arise in the discussion of bound states.

Differential Equation

$$\hat{z}_l''(x) + [1 - l(l+1)x^{-2}]\hat{z}_l(x) = 0. \tag{1}$$

Recursion Relations

$$\hat{z}_l'(x) + (l/x)\hat{z}_l(x) - \hat{z}_{l-1}(x) = 0, \tag{2a}$$

$$\hat{z}_l'(x) - [(l+1)/x]\hat{z}_l(x) + \hat{z}_{l+1}(x) = 0. \tag{2b}$$

Definition of the Riccati-Bessel Functions

$$\hat{j}_l(x) = \sin\left(x - l\frac{\pi}{2}\right) \sum_{n=0}^{\leqslant l/2} (-)^n (2x)^{-2n} \frac{(l+2n)!}{[(2n)!(l-2n)!]}$$

198

$$+ \cos \left(x - l\frac{\pi}{2}\right) \sum_{n=0}^{\leqslant (l-1)/2} (-)^n (2x)^{-2n-1} \frac{(l + 2n + 1)!}{[(2n + 1)!(l - 2n - 1)!]}, \quad (3a)$$

$$= x^{l+1} \sum_{n=0}^{\infty} \frac{(-x^2/2)^n}{[n!(2l + 2n + 1)!!]}, \quad (3b)$$

$$= \left(\frac{\pi x}{2}\right)^{1/2} J_{l+1/2}(x). \quad (3c)$$

$$\hat{n}_l(x) = -\cos \left(x - l\frac{\pi}{2}\right) \sum_{n=0}^{\leqslant l/2} (-)^n (2x)^{-2n} \frac{(l + 2n)!}{[(2n)!(l - 2n)!]}$$

$$+ \sin \left(x - l\frac{\pi}{2}\right) \sum_{n=0}^{\leqslant (l-1)/2} (-)^n (2x)^{-2n-1} \frac{(l + 2n + 1)!}{[(2n + 1)!(l - 2n - 1)!]}, \quad (4a)$$

$$= -x^{-l} \sum_{n=0}^{\infty} \left(\frac{x^2}{2}\right)^n \frac{(2l - 2n - 1)!!}{n!} \qquad \begin{array}{l} [(-2n - 1)!! \\ = (-)^n \{(2n - 1)!!\}^{-1}, (-1)!! = 1] \end{array}$$

$$\quad (4b)$$

$$= (-)^{l+1} \left(\frac{\pi x}{2}\right)^{1/2} J_{-(l+1/2)}(x). \quad (4c)$$

Here $J_\nu(x)$ is a standard Bessel function.

The First Riccati-Bessel Functions

$$\hat{j}_0(x) = \sin x, \qquad \hat{j}_1(x) = -\cos x + \frac{\sin x}{x},$$

$$\hat{j}_2(x) = \sin x \left(\frac{3}{x^2} - 1\right) - \frac{3}{x} \cos x; \quad (5a)$$

$$\hat{n}_0(x) = -\cos x, \qquad \hat{n}_1(x) = -\sin x - \frac{\cos x}{x},$$

$$\hat{n}_2(x) = -\cos x \left(\frac{3}{x^2} - 1\right) - \frac{3}{x} \sin x. \quad (5b)$$

Wronskian Relation

$$\hat{j}_l(x)\hat{n}_l'(x) - \hat{j}_l'(x)\hat{n}_l(x) = 1. \quad (6)$$

Behavior near the Origin

$$\hat{j}_l(x) = [x^{l+1}/(2l + 1)!!][1 + O(x^2)], \quad (7a)$$

$$\hat{n}_l(x) = -x^{-l}(2l - 1)!![1 + O(x^2)]. \quad (7b)$$

Asymptotic Behavior

$$\hat{j}_l(x) \xrightarrow[x \to \infty]{} \sin\left(x - l\frac{\pi}{2}\right) \qquad (x \gg l), \tag{8a}$$

$$\hat{n}_l(x) \xrightarrow[x \to \infty]{} -\cos\left(x - l\frac{\pi}{2}\right) \qquad (x \gg l). \tag{8b}$$

Parity

$$\hat{j}_l(-x) = (-)^{l+1}\hat{j}_l(x), \tag{9a}$$

$$\hat{n}_l(-x) = (-)^l\hat{n}_l(x). \tag{9b}$$

Amplitude and Phase of the Riccati-Bessel Functions

$$\hat{j}_l(x) = \hat{D}_l(x)\sin\hat{\delta}_l(x), \tag{10a}$$

$$\hat{n}_l(x) = -\hat{D}_l(x)\cos\hat{\delta}_l(x), \tag{10b}$$

$$\hat{D}_l(x) = [\hat{j}_l^2(x) + \hat{n}_l^2(x)]^{1/2}, \tag{11a}$$

$$\hat{\delta}_l(x) = -\tan^{-1}[\hat{j}_l(x)/\hat{n}_l(x)]. \tag{11b}$$

Here the phase $\hat{\delta}_l(x)$ is defined only mod(π). An absolute definition is the following:

$$\hat{\delta}_l(x) = \int_0^x dy\, \hat{D}_l^{-2}(y), \tag{12}$$

whose consistency with Eqs. (10) and (11) is ensured by the Wronskian relation (6). On the other hand, explicit definitions of $\hat{D}_l(x)$ are given by the following expressions:

$$\hat{D}_l^2(x) = \left\{\sum_{n=0}^{\leqslant l/2} (-)^n(2x)^{-2n}\frac{(l+2n)!}{[(l-2n)!(2n)!]}\right\}^2$$

$$+ \left\{\sum_{n=0}^{\leqslant (l-1)/2} (-)^n(2x)^{-2n-1}\frac{(l+2n+1)!}{[(l-2n-1)!(2n+1)!]}\right\}^2; \tag{13a}$$

$$\hat{D}_l^2(x) = \sum_{n=0}^{l} x^{-2n}\left[\frac{(l+n)!}{(l-n)!}\right]\left[\frac{(2n-1)!!}{(2n)!!}\right]. \tag{13b}$$

The first expression, Eq. (13a), follows immediately from Eqs. (3a) and (3b) and the definition of $\hat{D}_l(x)$, Eq. (11a); the second expression, Eq. (13b), may be proved as follows. We start with J. W. Nicholson's *integral representation* [45]

$$\hat{D}_l^2(x) = (4x/\pi) \int_0^\infty dt \, K_0(2x \sinh t) \cosh[(2l+1)t], \qquad (14)$$

where $K_0(z)$ is the usual Bessel function of the third kind of zeroth order. We then use the formula [46]

$$\cosh[(2l+1)t] = \cosh t \sum_{n=0}^{l} (2 \sinh t)^{2n}(l+n)!/[(2n)!(l-n)!]. \qquad (15)$$

Inserting this expression in the integral and setting $2x \sinh t = y$, we get

$$\hat{D}_l^2(x) = (2/\pi) \sum_{n=0}^{l} x^{-2n} \frac{(l+n)!}{[(2n)!(l-n)!]} \int_0^\infty dy \, y^{2n} K_0(y), \qquad (16)$$

having exchanged the order of summation and integration. But

$$\int_0^\infty dy \, y^{2n} K_0(y) = (\pi/2)[(2n-1)!!]^2. \qquad (17)$$

Inserting this expression in the preceding equation, we obtain Eq. (13b). Q.E.D.

It should be emphasized that both Eqs. (13) apply only if l is integral and nonnegative. If l is not a nonnegative integer, the series in Eq. (13b) does not terminate at $n = l$ nor does it converge; it provides, however, an asymptotic expansion of $\hat{D}_l^2(x)$. This is proved in the paper by Kolodner quoted in the Bibliography.

We also note that the amplitude function is characterized by the nonlinear *differential equation*

$$\hat{D}_l''(x) + [1 - l(l+1)x^{-2}]\hat{D}_l(x) = \hat{D}_l^{-3}(x), \qquad \hat{D}_l(\infty) = 1, \quad \hat{D}_l'(\infty) = 0, \tag{18a}$$

while the phase function obeys the integrodifferential equation

$$\delta_l'(x) = a + \pi^{-1} \int_{-\infty}^{\infty} dy(y-x)^{-2} \ln | \cos[a(y-x) - \delta_l(y) + \delta_l(x)] |, a \geqslant 1. \tag{18b}$$

This equation is implied by Eq. (7.21). (Recall that $-\delta_l(kR)$ is the scattering phase shift for the hard sphere potential, $V(r) = \infty$ for $r < R$, $V(r) = 0$ for $r > R$.)

Special Cases

$$\hat{D}_0(x) = 1, \quad \hat{D}_1(x) = (1 + x^{-2})^{1/2}, \quad \hat{D}_2(x) = [1 + 3x^{-2} + 9x^{-4}]^{1/2}; \quad (19a)$$

$$\hat{\delta}_0(x) = x, \quad \hat{\delta}_1(x) = x - \tan^{-1} x, \quad \hat{\delta}_2 = x - \tan^{-1}[3x/(3 - x^2)]. \quad (19b)$$

Behavior at the Origin

$$\hat{D}_l(x) = x^{-l}(2l - 1)!![1 + O(x^2)], \tag{20a}$$

$$\hat{\delta}_l(x) = \{x^{2l+1}/[(2l + 1)!!(2l - 1)!!]\}[1 + O(x^2)]. \tag{20b}$$

Asymptotic Behavior

$$\hat{D}_l(x) = 1 + O(x^{-2}), \tag{21a}$$

$$\hat{\delta}_l(x) = x - l\pi/2 + O(x^{-1}). \tag{21b}$$

Parity

$$\hat{D}_l(-x) = \hat{D}_l(x), \tag{22a}$$

$$\hat{\delta}_l(-x) = -\hat{\delta}_l(x). \tag{22b}$$

Qualitative Features

The amplitude $\hat{D}_l(x)$ is a decreasing function of x (except for $l = 0$). The phase $\hat{\delta}_l(x)$ is an increasing function of x. Short tables of these functions are given in the book by Morse and Feshbach [47]. Note that the function $\hat{\delta}_l(x)$ is called $\delta_l(x)$ there, while the function $D_l(x)$ given there is related to $\hat{D}_l(x)$ by $\hat{D}_l(x) = xD_l(x)$. It should be emphasized that the function $\hat{\delta}_l(x)$ is not the phase function that would be associated with the Riccati–Bessel functions in a straightforward application of the phase approach to the Riccati–Bessel equation.

Riccati-Hankel Functions

$$\hat{h}_l^{(1)}(x) = -\hat{n}_l(x) + i\hat{j}_l(x) = \hat{D}_l(x)\exp[i\hat{\delta}_l(x)], \tag{23a}$$

$$\hat{h}_l^{(2)}(x) = -\hat{n}_l(x) - i\hat{j}_l(x) = \hat{D}_l(x)\exp[-i\hat{\delta}_l(x)], \tag{23b}$$

$$\hat{j}_l(x) = (2i)^{-1}[\hat{h}_l^{(1)}(x) - \hat{h}_l^{(2)}(x)], \tag{24a}$$

$$\hat{n}_l(x) = -\tfrac{1}{2}[\hat{h}_l^{(1)}(x) + \hat{h}_l^{(2)}(x)]. \tag{24b}$$

Explicit Expressions

$$\hat{h}_l^{(1,2)}(x) = (\pm i)^{-l-1}e^{\pm ix}\sum_{n=0}^{l}(\mp 2ix)^{-n}(l+n)!/[n!(l-n)!]. \tag{25}$$

Special Cases

$$\hat{h}_0^{(1)}(x) = e^{ix},$$

$$\hat{h}_1^{(1)}(x) = (-i + x^{-1})e^{ix}, \tag{26a}$$

$$\hat{h}_2^{(1)}(x) = (-1 - 3ix^{-1} + 3x^{-2})e^{ix},$$

$$\hat{h}_0^{(2)}(x) = e^{-ix},$$

$$\hat{h}_0^{(2)}(x) = (i + x^{-1})e^{-ix}, \tag{26b}$$

$$\hat{h}_2^{(2)}(x) = (-1 + 3ix^{-1} + 3x^{-2})e^{-ix}.$$

The Riccati–Hankel functions are complex for real argument, but become purely real or imaginary (depending on the parity of l) for imaginary argument. For instance,

$$\hat{h}_0^{(1)}(ix) = e^{-x},$$

$$\hat{h}_1^{(1)}(ix) = -i(1 + x^{-1})e^{-x}, \tag{27a}$$

$$\hat{h}_2^{(1)}(ix) = -(1 + 3x^{-1} + 3x^{-2})e^{-x},$$

$$\hat{h}_0^{(2)}(ix) = e^{x},$$

$$\hat{h}_1^{(2)}(ix) = i(1 - x^{-1})e^{x}, \tag{27b}$$

$$\hat{h}_2^{(2)}(ix) = -(1 - 3x^{-1} + 3x^{-2})e^{x}.$$

Finally, we collect a few properties and explicit expressions of the functions $U_l(x)$, which are employed in Chapter 20 to discuss bound states.

Definitions

$$U_l(x) = x[\hat{h}_l^{(1)}(ix)]^{-2}\{\hat{h}_{l+1}^{(1)}(ix)\hat{h}_{l-1}^{(1)}(ix) - [\hat{h}_l^{(1)}(ix)]^2\}, \tag{28a}$$

$$U_l(x) = 2[\hat{h}_l^{(1)}(ix)]^{-2} \int_x^\infty dy[\hat{h}_l^{(1)}(iy)]^2, \tag{28b}$$

$$U_l(x) = -x\{1 + [\hat{h}_l^{(1)\prime}(ix)/\hat{h}_l^{(1)}(ix)]^2\} - l(l+1)x^{-1} - i\hat{h}_l^{(1)\prime}(ix)/\hat{h}_l^{(1)}(ix), \tag{28c}$$

$$U_l(x) = -x\{1 + [\hat{h}_{l\pm1}^{(1)}(ix)/\hat{h}_l^{(1)}(ix)]^2\} - i(2l+1)\hat{h}_{l\pm1}^{(1)}(ix)/\hat{h}_l^{(1)}(ix). \tag{28d}$$

In the last expression, either the plus or the minus sign can be chosen. Note that for real x, $U_l(x)$ is real, and for positive x, it is positive (see Eq. (28b); also note that Eq. (25) implies that $\hat{h}_l^{(1)}(ix)$ is positive for positive x, aside from a phase factor that cancels in the ratio).

The First Functions $U_l(x)$

$$U_0(x) = 1, \qquad U_1(x) = x(x+2)(1+x)^{-2},$$
$$U_2(x) = x(x^3 + 16x^2 + 12x + 6)(x^2 + 3x + 3)^{-2}. \tag{29}$$

Behavior at the Origin

$$U_l(x) = 2x(2l-1)^{-1}[1 + O(x^2)], \qquad l > \tfrac{1}{2}. \tag{30}$$

Asymptotic Behavior

$$U_l(x) = 1 + O(x^{-2}). \tag{31}$$

Derivative

$$U_l'(x) = -2\{1 + iU_l(x)[\hat{h}_l^{(1)\prime}(ix)/\hat{h}_l^{(1)}(ix)]\}. \tag{32}$$

Qualitative Features

For positive integral l, the function $U_l(x)$ has the form

$$U_l(x) = xP_{2l-1}(x)Q_l^{-2}(x), \tag{33}$$

where P_n and Q_n are polynomials of degree n. It vanishes in the origin (see Eq. (30)). For positive x, it is positive and continuous. For negative x, it has one discontinuity associated with a double pole if l is odd, but no discontinuity if l is even; it may have zeros but, of course, no more than $2l - 1$.

Appendix **II**

Variational and extremum principle for first-order differential equations

In this appendix we derive a variational principle for the solution of first-order differential equations. We also show that under certain conditions the variational principle becomes an extremum principle. Finally we specialize the results to the case of a Riccati equation, and in that case we also derive simple bounds on the solution. The approach employed is based on an ingenious mathematical trick (quasilinearization) due to Bellman [48].

We consider the real first-order differential equation

$$y'(x) = F(y(x), x),$$ (1)

with real boundary condition

$$y(0) = y_0.$$ (2)

We assume the real function $F(y(x), x)$ to be such that the differential equation (1) and the boundary condition (2) are sufficient to identify uniquely a real solution $y(x)$ for all positive values of x. In the following, we consider only nonnegative values of the variable. The extension to negative values is trivial.

We now introduce the functional $\bar{y}[v; x]$:

$$\bar{y}[v; x] = y_0 \exp \left[\int_0^x ds \, \frac{\partial F(v(s), s)}{\partial v} \right]$$

$$+ \int_0^x ds \left[F(v(s), s) - v(s) \frac{\partial F(v(s), s)}{\partial v} \right] \exp \left[\int_s^x dt \, \frac{\partial F(v(t), t)}{\partial v} \right].$$ (3)

This is a functional of the function $v(x)$, and a function of x. Clearly, for $x = 0$, we have

$$\bar{y}[v; 0] = y_0 .\qquad(4)$$

It is also easily seen that $\bar{y}[v; x]$ satisfies the differential equation

$$\bar{y}'[v; x] = F(v(x), x) + [\bar{y}[v; x] - v(x)]\frac{\partial F(v(x), x)}{\partial v},\qquad(5)$$

where the prime indicates (partial) differentiation with respect to x.

A comparison of these equations, (5) and (4), with Eqs. (1) and (2) implies that if we substitute in place of the trial function $v(x)$ the exact solution of the original differential equation $y(x)$, the functional $\bar{y}[y; x]$ reduces to the exact solution $y(x)$:

$$\bar{y}[y; x] = y(x).\qquad(6)$$

We show below that the functional $\bar{y}[v; x]$ is stationary for $v(x) = y(x)$. This implies that if $v(x)$ does not coincide with $y(x)$, but differs from it only by a small (first-order) term, then $\bar{y}[v; x]$ provides a better approximation to $y(x)$ than $v(x)$ itself because it differs from it only by second-order terms.

To exhibit this stationary property of the functional $\bar{y}[v; x]$, we compute its functional derivative. We find by a straightforward calculation:

$$\frac{\delta\bar{y}[v; x]}{\delta v(\bar{x})} = \theta(x - \bar{x}) \exp\left[\int_{\bar{x}}^{x} ds \frac{\partial F(v(s), s)}{\partial v}\right] \frac{\partial^2 F(v(\bar{x}), \bar{x})}{\partial v^2}[\bar{y}[v; \bar{x}] - v(\bar{x})].\qquad(7)$$

This is now a functional of $v(x)$ and a function of the two variables x and $\bar{x}$. Using Eq. (6), we immediately obtain

$$\frac{\delta\bar{y}[v; x]}{\delta v(\bar{x})}\bigg|_{v(x')=y(x')} = 0.\qquad(8)$$

Q.E.D. We may therefore write explicitly that

$$y(x) = \operatorname*{stat}_{v}\left\{y_0 \exp\left[\int_0^x ds \frac{\partial F(v(s), s)}{\partial v}\right]\right.$$
$$\left. + \int_0^x ds \left[F(v(s), s) - v(s)\frac{\partial F(v(s), s)}{\partial v}\right] \exp\left[\int_s^x dt \frac{\partial F(v(t), t)}{\partial v}\right]\right\},\qquad(9)$$

where by the symbol stat$_v$ we indicate a value of the functional in the braces that is stationary for variations of the trial functions $v(x)$. The optimal trial function $v_{opt}(x)$, which yields the stationary result, is, of course, just $y(x)$,

$$v_{opt}(x) = y(x). \tag{10}$$

It may be easily verified that if $F(y(x), x)$ is either independent of $y(x)$ or linear in $y(x)$, the expression in braces in the r.h.s. of Eq. (9) is independent of the trial function $v(x)$ and, in fact, reproduces the correct solution $y(x)$—i. e., the same expression that may be obtained by direct integration of the original differential equation (1), which is integrable by quadrature under these conditions.

We now proceed to show that provided (i) *the function $y(x)$ is continuous* and (ii) *the relationship*

$$\frac{\partial^2 F(y(x), x)}{\partial y^2} \geqslant 0 \tag{11}$$

holds, the stationary principle just derived becomes a maximum principle. This observation is due to Bellman [48]. If the inequality sign in Eq. (11) were reversed, we would obtain a minimum principle instead of a maximum principle. What is essential for the transition from the variational principle to the extremum principle is, beside condition (i) above, that the quantity $\partial^2 F(y(x), x)/\partial y^2$ be semidefinite. Note that this property is required to hold only for the function $y(x)$ which is the solution of the original differential equation; it must, of course, hold for the whole range of values of x from zero to those in which one is interested.

Before proving the maximum principle, we introduce and prove a very simple lemma.

LEMMA.   *If the two continuous real functions $y_1(x)$, $y_2(x)$ are defined by the first-order differential equations*

$$y_1'(x) = F_1(y_1(x), x), \tag{12a}$$

$$y_2'(x) = F_2(y_2(x), x), \tag{12b}$$

and the same boundary condition

$$y_1(0) = y_2(0) = y_0, \tag{13}$$

and if for all positive x and arbitrary real y we have

$$F_2(y, x) \geqslant F_1(y, x), \tag{14}$$

then for all positive x we also have

$$y_2(x) \geqslant y_1(x). \tag{15}$$

The proof of this lemma is quite trivial and may be stated as follows: $y_1(x)$ can never overtake $y_2(x)$ because at the point where the overtaking would occur, y_1' should exceed y_2', in violation of Eqs. (12) and (14). It should be emphasized, however, that this lemma holds only for *continuous* functions, as is also implied by its proof. If this essential condition is dropped, it is very easy to construct counterexamples. (For instance, $y_1'(x) = 1$, $y_2'(x) = 1 + y_2^2(x)$, $y_1(0) = y_2(0) = 0$ is one such counterexample because, for $\pi/2 < x < \pi$, $y_2(x) = \tan x$ is negative and is therefore smaller than $y_1(x) = x$.)

We now derive the maximum principle. First of all we note that .the concavity condition, Eq. (11), implies the inequality

$$F(y(x), x) \geqslant F(v(x), x) + [y(x) - v(x)] \frac{\partial F(v(x), x)}{\partial v}. \tag{16}$$

This equation holds for all the trial functions $v(x)$ for which the concavity condition

$$\frac{\partial^2 F(v(x), x)}{\partial v^2} \geqslant 0 \tag{17}$$

holds. From now on we consider only such trial functions. Note that we have the equality sign in Eq. (16) if $v(x)$ coincides with $y(x)$.

We now compare the functional $\bar{y}[v; x]$, which we may consider to be defined by Eqs. (5) and (4), with the unknown function $y(x)$, defined by Eqs. (1) and (2). Assumption (i) preceding the lemma proved above implies the applicability of the lemma. (Note that the continuity of the functional $\bar{y}[v; x]$, considered as a function of x, is implied by its definition; of course, we exclude from consideration the trial functions that would make it discontinuous.) We therefore assert that

$$y(x) \geqslant \bar{y}[v; x]. \tag{18}$$

But this equation, together with Eq. (6), is equivalent to the extremum property

$$y(x) = \max_v \{\bar{y}[v; x]\}, \tag{19}$$

or, more explicitly,

$$y(x) = \max_{v} \left\{ y_0 \exp \left[\int_0^x ds \, \frac{\partial F(v(s), s)}{\partial v} \right] \right.$$

$$\left. + \int_0^x ds \left[F(v(s), s) - v(s) \frac{\partial F(v(s), s)}{\partial v} \right] \exp \left[\int_s^x dt \, \frac{\partial F(v(t), t)}{\partial v} \right] \right\}. \quad (20)$$

This is our maximum principle. Here the symbol $\max_v$ indicates the maximum value of the functional within the braces on variation of the trial functions $v(x)$. We recall, however, that the trial functions are not completely arbitrary; they must satisfy condition (17). We also emphasize that the optimal trial function $v_{\mathrm{opt}}(x)$ which attains the maximum is again just the unknown solution $y(x)$, as in the case of the variational principle (see Eq. (10)). We are guaranteed by the original assumption, Eq. (11), that this optimal trial function is contained within the manifold of trial functions satisfying Eq. (17).

It is trivial to extend the result to the case when the inequality sign in Eq. (11) is reversed. There is no change other than the substitution of min for max in the final equations.

We emphasize that extremum principles are much more powerful than variational principles for any kind of application. For one thing, they provide rigorous bounds for the exact solution. Moreover, because the sign of the error is determined *a priori*, we have a criterion for selecting the better trial function among several possible ones. Thus any approximation based on an extremum principle may be refined *ad libitum* by successive trials, whereas there is no definite prescription to improve an approximate result obtained variationally.

Finally, we apply these general results to the case of a Riccati equation of the form

$$y'(x) = P(x)[a(x) + b(x)y(x)]^2, \quad (21)$$

with boundary condition

$$y(0) = 0. \quad (22)$$

(We note, incidentally, that we could have set either $a(x) = 1$ or $b(x) = 1$, without loss of generality. We keep both terms to make the final formulas more convenient for application.) It is obvious that in this case the concavity condition (11) becomes

$$2P(x)b^2(x) \geqslant 0, \quad (23a)$$

or, equivalently,

$$P(x) \geqslant 0. \tag{23b}$$

Notice that now the concavity condition is independent of the dependent variable y. Thus we have no restriction, in this case, on the trial functions to be used in the extremum principle (besides the obvious requirement that they keep all integrations finite). The only conditions required for a maximum principle to hold in this case are the validity of Eq. (23b) and the continuity of $y(x)$ in the interval 0 to $x > 0$. Under these conditions, we may write

$$y(x) = \max_{v} \left\{ \int_0^x ds\ P(s)[a^2(s) - b^2(s)v^2(s)] \right.$$

$$\left. \times \exp\left[2\int_s^x dt\ P(t)b(t)(a(t) + v(t)b(t)) \right] \right\}. \tag{24}$$

The optimal trial function coincides, as usual, with the function $y(x)$ itself, Eq. (10). Another convenient form of the maximum principle is the following:

$$y(x) = \max_{w} \left\{ \int_0^x ds\ P(s)a^2(s)[2 - w(s)]w(s) \exp\left[2\int_s^x dt\ P(t)a(t)b(t)w(t) \right] \right\}. \tag{25}$$

This form is obtained from the previous one, Eq. (24), by a renormalization of the trial functions. The optimal trial function $w_{\mathrm{opt}}(x)$ is now related to the exact solution $y(x)$ by

$$w_{\mathrm{opt}}(x) = 1 + y(x)b(x)/a(x). \tag{26}$$

There is a third form of this maximum principle that is very convenient in certain cases. It obtains with a redefinition of the trial function, selected so as to make one partial integration simple. It reads

$$y(x) = \tfrac{1}{2}\max_{z} \left\{ z(0)E(x) - z(x) + E(x)\int_0^x ds\ z'(s)/E(s) \right\}, \tag{27}$$

where

$$E(x) = \exp\left\{ 2\int_0^x ds\ P(s)b(s)[2a(s) - b(s)z(s)] \right\}. \tag{28}$$

The optimal value of $z(x)$ is

$$z_{\mathrm{opt}}(x) = -y(x) + a(x)/b(x). \tag{29}$$

This form of the maximum principle is especially suited for establishing lower bounds to the solution $y(x)$ because it implies the inequality

$$y(x) \geqslant \tfrac{1}{2}[z(0)E(x) - z(x)], \qquad (30)$$

provided

$$z'(0) \geqslant 0. \qquad (31)$$

The equality sign in Eq. (30) might prevail only if $z(x)$ is a constant (see below). Needless to say, the validity of Eq. (30) is subject to the same conditions necessary for the validity of the maximum principle—i. e., positive semidefiniteness of $P(s)$ and continuity of $y(s)$ for $0 \leqslant s \leqslant x$. The choice

$$z(x) = z = \text{const} \qquad (32)$$

in Eq. (30) is convenient to secure a simple lower bound to $y(x)$, which depends only on the evaluation of the two integrals

$$A(x) = \int_0^x ds\, P(s)\, a(s)\, b(s), \qquad (33)$$

$$B(x) = \int_0^x ds\, P(s)\, b^2(s). \qquad (34)$$

In fact, it is easily seen that Eq. (30) implies

$$|y(x)| \geqslant |[A(x)/B(x)]L[A(x)]|, \qquad (35)$$

where the universal function L is defined by

$$L(t) = (t/|t|) \max_{0 \leqslant c \leqslant 1} |c[e^{4t(1-c)} - 1]|. \qquad (36)$$

The function $L(t)$ is plotted in Fig. 1 and is tabulated in Table I, together with the values of c corresponding to the maximum. The factor $(t/|t|)$ has been introduced for convenience in plotting, and also because with this definition $L(t)$ is a smooth function of t at $t = 0$. In Table I we have also recorded the asymptotic behavior of the function $L(t)$ for large $|t|$, which is easily evaluated. It may be verified that the last values explicitly given in the table, i. e., those for $t = 3$ and $t = -18$, are already very accurately reproduced by the asymptotic formulas.

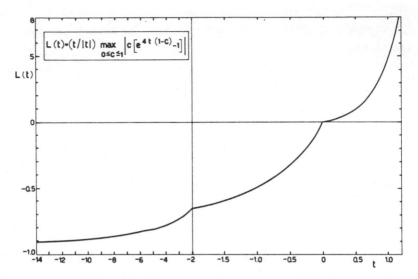

FIG. 1.   The universal function $L(t)$, Eq. (36), is plotted as a function of t. Notice that there is a change of scale both in the abscissae and in the ordinates. The corresponding data are tabulated in Table I.

The inequality (35) has been derived under the assumption that $P(s)$ is positive semidefinite in the interval $0 \leqslant s \leqslant x$; in this case, the modulus sign in Eq. (35) is superfluous because the fact that $P(s)$ is positive semidefinite implies that $y(x)$ and $B(x)$ are positive, and $t \cdot L(t)$ is positive by definition. But it is easily seen that Eq. (35) also holds if $P(s)$ is negative semidefinite in the interval $0 \leqslant s \leqslant x$. Thus the only requirements for the validity of Eq. (35) are the continuity of $y(s)$ and the fact that $P(s)$ does not change sign in the interval $0 \leqslant s \leqslant x$.

The fact that $L(t)$ becomes quite large for $t > 1$ indicates that if the functions $a(s)$, $b(s)$, and $P(s)$ are such that $A(x)$, Eq. (33), is large while $P(s)$ does not change sign for $0 \leqslant s \leqslant x$, then generally either $y(x)$ has a large modulus or it is discontinuous in the interval $0 \leqslant s \leqslant x$.

It is easy to verify that the inequality (35) is best possible, namely, that there exist cases such that the equality sign prevails in it. The condition for this to happen is

$$b^{-2}(x)\{2a(x)\,b(x) - \sqrt{[a'(x)\,b(x) - a(x)\,b'(x)]}/P(x) = \lim_{x \to 0}[a(x)/b(x)]. \quad (37)$$

TABLE I

THE UNIVERSAL FUNCTION $L(t)$ AS A FUNCTION OF x AND
VALUES OF c CORRESPONDING WITH THE MAXIMUM

t	$L(t)$	c_{opt}
$\gg 1$	$(4t)^{-1} \exp[4t - 1 + O(t^{-1})]$	$(4t)^{-1}$
3.0	5.10^3	0.08
2.5	810	0.10
2.0	137	0.125
1.5	25	0.17
1.0	4.78	0.24
0.5	0.935	0.36
0.4	0.645	0.39
0.3	0.42	0.42
0.2	0.25	0.45
0.1	0.11	0.47
0	0	0.5
-0.1	-0.091	0.52
-0.2	-0.166	0.55
-0.3	-0.230	0.57
-0.4	-0.284	0.59
-0.5	-0.330	0.60
-0.6	-0.371	0.62
-0.7	-0.407	0.64
-0.8	-0.438	0.65
-0.9	-0.466	0.66
-1.0	-0.491	0.67
-2	-0.649	0.76
-3	-0.728	0.80
-4	-0.775	0.83
-5	-0.808	0.86
-6	-0.832	0.87
-7	-0.850	0.88
-8	-0.864	0.89
-9	-0.876	0.90
-10	-0.885	0.91
-12	-0.900	0.92
-14	-0.912	0.93
-16	-0.920	0.94
-18	-0.928	0.94
$\ll -1$	$-1 + \dfrac{\ln\lvert 4t \rvert}{\lvert 4t \rvert} + \dfrac{1}{\lvert 4t \rvert} + O\left(\dfrac{\ln\lvert t \rvert}{t^2}\right)$	$1 - \dfrac{\ln\lvert 4t \rvert}{\lvert 4t \rvert} + \dfrac{\ln\lvert 4t \rvert}{\lvert 4t \rvert^2}$

Note that this requires that the l.h.s. be constant. In this case, the solution $y(x)$ is also given by the simpler equation

$$y(x) = [a(x)/b(x)] - \lim_{x \to 0}[a(x)/b(x)]. \tag{38}$$

Summarizing, we assert that the solution of the Riccati equation (21) with boundary condition (22) is given by the maximum principle (24), (25), or (27), provided, in the interval from 0 to x, $y(s)$ is continuous and $P(s)$ is positive semidefinite. If $P(s)$ is negative semidefinite, in place of the maximum principle we have a minimum principle, obtained by substituting *min* in place of *max* in Eqs. (24), (25), and (27). If $P(s)$ is not definite, the extremum principle is invalid, but the variational principle obtained by substituting *stat* in place of *max* in Eqs. (24), (25), and (27) still holds. Moreover, if $y(s)$ is continuous in the interval 0 to x, and $P(s)$ is semidefinite in that interval, then Eq. (35), together with Eq. (36), provides a simple lower bound to the modulus of $y(x)$.

Appendix III

Asymptotic behavior of scattering phase shifts at large energy

In this appendix we discuss the asymptotic behavior of the scattering phase shift as k diverges (l fixed). We are interested here only in assessing the behavior of the dominant term in the asymptotic expansion of the phase shift at large k. Thus our results depend only on the behavior of the potential at the origin, not on l. For this reason, we indicate the phase shift simply as δ, dropping the subscript l. The results are in Table I (page 220).

To obtain more precise results one should evaluate more accurately the asymptotic behavior of the Born approximation, Eq. (8.6) or (4), in the case of regular potentials, or of the expression (15.17) or (12), in the case of singular potentials. (For singular potentials that behave in the origin as a power, results are given in Chapter 15.)

The precise meaning of the symbol $\sim$ used below is the following: $y(k) \sim x(k)$ iff there exist two constants M and K such that for all $k > K$, $|y(k)| \leqslant M|x(k)|$ and $|x(k)| \leqslant M|y(k)|$; $y(r) \sim x(r)$ iff there exist two constants M and R such that for all $r < R$, $|y(r)| \leqslant M|x(r)|$ and $|x(r)| \leqslant M|y(r)|$.

First we consider regular potentials, namely, potentials for which

$$\lim_{r \to 0} r^2 V(r) = 0. \tag{1}$$

For the sake of definiteness, we characterize their behavior in the origin by writing

$$V(r) \sim V_0(r) = r^{-m} \ln^n r \qquad (m \leqslant 2; \quad \text{if} \quad m = 2, n < 0). \tag{2}$$

The results given in Table I also include a more general case.

The asymptotic behavior in k of the corresponding phase shift is determined by the Born approximation. While we do not provide here a rigorous proof of this well-known fact, we note that it may be justified from the exact formula

$$\delta_l = -k^{-1} \int_0^\infty dr \; V(r)[\cos \delta_l(r) \, \hat{\jmath}_l(kr) - \sin \delta_l(r) \, \hat{n}_l(kr)]^2 \qquad (3)$$

and the remark that as k diverges, the scattering phase shift, and therefore also the phase function, vanishes. Thus, in general,

$$\delta_l \sim \delta_l^B = -k^{-1} \int_0^\infty dr \; V(r) \, \hat{\jmath}_l^2(kr). \qquad (4)$$

(Incidentally, the equality in this equation is compatible with Eq. (8.6) because we are considering small quantities, so that the tangent and the angle coincide.)

We now wish to extract the explicit behavior as k diverges from Eq. (4); as is easily seen, this depends only on the behavior of the potential near the origin, Eq. (2). It is convenient to separate the integral in Eq. (4) into two parts:

$$\delta_l \sim -k^{-1} \int_0^R dr \; V(r) \, \hat{\jmath}_l^2(kr) - k^{-1} \int_R^\infty dr \; V(r) \, \hat{\jmath}_l^2(kr). \qquad (5)$$

We consider separately the two terms in the r.h.s.

To evaluate the second term, we assume that $k > K$, with $KR \gg l$, so that we may substitute in place of the Riccati–Bessel function its asymptotic expressions, Eq. (I.8a), and we thus obtain

$$k^{-1} \int_R^\infty dr \; V(r) \, \hat{\jmath}_l^2(kr) \sim k^{-1} \int_R^\infty dr \; V(r) \sin^2 kr \sim k^{-1}. \qquad (6)$$

As for the first term, assuming that R is small enough so that we may use Eq. (2) and performing a change of variable, we obtain

$$k^{-1} \int_0^R dr \; V(r) \, \hat{\jmath}_l^2(kr) \sim k^{-1} \int_0^{kR} dx \; V_0(x/k) \, \hat{\jmath}_l^2(x)$$

$$= k^{m-2} \int_0^{kR} dx \; x^{-m} \ln^n(x/k) \, \hat{\jmath}_l^2(x). \qquad (7)$$

Using Eqs. (I.8a) and (I.7a), it is easily seen that the only effect of the Riccati–Bessel function is to ensure convergence of the integral at the lower limit. Thus we may also write

$$k^{m-2} \int_0^{kR} dx\, x^{-m} \ln^n(x/k)\, \hat{j}_l^2(x) \sim k^{m-2} \int_1^{kR} dx\, x^{-m} \ln^n(x/k). \tag{8}$$

That this step is correct may be checked, in each case, by dividing the interval of integration into two parts and treating each part separately.

We are now left with the problem of evaluating the integral in the r.h.s. of Eq. (8) as k diverges. We must distinguish three cases. If $m < 1$, we note that it diverges if the upper limit diverges. We may then easily ascertain its behavior by partial integration, and we find

$$k^{m-2} \int_1^{kR} dx\, x^{-m} \ln^n(x/k) \sim k^{-1}. \tag{9}$$

Thus from this equation and Eq. (6), we conclude, in this case,

$$\delta \sim k^{-1}. \tag{10}$$

(Incidentally, we note that essentially this result was proved in Ref. [13], without using the Born approximation.)

(In this derivation, however, we have disregarded the possibility that the two contributions, Eqs. (6) and (9), cancel each other exactly. A necessary and sufficient condition for this to happen is that the quantity $I_0 = \int_0^\infty dr\, V(r)$ vanish. In fact it is well known [28] that, if the behavior of the potential in the origin is such that this integral exists, the scattering phase shift behaves at high energy as $-\frac{1}{2}I_0/k$. This remark applies also to the last case, which now follows.)

If $m = 1$, we perform an exact integration and obtain

$$k^{-1} \int_1^{kR} dx\, x^{-1} \ln^n(x/k) \sim \begin{cases} k^{-1} \ln^{n+1} k, & n \neq -1, \\ k^{-1} \ln \ln k, & n = -1. \end{cases} \tag{11}$$

From this equation and Eq. (6), we conclude, in this case,

$$\delta \sim \begin{cases} k^{-1} \ln^{n+1} k & \text{if } n > -1, \\ k^{-1} \ln \ln k & \text{if } n = -1, \qquad (m = 1). \\ k^{-1} & \text{if } n < -1. \end{cases} \tag{12}$$

If $1 < m \leqslant 2$, the integral in the r.h.s. of Eq. (8) converges even if the upper limit diverges. Therefore, we obtain immediately

$$k^{m-2} \int_1^{kR} dx\, x^{-m} \ln^n(x/k) \sim k^{m-2} \ln^n k, \tag{13}$$

and from this we conclude

$$\delta \sim k^{m-2} \ln^n k \quad (1 < m \leqslant 2; \text{ if } m = 2, n < 0). \tag{14}$$

We proceed now to consider singular potentials, namely, potentials for which, given any positive quantity M, there exists an R such that for $r \leqslant R$,

$$r^2 V(r) > M. \tag{15}$$

(We consider only singular potentials that are repulsive in the singular region, as emphasized in Chapter 15.) We continue to characterize the behavior of the potential near the origin by writing

$$V(r) \sim V_0(r) = r^{-m} \ln^n r \quad (m \geqslant 2; \text{ if } m = 2, n > 0). \tag{16}$$

The results obtaining in more general cases are also given below.

As explained in Chapter 15, the asymptotic behavior of the scattering phase shift is given by Eq. (15.17), which we write

$$\delta \sim k^{-1} \int_0^R dr\, V(r) \sin^2 k[V(r)]^{-1/2} + k^{-1} \int_R^\infty dr\, V(r) \sin^2 k[V(r)]^{-1/2}. \tag{17}$$

The second term behaves as k^{-1} at large k, and is certainly negligible with respect to the first term (see below), so from here on we neglect it. Moreover, we choose the distance R small enough so that we may substitute $V_0(r)$ in place of $V(r)$, and we divide the interval of integration into two parts:

$$\delta \sim k^{-1} \int_0^{R(k)} dr\, V_0(r) \sin^2 k[V_0(r)]^{-1/2} + k^{-1} \int_{R(k)}^R dr\, V_0(r) \sin^2 k[V_0(r)]^{-1/2}. \tag{18}$$

We now chose the quantity $R(k)$ as the solution of the equation

$$k^2 = V_0[R(k)]. \tag{19}$$

Since $V_0(r)$ is by definition a decreasing function of r that diverges in the origin, this equation has, for sufficiently large k, one and only one solution; moreover, as k diverges, $R(k)$ vanishes. We note incidentally that the distance $R(k)$ has a simple physical meaning, as implied by its definition, Eq. (19): It is the classical value of the minimum distance of approach to the scattering center. That this distance plays an important role in determining the high-energy behavior of the scattering phase shift is very reasonable; its relevance in this connection has been already noted [49, 50].

Going back to Eq. (18), we note that the argument of the sine function in the first integral is always smaller than unity, and in the second integral is always larger than unity. We may therefore substitute for the sine, in our asymptotic estimate, its argument in the first integral, and a constant in the second. Thus we obtain

$$\delta \sim kR(k) + k^{-1} \int_{R(k)}^{R} dr \, V_0(r). \tag{20}$$

It remains to evaluate this expression; to do this, we must use the explicit form of $V_0(r)$, Eq. (16). From this equation and Eq. (19), we easily obtain

$$R(k) \sim k^{-2/m}[\ln k]^{n/m}, \tag{21}$$

and (by partial integration)

$$k^{-1} \int_{R(k)}^{R} dr \, r^{-m} \ln^n r \sim k^{-1}[R(k)]^{1-m} \ln^n R(k), \tag{22}$$

which yields, using Eq. (21),

$$k^{-1} \int_{R(k)}^{R} dr \, r^{-m} \ln^n r \sim k^{1-2/m}[\ln k]^{n/m} \qquad (m > 2). \tag{23}$$

We thus see that both terms in Eq. (20) give an asymptotic contribution of the same order, and we finally conclude

$$\delta \sim k^{1-2/m}[\ln k]^{n/m}. \tag{24}$$

(The possibility that the two contributions in Eq. (20) cancel each other exactly is excluded, because it is easily seen that they have the same sign.) This result of course agrees, for $n = 0$, with the more detailed one obtained in Chapter 15.

Finally we consider the case in which the potential diverges at the origin faster than any power, say,

$$V_0(r) \sim \exp|f(r)|, \tag{25a}$$

with

$$f(r) \sim r^{-q}, \qquad q > 0. \tag{25b}$$

It is then easy to prove by partial integration that the second term in the r.h.s. of Eq. (20) behaves as $k[R(k)]^{1+q}$, so that it is dominated by the first term. We may therefore conclude quite generally that in the case of singular potentials, the asymptotic behavior is given by the rule

$$\delta \sim kR(k), \qquad (26)$$

with $R(k)$ defined by Eq. (19). For the potential of Eqs. (25) we find

$$\delta \sim k[\ln k]^{-q}. \qquad (27)$$

This result holds even if $f(r)$ contains other singular terms beside the leading one displayed in Eq. (25b).

All the results of this appendix are summarized in Table I. We have also included a slightly more general case than those discussed above. This generalization—or, for that matter, any other generalization—is easily accounted for by a discussion completely analogous to that given above.

TABLE I

ASYMPTOTIC BEHAVIOR AT LARGE ENERGY OF SCATTERING PHASE SHIFTS

	Behavior of potential near the origin	Behavior of scattering phase shifts at large energy	Remarks
$V(r) \sim r^{-m}(\ln r)^n (\ln \ln r)^p$	$m < 1;\quad n, p$ arbitrary $m = 1;\quad n < -1;\quad p$ arbitrary $m = 1;\quad n = -1;\quad p < -1$	k^{-1} (unless $I_0 = 0$)	*Regular potentials* ($\lim_{r \to 0} r^2 V(r) = 0$) asymptotic behavior given by Born approximation, Eq. (4); phase shifts vanish at large k.
	$m = 1;\quad n = -1;\quad p = -1$	$k^{-1} \ln \ln \ln k$	
	$m = 1;\quad n = -1;\quad p > -1$	$k^{-1}(\ln \ln k)^{1+p}$	
	$m = 1;\quad n > -1;\quad p$ arbitrary	$k^{-1}(\ln k)^{n+1}(\ln \ln k)^p$	
	$1 < m < 2;\quad n, p$ arbitrary $m = 2;\quad n < 0;\quad p$ arbitrary $m = 2;\quad n = 0;\quad p < 0$	$k^{m-2}(\ln k)^n(\ln \ln k)^p$	
	$m = 2;\quad n = 0;\quad p > 0$ $m = 2;\quad n > 0;\quad p$ arbitrary $m > 2;\quad n, p$ arbitrary	$k^{1-2/m}(\ln k)^{n/m}$ $\times\ (\ln \ln k)^{p/m}$	*Singular potentials* ($\lim_{r \to 0} r^2 V(r) = +\infty$) asymptotic behavior given by Eqs. (26) and (19); phase shifts diverge less than linearly at large k.
	$V(r) \sim \exp|f(r)|,\quad f(r) \sim r^{-q}$	$k(\ln k)^{-q}$	

Appendix IV

Derivation of the pole equation and discussion of the pole functions for q < 0

In this appendix we derive the pole equation (20.14), i. e., the equation satisfied by the pole functions $q_i(r)$, which give the locations of the poles of the S-matrix function $S(q, r)$. We also discuss the behavior of the pole functions (also in the $q \leqslant 0$ region), mainly from the point of view of the mathematical structure of the pole equation; the physical significance of the pole functions (also in the $q \leqslant 0$ region and when they become complex) is also mentioned. We stick, for simplicity, to the case of S waves; the subscript 0 to indicate S waves is not explicitly indicated. The generalization to all partial waves presents no problem; the main differences from the S-wave case are mentioned at the end of this appendix.

Before beginning our discussion, we introduce several auxiliary functions, whose relationship with the S-matrix function and among themselves may prove useful in various applications. First of all we note that in place of the S-matrix function $S(q, r)$, we may consider the function

$$A(q, r) = (2q)^{-1}[1 \doteq S(q, r)] \tag{1}$$

or

$$Y(q, r) = e^{-2qr} S(q, r). \tag{2}$$

Obviously these functions have the same poles as $S(q, r)$. The function $A(q, r)$ is the "scattering amplitude function" of Chapter 6, for $k = iq$. It satisfies the differential equation

$$A'(q, r) = -V(r)[q^{-1} \sinh(qr) + A(q, r) e^{-qr}]^2, \tag{3}$$

221

with boundary condition

$$A(q, 0) = 0. \tag{4}$$

This function is a convenient one for studying the $q = 0$ limit, when it reduces exactly to the "scattering length function" of Chapter 11:

$$A(0, r) = a(r). \tag{5}$$

This may be verified noting that $A(0, r)$ and $a(r)$ satisfy the same differential equation with the same boundary condition. As for the function $Y(q, r)$, it satisfies the differential equation

$$Y'(q, r) = -2qY(q, r) + (2q)^{-1} V(r)[Y(q, r) - 1]^2, \tag{6}$$

with boundary condition

$$Y(q, 0) = 1. \tag{7}$$

Its use instead of $S(q, r)$ is advantageous in certain connections, owing to the disappearance of the exponential functions in the equation it satisfies. Moreover, it provides a simple means for bypassing the convergence difficulty for the case of potentials that vanish slowly at infinity, even for bound states that fall outside the Bargmann strip. In fact, as is implied by the differential equation (6) (also see below), $Y(q, \infty)$ vanishes unless q corresponds to the energy of a bound state. (For an explicit example, see Ref. [13].)

But the function on which we prefer to focus attention is $M(q, r)$, defined through

$$M(q, r) = q^{-1}[e^{2qr} - S(q, r)][e^{2qr} + S(q, r)]^{-1}, \tag{8a}$$

$$M(q, r) = q^{-1}[1 - Y(q, r)][1 + Y(q, r)]^{-1}, \tag{8b}$$

$$M(q, r) = [q^{-1} \sinh(qr) + e^{-qr} A(q, r)][\cosh(qr) - qe^{-qr} A(q, r)]^{-1}, \tag{8c}$$

$$M(q, r) = u(q, r)/u'(q, r). \tag{8d}$$

This function possesses both of the advantages previously mentioned. In the $q = 0$ limit, we find

$$M(0, r) = r + a(r), \tag{9}$$

so that the poles of $M(0, r)$ coincide with the poles of the scattering length function $a(r)$. On the other hand, $M(q, r)$ satisfies the differential equation

$$M'(q, r) = 1 - [q^2 + V(r)] M^2(q, r), \tag{10}$$

with boundary condition

$$M(q, 0) = 0. \tag{11}$$

This differential equation is clear of exponential functions, and it implies that

$$M(q, \infty) = \pm q^{-1} \tag{12}$$

because only for these values does the derivative vanish in the region where $V(r)$ vanishes. (A third possibility that cannot be excluded simply by inspection of the differential equation is $M(q, \infty) = -\infty$; it is easily excluded, however, e. g., by noticing the relationship between $M(q, r)$ and the radial wave function $u(q, r)$, Eq. (8d).) On the other hand, the bound state condition is

$$M(q, \infty) - -q^{-1}, \tag{13}$$

as is implied, e. g., by Eq. (8a); it corresponds therefore to one of the two possibilities of Eq. (12). As is easily seen, the differential equation (10) implies that the asymptotic solution (13) is unstable against small perturbations, while the other asymptotic possibility

$$M(q, \infty) = +q^{-1} \tag{14}$$

is stable. (This point is further elaborated at the end of Chapter 21.) Finally we note that $M(q, r)$ is just the inverse of the logarithmic derivative of the radial wave function, Eq. (8d); thus the two values of Eq. (13) correspond to the two possibilities $e^{\pm qr}$ for the asymptotic behavior of the radial wave function $u(q, r)$.

The poles of the S-matrix function are now defined by the equation

$$M[q_i(r), r] = -[q_i(r)]^{-1}, \tag{15}$$

which corresponds to Eq. (20.12).

It is advantageous to introduce yet another function, which is related in a simple way to $M(q, r)$. This we do by setting

$$M(q, r) = R \tan \varphi(q, r), \tag{16}$$

where R is an arbitrary constant, with the dimensions of a length. (To be definite, we always assume that R is positive.) From this definition and Eq. (10), we obtain for $\varphi(q, r)$ the differential equation

$$\varphi'(q, r) = R^{-1} \cos^2 \varphi(q, r) - [q^2 + V(r)] R \sin^2 \varphi(q, r) \tag{17}$$

(the prime always indicating differentiation with respect to the last argument, r) with boundary condition

$$\varphi(q, 0) = 0. \tag{18}$$

(Incidentally, we note that this boundary condition is sufficient to identify the function $\varphi(q, r)$ if the potential is regular, namely, if $\lim_{r \to 0} r^2 V(r) = 0$. Otherwise the situation is completely analogous to that discussed in Chapter 15; as is explained there, extra conditions are required to identify $\varphi(q, r)$. Aside from this point, all our discussion of bound states may be extended without reservation to include the case of singular potentials such as those considered in Chapter 15).

We assume $\varphi(q, r)$ to be a continuous function of r; this is consistent with Eq. (17) and, together with Eq. (18), eliminates the mod (π) ambiguity associated with the definition of $\varphi(q, r)$ through Eq. (16). We note that corresponding to Eq. (12), we have

$$\tan^2 \varphi(q, \infty) = (qR)^{-2}, \tag{19}$$

while the bound state condition, Eq. (13) becomes

$$\tan \varphi(q, \infty) = -(qR)^{-1}. \tag{20}$$

The poles of the S matrix function are characterized now by the equation

$$\tan \varphi[q_i(r), r] = -[Rq_i(r)]^{-1}. \tag{21}$$

Of course, the pole functions $q_i(r)$ are independent of the value assigned to the constant R (see below).

To study the behavior of the pole functions $q_i(r)$, we differentiate Eq. (21) with respect to r. We obtain

$$\frac{\partial \varphi[q_i(r), r]}{\partial q} \frac{dq_i(r)}{dr} + \frac{\partial \varphi[q_i(r), r]}{\partial r} = R\{1 + [Rq_i(r)]^2\}^{-1} \frac{dq_i(r)}{dr}. \tag{22}$$

It should be emphasized that $\partial \varphi[q_i(r), r]/\partial r$ indicates the partial derivative of $\varphi(q, r)$ with respect to r, evaluated for $q = q_i(r)$, and similarly for $\partial \varphi[q_i(r), r]/\partial q$. We have also used Eq. (21) to express $\cos^2 \varphi[q_i(r), r]$ in terms of $Rq_i(r)$. But from the differential equation (17) and the pole condition (21), we see that

$$\frac{\partial \varphi[q_i(r), r]}{\partial r} = -RV(r)\{1 + [Rq_i(r)]^2\}^{-1}, \tag{23}$$

so that, by inserting this relation in Eq. (22), we secure

$$\frac{dq_i(r)}{dr} = -V(r)\{1 + 2q_i(r)\,\bar{P}[q_i(r), r]\}^{-1},\tag{24}$$

where we have defined

$$\bar{P}(q, r) = -(2Rq)^{-1}[1 + (Rq)^2]\frac{\partial\varphi(q, r)}{\partial q}.\tag{25}$$

We have thus produced an equation, Eq. (24), that closely resembles the pole equation (20.14). To complete our derivation it remains to be shown that at the pole, the functions $P(q, r)$ and $\bar{P}(q, r)$, Eqs. (20.15) and (25), coincide:

$$P[q_i(r), r] = \bar{P}[q_i(r), r].\tag{26}$$

To achieve this aim, we perform a partial differentiation with respect to q on Eqs. (17) and (18). We obtain in this manner the first-order linear differential equation for $\partial\varphi/\partial q$,

$$\frac{\partial}{\partial r}\left[\frac{\partial\varphi(q, r)}{\partial q}\right] = -2qR\sin^2\varphi(q, r)$$
$$- \{R^{-1} + R[q^2 + V(r)]\}\sin 2\varphi(q, r)\left[\frac{\partial\varphi(q, r)}{\partial q}\right],\tag{27}$$

with boundary condition

$$\frac{\partial\varphi(q, 0)}{\partial q} = 0.\tag{28}$$

From these equations we obtain by formal quadrature,

$$\frac{\partial\varphi(q, r)}{\partial q} = -2qR\int_0^r ds\,\sin^2\varphi(q, s)$$
$$\times \exp\left\{-\int_s^r dt\{R^{-1} + R[q^2 + V(t)]\}\sin 2\varphi(q, t)\right\}.\tag{29}$$

We now substitute in this equation the radial wave function $u(q, r)$ and its derivative in place of $\varphi(q, r)$ and $V(r)$, using the formulas

$$\sin^2\varphi(q, r) = u^2(q, r)\{[Ru'(q, r)]^2 + u^2(q, r)\}^{-1},\tag{30a}$$

$$\sin 2\varphi(q, r) = 2u(q, r)\,Ru'(q, r)\{[Ru'(q, r)]^2 + u^2(q, r)\}^{-1},\tag{30b}$$

which follow from the definitions of $\varphi(q, r)$ and $M(q, r)$, Eqs. (16) and (8d), and the relation

$$q^2 + V(r) = u''(q, r)/u(q, r), \tag{31}$$

which follows from the radial Schrödinger equation. It is then immediately recognized that the integrand in the exponential is a perfect differential; and, carrying out the integration, we find

$$\frac{\partial \varphi(q, r)}{\partial q} = -2qR\{[Ru'(q, r)]^2 + u^2(q, r)\}^{-1} \int_0^r ds\, u^2(q, s). \tag{32}$$

But at the pole, $u' = -qu$ (see Eqs. (15) and (8d)), so that Eq. (32) yields

$$\frac{\partial \varphi[q_i(r), r]}{\partial q} = -2Rq_i(r)\{1 + [Rq_i(r)]^2\}^{-1}\, u^{-2}[q_i(r), r] \int_0^r ds\, u^2[q_i(r), s]; \tag{33}$$

inserting this in Eq. (25), we secure

$$\bar{P}[q_i(r), r] = u^{-2}[q_i(r), r] \int_0^r ds\, u^2[q_i(r), s], \tag{34}$$

which, through Eq. (20.15), implies Eq. (26). Q.E.D.

We note, incidentally, that the pole equation might also have been derived by differentiating the pole relation $u' = -qu$ with respect to q and using the Wronskian theorem. Although such a derivation is more straightforward, we have preferred a formulation based on the function $\varphi(q, r)$, which is generally more convenient for numerical computations (see Chapter 21).

It remains to discuss the boundary condition to be imposed on the functions $q_i(r)$; it is convenient to assign the distance b_i at which these functions vanish:

$$q_i(b_i) = 0. \tag{35}$$

It is immediately recognized (see Eqs. (15) and (8d)) that these distances b_i are just the zeros of $u'(0, r)$:

$$u'(0, b_i) = 0. \tag{36}$$

Equivalently, they are defined by the equation

$$\varphi(0, b_i) = \frac{\pi}{2} + n\pi, \qquad b_i < \infty, \quad n = 0, 1, 2,..., \tag{37}$$

where $\varphi(0, r)$ is the function $\varphi(q, r)$ for $q = 0$, i. e., the solution of the differential equation

$$\varphi'(0, r) = R^{-1} \cos^2 \varphi(0, r) - RV(r) \sin^2 \varphi(0, r), \tag{38}$$

with boundary condition

$$\varphi(0, 0) = 0. \tag{39}$$

Of course, the distances b_i are independent of the choice of the arbitrary constant R, as is implied by their equivalent definition through Eq. (36). This is a remarkable property of the differential equation (38). It should be emphasized that the function $\varphi(0, r)$, at any distance $r \neq b_i$, in general depends on the value of R.

In Eq. (37), different values of i need not correspond to different values of n; however, in the case of a nowhere repulsive potential, $\varphi(0, r)$ is a monotonically increasing function (see Eq. (38)), and we may therefore identify the label i with the integer n, this identification also being consistent with the ordering convention

$$b_{i+1} > b_i, \tag{40}$$

which is always assumed. On the other hand, the restriction

$$\varphi(0, r) \geqslant 0 \tag{41}$$

holds quite generally because when $\varphi(0, r)$ vanishes, $\varphi'(0, r)$ is positive (see Eq. (38)). (This justifies our neglect of negative values of n in Eq. (37).) At the pole locations, Eq. (37), we have, instead,

$$\varphi'(0, b_i) = -RV(b_i), \tag{42}$$

so that $\varphi(0, r)$ increases or decreases through the pole values, at the distances b_i, depending on whether the potential there is attractive or repulsive. If, as in Chapter 20, we call $b^{(+)}$'s the solutions of Eq. (37) such that $\varphi(0, r)$ increases though the value $\pi/2 + n\pi$, and $b^{(-)}$'s those at which $\varphi(0, r)$ is decreasing, we easily conclude that

$$\varphi(0, \infty) = \frac{\pi}{2} + N\pi, \tag{43}$$

where

$$N = n^{(+)} - n^{(-)}, \tag{44}$$

$n^{(+)}$ being the number of $b^{(+)}$'s and $n^{(-)}$ the number of $b^{(-)}$'s. To reach this conclusion, we have also used the remark that $\varphi(0, \infty)$ must equal $\pi/2$ (mod (π)) because the asymptotic vanishing of the potential implies, through Eq. (38), that this is the only value that secures asymptotically $\varphi'(0, \infty) = 0$. (Incidentally, this remark justifies the restriction to finite b's in Eq. (37)). As noted in Chapter 20, the number N is just the total number of (S-wave) bound states possessed by the potential $V(r)$. This fact is the origin of Levinson's theorem, as is shown in Chapter 22. Moreover, the connection of N with the value of $\varphi(0, r)$ for large r is a convenient starting point for establishing limitations on the number of bound states, as is shown in Chapter 23.

In conclusion, we have seen that the behavior of the poles of the S-matrix function $S(q, r)$ is described by the pole equation (24), where the quantity $\bar{P}[q_i(r), r]$ is defined by Eq. (25), or, in terms of the radial wave function $u(q, r)$, by Eq. (34). The distances b_i at which the functions $q_i(r)$ start from their initial vanishing value are determined though Eq. (36), or, equivalently, though Eq. (37).

The relevance of these equations for the evaluation of the binding energies of bound states is described in Chapter 20; there we analyze the behavior of the pole functions $q_i(r)$ in the region $q \geqslant 0$, the only region directly relevant for the discussion of bound states. Here we discuss the behavior of the pole functions in the region $q < 0$; as we shall see, beside clarifying the mathematical structure of the pole equation, this discussion is quite illuminating for the understanding of the physical significance of certain singularities of the analytic continuation of the S matrix in the complex k plane. We shall refrain, however, from any detailed investigation of this topic. For specific examples, see Chapter 21.

For the sake of simplicity, we consider first the simpler case of attractive potentials, $V(r) < 0$. Then, in the region $q \geqslant 0$, the functions $q_i(r)$ are increasing; integrating forward from the initial values $q_i(b_i) = 0$, we never reach the $q \leqslant 0$ region. Let us therefore integrate backward; then $q_i(r)$ becomes negative and keeps decreasing as r decreases. In general, as $q_i(r)$ decreases, the denominator D in the r.h.s. of Eq. (24),

$$D[q_i(r), r] = 1 + 2q_i(r) P[q_i(r), r],\tag{45}$$

also decreases. There are three possibilities: (i) as r approaches zero, $q_i(r)$ tends to a finite (negative) value $q_i(0)$, and D does not vanish, so $D(q_i(0), 0)$ is positive; (ii) as r approaches zero, $q_i(r)$ diverges to minus infinity, but D always stays positive; and (iii) at a finite value r_i, D vanishes,

$$D[q_i(r_i), r_i] = 0. \tag{46}$$

In Chapter 21 we show that the first possibility does not occur, while the second one does occur for any regular potential that is attractive at the origin, but only for the first pole trajectory. The behavior of this trajectory is discussed there in some detail. Here we consider the third possibility, which manifests itself as a singularity of the differential equation (24) because it implies that dq_i/dr becomes unbounded at the distance r_i. (This phenomenon occurs also, for all higher partial waves, at the initial values $q(b_i) = 0$; see Chapter 20).

To understand what happens at the singular points r_i, we investigate the pole equation in their neighborhood. We set

$$D[q_i(r), r] = [q_i(r) - q_i(r_i)] A_i + [r - r_i] B_i, \tag{47}$$

where, of course,

$$A_i = \frac{\partial D[q_i(r_i), r_i]}{\partial q}, \tag{48a}$$

and

$$B_i = \frac{\partial D[q_i(r_i), r_i]}{\partial r}. \tag{48b}$$

We assume for the moment that both A_i and B_i are different from zero. The pole equation then becomes

$$\frac{dq_i(r)}{dr} = -V(r_i)\{A_i[q_i(r) - q_i(r_i)] + B_i[r - r_i]\}^{-1}. \tag{49}$$

Note that we have also substituted $V(r_i)$ in place of $V(r)$. This equation is easily integrated, and we find

$$r - r_i = \left[-\frac{A_i}{B_i}[q_i(r) - q_i(r_i)] + \frac{A_i V(r_i)}{B_i^2} \right]$$
$$\times \left\{ \exp\left(\frac{B_i}{V(r_i)}[q_i(r) - q_i(r_i)] \right) \right\} - \frac{A_i V(r_i)}{B_i^2}. \tag{50}$$

Because we are interested only in the neighborhood of the singular points, we may develop the exponential; we thus find

$$r - r_i = -\frac{A_i}{2V(r_i)}[q_i(r) - q_i(r_i)]^2. \tag{51}$$

Notice that we might have obtained this result directly by neglecting in the expansion of D, Eq. (47), the term proportional to $r - r_i$. This incidentally implies that this result also holds if B_i happens to vanish. On the other hand, if A_i vanishes, Eq. (51) does not stand; this possibility is considered below.

Let us now discuss the behavior of the pole functions in the neighborhood of the singular point. From Eq. (51), we find

$$q_i(r) = q_i(r_i) \pm \left[- \frac{2V(r_i)}{A_i} (r - r_i) \right]^{1/2}. \tag{52}$$

Consider first the region $r > r_i$. In this region, we know that we have at least one real solution; therefore, also recalling that $V(r) < 0$, we infer that

$$A_i > 0. \tag{53}$$

We then see that in this region we have in fact *two* real solutions: the first one (plus sign in Eq. (52)) is the one we were discussing to begin with; the second one (minus sign in Eq. (52)) decreases as r increases. This is consistent with the pole equation (24) because, in the second case, with $q_i(r)$ being more negative than the critical value, the denominator in the r.h.s. is negative. The two solutions coincide for $r = r_i$; this accounts for the singularity of the pole equation at these points.

And what happens for $r < r_i$? Obviously we still have two solutions, but they are complex; the values of their imaginary parts, as they move into the complex plane, may be read from Eq. (52); they are equal and opposite, so the two solutions are complex conjugate. Because the pole equation and the boundary conditions are real, we may, in fact, assert that the complex solutions always occur in conjugate pairs.

In conclusion, a typical situation is illustrated schematically in Fig. 1. We have indicated with a continuous line the solutions in the region where the denominator D in the r.h.s. of the pole equation is positive, and with a dashed line the solutions in the region where D is negative. The points at which they meet are the singular points $D = 0$ of the equation; and from these points, two complex solutions (not indicated in the figure) move off. The first graph corresponds to a case when, integrating backward from the starting value $q_1(b_1) = 0$, we do not encounter any singularity, the denominator D never vanishes, and $q_1(r)$ diverges to minus infinity. (Such behavior

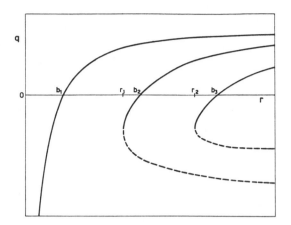

FIG. 1.   Pole functions for attractive potential.

is characteristic of the first pole trajectory; this is proved in Chapter 21 by considering explicitly the case of a square well.) The other graphs correspond to the situation discussed above.

We are now in a position to understand what situation corresponds to the exceptional case when $A_i = 0$. There occurs then at the corresponding values of r and q a confluence of more than two solutions of the pole equation. While this phenomenon need not happen generally, we have no argument to exclude it altogether. In any case, it is easily seen that the topology of the graphs $q_i(r)$ representing the real solutions of the pole equation (see Chapter 21) is not modified by this possibility. This remark also applies to potentials whose sign may change, which are discussed below.

Incidentally, as is implied by their definition, all the singular points must lie on the curve defined by the equation

$$2q = -u^2[q, r]\Big/\int_0^r ds\, u^2[q, s].\tag{54}$$

This equation is obtained by setting $D = 0$, where D is the denominator of the pole equation (20.14). Another curve on which all the double poles lie is characterized by the equation obtained by setting equal to zero the denominator of the pole equation written in the form of Eq. (24). These two curves need not coincide. For a discussion of this point, see Chapter 21, where we also ascertain the behavior of the curve characterized by Eq. (54) as r vanishes.

The generalization of this discussion to the case of a potential that may change sign presents no difficulty. The only difference is that if a singular point occurs in a region where the potential is positive, then the upper solution (corresponding to $D > 0$) decreases, while the lower one (corresponding to $D < 0$) increases; and again from the point at which they meet (characterized by $D = 0$), a pair of complex conjugate solutions emerges. Another possibility also present in this case is that of a graph entering the $q < 0$ region and then leaving it again, without encountering any singular point. A possible situation is illustrated in Fig. 2 (which is a completion of Fig. 20.1): solid line graphs correspond to the solutions with $D > 0$; broken line graphs to the solutions with $D < 0$. The occurrence of "closed" graphs should be noticed; for realistic examples, see Chapter 21. As was noted in Chapter 20, the graphs that do not extend to infinity may be completely ignored if one is interested only in the properties of the whole potential because they are related only to the singularities of the S matrix associated with truncated potentials.

Again all the singular points (meeting points of two trajectories) lie on the curve defined by Eq. (54).

. Finally, let us discuss the physical significance of these poles of the S matrix function $S(q, r)$. In Chapter 20 we treated the $q \geqslant 0$

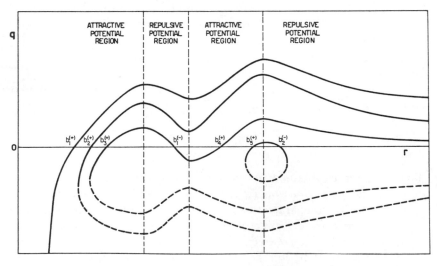

FIG. 2. Pole functions for a potential with attractive and repulsive sectors.

region; there the poles correspond to the bound states of truncated potentials. For $q < 0$, there are two types of poles. (Notice that we consider for the moment only the poles occurring at real values of q.) There are those occurring at values of r and q such that $D(q, r) > 0$, D being defined by Eq. (45), and those occurring at values of r and q such that $D(q, r) < 0$. Their locations are indicated, respectively, by solid and broken lines in Figs. 1 and 2. The poles of the first type correspond to the so-called virtual states of the truncated potential. As more chunks of attractive potential are taken progressively into account, these virtual states may graduate to real bound states; this happens at the distances $b_i^{(+)}$'s, where the graphs we have been describing cross from negative to positive values of q. Conversely, as more repulsive chunks of potential are progressively taken into account, a real bound state may go into a virtual state; this happens at the distances $b_i^{(-)}$'s. As is seen in the complex k plane, these poles move upward along the imaginary axis as more portions of attractive potential are added; they move downward as more portions of repulsive potential are added.

The poles of the second type behave in the opposite way: they move upward along the imaginary axis in the k plane as more chunks of repulsive potential are taken into account; they move downward as more chunks of attractive potential are added. They may be termed to correspond to "antibound" or "antivirtual" states of the truncated potential. These poles can never reach the upper half of the k plane.

In a region of repulsive potential, as r increases, a "virtual" pole, which slides down along the k imaginary axis, may collide head-on with an "antivirtual" pole, which is coming up along the same axis; thence the two poles leave the imaginary axis and wander off at real conjugate positions in the lower half of the complex k plane. Of course, if the potential turns attractive again, these two poles may come back to the negative imaginary axis and collide again as they touch it; then one of them moves down, representing an "antivirtual" state, while the other one moves up as a virtual state and perhaps emerges again into the upper half of the k plane to graduate as a real bound state. Of course, eventually, as r keeps increasing, we reach the asymptotic region where the potential becomes negligibly small and the poles cease to move. Their final positions correspond to the singularities of the scattering matrix associated with the whole potential.

234   APPENDIX IV

As is seen from this discussion, in general the poles of the S matrix occur in pairs: either a real conjugate pair, if they are off the imaginary axis in the lower half of the k plane, or a pair on the imaginary axis, one of which, at most, may be on the upper half of the k plane and thus correspond to a bound state. There is only one exception to this rule, which occurs in the case of regular potentials attractive near the origin, as discussed in Chapter 21. In such a case, there is always one unpaired pole, characterized by a trajectory, which is the uppermost one at least so long as the potential remains attractive, and which diverges to minus infinity as r vanishes. (For a similar result in the context of complex angular momentum, see Ref. [51].)

It is perhaps worth emphasizing that this distinction between "virtual" and "antivirtual" or "antibound" poles is not usually made in the literature; in fact, the adjectives "virtual" and "antibound" are generally used synonymously to characterize poles of the S matrix occurring on the negative imaginary axis in the complex k plane [52]. This is, we believe, one instance of the additional insight gained with the approach used in this monograph. We also note that once the distinction between "virtual" and "antivirtual" poles is introduced according to the value of D at the pole, it is also easy to characterize it by other means. For instance, at least in the case of a nowhere attractive potential, the behavior of the pole locations in the complex k plane as functions of r (r being the truncation distance of the potential), discussed above, is identical to the behavior of the poles associated with the whole potential ($r = \infty$) as the strength of the potential (coupling constant) is varied.

In conclusion, we see that to all values of the pole functions $q_i(r)$ we may associate a physical interpretation: They correspond to various possible singularities of the S matrix associated with the truncated potential. It should be emphasized, however, that they do not yield all the singularities of this S matrix because, with our choice of boundary conditions, we have selected only those singularities that at some value of $r = b_i$, occur at the origin in the k plane. On the other hand, the pole equation does describe the motion of all the poles of the S-matrix function associated with the potential truncated at r, as the truncation distance r is varied. These poles are the only type of singularities possessed by an S matrix associated with a truncated potential (see Chapter 20). Thus, by giving appropriate boundary conditions (e. g., the location of all the poles for $r \approx 0$), the pole equation might be used to investigate the whole analytic structure of the S matrix. (The limit as r diverges is nontrivial, however, unless the potential vanishes faster than exponentially.) Moreover, by using the same approach generalized to all values of l (see the end of Chapter 20), it is also possible to investigate the analytic structure of the S matrix for complex l. But such studies are beyond the scope of this monograph.

We end this appendix by mentioning the two main differences in the behavior of the pole functions for $l > 0$ and for $l = 0$. The first is the absence of the first "unpaired" trajectory, for all odd values of l, in the case of potentials that are attractive near the origin (and for all even values of l, in the case of regular potentials that are repulsive near the origin; see Chapter 21). The second is the occurrence of double poles at $q = 0$ for $l > 0$ (see Chapter 20). This last result implies a somewhat more complex pattern of the pole trajectories in the $q < 0$ region, even for potentials which are attractive everywhere—a fact physically quite relevant, being connected with the possible existence of resonances. For a thorough discussion of an example (Coulomb potential) that should be adequate to illustrate the general situation, see Ref. [36].

References

1. R. Courant and D. Hilbert, "Methoden der Mathematischen Physik," p. 303. Berlin, 1924.
2. P. M. Morse and W. P. Allis, *Phys. Rev.* **44**, 269 (1933).
3. G. F. Drukarev, *Zh. Eksperim. i Teor. Fiz.* **19**, 247 (1949). (In Russian.)
4. O. Bergmann, *Acta Phys. Austriaca* **4**, 62 (1950).
5. G. J. Kynch, *Proc. Phys. Soc.* **65A**, 83, 94 (1952).
6. P. O. Olsson, *Arkiv Fysik* **4**, 217 (1951).
7. S. Franchetti, *Nuovo Cimento* **6**, 601 (1957).
8. D. R. Swanson, *Phys. Rev.* **89**, 740 (1952).
9. R. A. Bonham and J. Karle, *J. Phys. Soc. Japan* **17**, 6 (1962), Suppl. B II.
10. B. R. Levy and J. B. Keller, *J. Math. Phys.* **4**, 54 (1963).
11. R. F. Dashen, *J. Math. Phys.* **4**, 388 (1963).
12. L. Spruch, Minimum principles in scattering theory. *In* "Lectures in Theoretical Physics" (W. E. Brittin, B. W. Downs, and J. Downs, eds.). Wiley, New York, 1962.
13. F. Calogero, *Nuovo Cimento* **27**, 261 (1963).
14. F. Calogero, *Nuovo Cimento* **27**, 947 (1963).
15. F. Calogero, *Nuovo Cimento* **27**, 1007 (1963).
16. F. Calogero, *Nuovo Cimento* **28**, 320 (1963).
17. F. Calogero and D. G. Ravenhall, *Nuovo Cimento* **32**, 1755 (1964).
18. F. Calogero, *Nuovo Cimento* **33**, 352 (1964).
19. F. Calogero, *Phys. Rev.* **135**, B693 (1964).
20. A. Degasperis, *Nuovo Cimento* **34**, 1667 (1964).
21. C. Zemach, *Nuovo Cimento* **33**, 939 (1964).
22. J. R. Cox and A. Perlmutter, *Nuovo Cimento* **37**, 76 (1965).
23. J. R. Cox, *Nuovo Cimento* **37**, 474 (1965).
24. F. Calogero, *Nuovo Cimento* **28**, 66, 761 (1963).
25. F. Calogero and J. M. Charap, *Nuovo Cimento* **32**, 1665 (1964).
26. K. Chadan and J. Y. Guennéguès, *Nuovo Cimento* **34**, 665 (1964).
27. N. Levinson, *Kgl. Danske Videnskab. Selskab., Mat. fys. Medd.* **25**, No. 9 (1949).
28. R. G. Newton, *J. Math. Phys.* **1**, 319 (1960).
29. E. P. Wigner, *Phys. Rev.* **98**, 145 (1955).
30. K. Chadan, *Nuovo Cimento* **40A**, 1194 (1965); **41A**, 115 (1965).
31. R. Kalaba, *J. Math. and Mech.* **8**, 519 (1959).
32. S. Rosendorff and S. Tani, *Phys. Rev.* **131**, 396 (1963).
33. G. Molière, *Z. Natur.* **2A**, 133 (1947).
34. R. G. Glauber, High energy collision theory. *In* "Lectures in Theoretical Physics" (W. E. Brittin and L. G. Dunham, eds.). Wiley, New York, 1959.
35. G. Parzen, *Phys. Rev.* **80**, 261 (1950); **104**, 835 (1956).
36. E. M. Ferreira and A. F. F. Teixeira, *J. Math. Phys.* **7**, 1207 (1966).
37. F. Calogero and G. Jagannathan, *Nuovo Cimento* **47A**, 178 (1967).
38. F. Calogero, *J. Math. Phys.* **6**, 161 (1965).
39. F. Calogero, *J. Math. Phys.* **6**, 1105 (1965).

40. F. Calogero, *Nuovo Cimento* **36**, 199 (1965).
41. F. Calogero, *Commun. math. Phys.* **1**, 80 (1965).
42. V. Bargmann, *Proc. Acad. Sci. U.S.A.* **38**, 961 (1952).
43. J. Schwinger, *Proc. Acad. Sci. U.S.A.* **47**, 122 (1961).
44. F. H. Brownell, *Arch. Rat. Mech. Anal.* **8**, 59 (1961).
45. G. N. Watson, "A Treatise on the Theory of Bessel Functions," p. 444. Cambridge Univ. Press, Cambridge, England, 1944.
46. T. J. Bromwich, "Introduction to the Theory of Infinite Series," p. 204. Macmillan, London, 1926.
47. P. M. Morse and H. Feshbach, "Methods of Theoretical Physics," Vol. II, pp. 1931ff. McGraw-Hill, New York, 1953.
48. R. Bellman, *Proc. Nat. Acad. Sci. U.S.A.* **41**, 743 (1955). See also, by the same author, "Adaptive Control Processes," p. 171. Princeton Univ. Press, Princeton, New Jersey, 1956.
49. L. Bertocchi, S. Fubini, and G. Furlan, *Nuovo Cimento* **32**, 745 (1964).
50. N. Limić, *Nuovo Cimento* **42A**, 516 (1966).
51. R. G. Newton, *J. Math. Phys.* **3**, 867 (1962).
52. V. de Alfaro and T. Regge, "Potential Scattering." North-Holland, Amsterdam, 1965.

Bibliography

These papers are not quoted in the text but refer to the phase method or to some topic treated in this monograph. Other relevant papers may be traced from the references given in these.

I. On the Phase Method

R. F. Dashen, Some extensions of the Born approximation for phase shifts. *Nuovo Cimento* **28**, 229 (1963).

V. V. Babikov, Method of phase functions in quantum mechanics (Dubna preprint P-2758, 1966). *Usp. Fiz. Nauk* **92**, No. 1 (1967) (to be published). See also, by the same author: *Yadernaya Fiz.* **1**, 369, 793, 984 (1965) [English transl. *Sov. J. Nucl. Phys.* **1**, 261, 567, 701 (1965).

D. J. Kouri and C. F. Curtiss, Phase shifts and the quantum mechanical Hamilton-Jacobi equation. *J. Chem. Phys.* **43**, 1919 (1965).

B. H. J. McKellar and R. M. May, Theory of low energy scattering by velocity dependent potentials. *Nuclear Physics* **65**, 289 (1965).

H. Brysk and M. L. Buchanan, Scattering by a cilindrical Gaussian potential: exact solution. *Canad. J. Phys.* **43**, 28 (1965).

J. Kane and E. R. Surynarayan, Integrals of the second order linear differential equation. *J. Math. Phys.* **6**, 966 (1965).

T. Tiesz, A generalization of the Levy and Keller method for finding the phase shifts. *Nuovo Cimento* **35**, 308 (1965).

H. Klar and H. Krüger, A new approach to potential scattering. Part I. Foundation of theory. *Z. Phys.* **191**, 409 (1966).

S. Flügge, H. Klar and H. Krüger, A new approach to potential scattering. Part II. Application to scattering at low and high energies. *Z. Phys.* **191**, 417 (1966).

II. On Related Techniques

J. W. Nicholson, The asymptotic expansions of Bessel functions. *Philos. Mag.* **19**, 228 (1910).

I. I. Kolodner, Phase shift of solutions of second order linear ordinary differential equations and related problems. *J. Math. Anal. Appl.* **4**, 422 (1962).

P. B. Bailey and G. M. Wing, Some recent developments in invariant imbedding with applications. *J. Math. Phys.* **6**, 453 (1965).

R. E. Bellman and R. E. Kalaba, "Quasilinearization and Boundary-Value Problems." Elzevier, New York, 1965.

W. A. Beyer, Asymptotic phase and amplitude for a modified Coulomb potential in scattering theory: An application of invariant imbedding. *J. Math. Anal. Appl.* **13**, 348 (1966).

III. *On the Number of Bound States in a Given Potential*

J. H. E. Cohn, On the number of bound states of a certain potential. *Acad. Roy. Belg. Bull. Cl. Sci.* **49**, 1195 (1963).

H. M. Schey and J. L. Schwartz, Counting the bound states in short-range central potentials. *Phys. Rev.* **139B**, 1428 (1965).

L. Spruch, Necessary conditions for the existence of bound states. *In* "Few nucleon problems" (Proc. Ninth Summer Meeting of Nuclear Physicists, Hercegnovi, 1964) (Miho Cerineo, ed.), Vol. I. Federal Nuclear Energy Commission of Yugoslavia, 1965.

G. C. Ghirardi and A. Rimini, On the number of bound states of a given interaction. *J. Math. Phys.* **6**, 40 (1965).

L. Fonda and G. C. Ghirardi, Approximate determination of the number and energies of the bound states of a physical system. *Nuovo Cimento* **46A**, 47 (1966).

F. Calogero and G. Cosenza, Properties of bound states and Regge poles derivable from modified Wronskian relations. *Nuovo Cimento* **45A**, 867 (1966).

IV. *On the Asymptotic Behavior of Scattering Phase Shifts*

M. Verde, Asymptotic expansions of phase shift at high energies. *Nuovo Cimento* **2**, 1001 (1955); The high energy limit of the potential scattering: I. Non relativistic kinematics; II. Relativistic kinematics, *Nuovo Cimento* **6**, 340 (1957); **8**, 560 (1958).

A. Klein, Mandelstam representation for potential scattering. *J. Math. Phys.* **1**, 41 (1960); A. Klein and D. I. Fivel, On the analytic properties of partial wave amplitudes in Yukawa potential scattering, *J. Math. Phys.* **1**, 274 (1960).

I. C. Percival, Energy moments of scattering phase shift. *Proc. Phys. Soc. (London) Ser. A* **80**, 1290 (1962); I. C. Percival and M. J. Roberts, Energy moments of scattering phase shifts. II. Higher partial waves, *Proc. Phys. Soc. (London) Ser. A* **82**, 519 (1963).

Author Index

Numbers in parentheses are reference numbers and indicate that an author's work is referred to although his name is not cited in the text. Numbers in italic show the page on which the complete reference is cited.

Subject Index

Page numbers in italics indicate the page on which the entry is defined or treated more fully.

Amplitude function, *31ff*, *116ff*, 127, 130
Analyticity properties of scattering parameters, as functions of angular momentum, 2, 235
of energy, 2, 143ff, 235
of potential strength, 100
Antibound state, 156, 159, *233ff*
Antivirtual state, 156, 159, *233ff*
Asymptotic convergence of pole functions, *171ff*

Born approximation, *43ff*, 53ff, 77ff, 216
Bounds
on energies of bound states, 195ff
on energy derivative of phase shift, *38ff*
on number of bound states, *182ff*
on scattering length, 70ff
on scattering phase shift, *37ff*, 51ff
on zero-energy cross section, 70ff
Bound states, *143ff*

Comparison functions, *86*, *114*
Condition for existence of bound states, 187, 189ff
Cotangent function, *17*
Cross section
absorption, 133
differential, 3, 121
total, 70ff

Dirac equation, 98, 120

Eigenphase shift, *139ff*
Eigenphase function, *140ff*
Extremum principle

for first-order differential equations, *205ff*
for scattering phase shift, 50, 57, *93ff*

High-energy behavior of scattering phase shift, 6, 105ff, 108, 125, *215ff*, 239

Improved Born approximation, *46*, 54ff, 77ff
Interpolating functions, 12

Jost function, 35

Klein-Gordon equation, 98

Levinson's theorem, 19, 21, 71, 147, 150, 153, 157, 160, *176ff*, 228
Low-energy behavior of scattering phase shift, *67ff*, 109

Mixing parameter, *139ff*
Mixing parameter function, *140ff*

Number of bound states, 150, 153, 187, 228, 239
Numerical computation
of bound state energies, 173
of pole functions, 160
of scattering phase shifts, 20, 21ff, 112

Partial wave amplitude, *5*
Phase equation, *11ff*, 13ff, 87ff, 116ff, 124, 127ff, 130ff
Phase functions, *11ff*, 13ff, 18, 21ff, 115ff, 130
radial wave function and, *31ff*, 86ff, 130